JOHN CATT'S

Which London School? & the South-East

2023/24

34th Edition
Editor: Phoebe Whybray

JOHN CATT

Published in 2023 by
John Catt Educational Ltd,
15 Riduna Park,
Melton, Suffolk IP12 1QT UK
Tel: 01394 389850   Fax: 01394 386893
Email: enquiries@johncatt.com
Website: www.johncatt.com

Designed and typeset by John Catt Educational Limited

**A CIP catalogue record for this book is available from the
British Library.**

ISBN: 978 1 036001 50 6

Contacts
Editor
Phoebe Whybray

Advertising & School Profiles
Tel: +44 (0) 1394 389850
Email: sales@johncatt.com

Distribution/Book Sales
Tel: +44 (0) 1394 389863
Email: booksales@johncatt.com

Contents

How a focus on belonging and wellbeing links to positive academic outcomes

Hendon Prep School Headteacher, Tushi Gorasia, shares the benefits of creating a sense of belonging for students

At Hendon Prep, we believe that academic achievement is enhanced when it goes hand in hand with mental and physical wellbeing, along with a sense of feeling valued and belonging. The relationship between wellbeing, belonging, and academic attainment is multi-layered, and it is important as educators to understand how these elements can be linked to create a supportive and authentic learning environment.

Our focus on developing, establishing, and building upon an ethos of 'stretch, diversity and inclusion' has not only created a whole school approach which nurtures a sense of belonging and wellbeing but one that has led to increased academic attainment and positive outcomes for not only students, but staff as well. And, as Hendon Prep fast approaches its 150th birthday, this traditionally 'Good' school has now been recognised in our recent ISI Inspection for the first time as 'Excellent in all areas'.

We see how students who experience positive mental health and feel included are more likely to be able to focus on their academic goals and succeed in their studies. In contrast, students who experience negative mental health issues such as anxiety, stress, or depression find it more difficult to concentrate on their studies.

Physical health is also linked to academic achievement and forms part of our student wellbeing charter which highlights the importance of not only physical exercise, but also healthy eating and sleep. All these aspects of physical wellbeing are woven throughout our curriculum, alongside an academic curriculum that is diverse and representative, and regularly reviewed for purpose.

Belonging at Hendon Prep refers to the sense of community and connectedness that our students feel within their academic environment. Students who feel

TEACHING WALKTHRUs

FIVE-STEP GUIDES TO INSTRUCTIONAL COACHING

Books

TEACHING WALKTHRUs
FIVE-STEP GUIDES TO INSTRUCTIONAL COACHING

TOM SHERRINGTON
OLIVER CAVIGLIOLI

TEACHING WALKTHRUs 2
FIVE-STEP GUIDES TO INSTRUCTIONAL COACHING

TOM SHERRINGTON
OLIVER CAVIGLIOLI

TEACHING WALKTHRUs 3
FIVE-STEP GUIDES TO INSTRUCTIONAL COACHING

TOM SHERRINGTON
OLIVER CAVIGLIOLI

SCHOOLS CAN SIGN UP TO OUR PD RESOURCES PACK

GET STARTED

Start planning your
CPD programme

Get going with
Instructional Coaching

Visit our website

Email us for a discussion

Visit the John Catt website for bulk
book orders

For more information visit

WALKTHRUS.CO.UK | JOHNCATTBOOKSHOP.COM

a sense of belonging are more likely to be motivated to focus in their classes, engage with their peers and teachers, and participate in extracurricular activities. This sense of belonging is fostered by creating a welcoming, safe, and inclusive environment that promotes diversity, equity and inclusion, and is delivered by all staff, not just those that teach.

Numerous studies have shown that student wellbeing and a sense of belonging are linked to academic attainment. Focusing on boosting students' self-confidence, resilience, self-esteem, and self-worth can only benefit their ability to perform and thrive in an educational environment and in life beyond the school gate. This is an idea that Professor Donna Cross, a renowned expert in child and adolescent health and wellbeing, has championed.

In a recent literature review by the Association of Independent Schools of New South Wales (AISNSW), Cross's work is cited as an important contribution to understanding how student wellbeing can impact academic outcomes. The review emphasises that a focus on wellbeing is not just about improving mental health but also about promoting positive social and emotional development, which in turn can lead to better academic outcomes. It found that students who felt more connected to their school community had better academic outcomes than those who did not.

In Nov 2014, the Public Health England report – *The link between pupil health and well-being and attainment stated*: Pupil wellbeing predicted their later academic progression and engagement in school. For example, pupils with better emotional wellbeing at age seven had a value-added Key Stage 2 score 2.46 points higher (equivalent to more than one term's progress) than pupils with poorer emotional wellbeing.

The feeling of being accepted and included is an important psychological need that helps individuals feel connected and supported, and it has been linked to numerous positive outcomes, including academic attainment. When our social identity, whether via race, gender, religion, or nationality is valued and respected by others in our community, we are more likely to feel a sense of belonging. On the other hand, when we feel excluded or discriminated against because of our identity, we are more likely to feel a sense of alienation which can impact focus on learning.

A sense of belonging is particularly important in educational settings. Students who feel that they belong in their school or classroom are more likely to be engaged and motivated in their learning. Conversely, students who feel that they do not belong in their school or classroom are more likely to be disengaged and unmotivated. They may also be more likely to disengage from school or perform poorly academically.

So why does a sense of belonging have such a strong link to academic attainment? There are several potential explanations. Firstly, when students feel that they belong in their school or classroom, they are more likely to feel that they have a stake in their academic success. They may also feel more comfortable seeking help from their teachers or classmates when they need it, which can help them to overcome academic challenges.

Second, a sense of belonging can help to reduce stress and anxiety, which can have a negative impact on academic performance. When students feel that they do not belong in their school or classroom, they may experience stress and anxiety, which can make it difficult to concentrate on their studies or perform well in exams.

Finally, a sense of belonging can help to foster a growth mindset, which is the belief that one's abilities can be developed through hard work and dedication. When students feel that they belong in their school or classroom, they may be more likely to adopt a growth mindset, which can help them to overcome academic setbacks and persist in the face of challenges.

Creating a sense of belonging through an inclusive and welcoming environment is a team effort, but students and staff who feel like they belong in their academic and work environment are more likely to be engaged, motivated, and successful. By fostering a sense of belonging among students, schools can help create a supportive and inclusive community that promotes academic achievement and re-evaluate what student success means.

Ultimately, by prioritising a sense of value, representation and belonging in our schools and celebrating diversity, we can help ensure that all students have the opportunity to reach their full potential and achieve their goals in our ever-changing world.

For more information about Hendon Prep School, see page 48

How to use this guide

Are you looking for...

Help and advice?

If so, take a look at our editorial section (pages 5-35). Here you will find articles written by experts in their field covering issues you may well come across when choosing a school for your child.

A school or college in a certain geographical area?

Then you need to go to page D103 to find the directory page reference to a particular area. We suggest that you look first in the directory for basic information about all the schools in each region, complete with contact details, so that you will be better informed about the choices

available to you. From this section you will be directed to more detailed information in the profile section, where this is available.

A certain type of school or college in a particular area?

Look in the directories for the area you want (again, you can find the directory page reference on D103). Underneath each school listed you will find icons that denote different types of schools or qualifications that they offer. You can find a key to these icons on the following page; this key is repeated at the front of each section of the directory.

Schools featured in this guidebook are also profiled on its accompanying website: www.whichlondonschool.co.uk and www.schoolsearch.co.uk

School profiles include embedded Twitter feed and YouTube/Vimeo video, direct links to email, website and social media. Users can search by region, county, or postcode; and by age, gender and day/boarding.

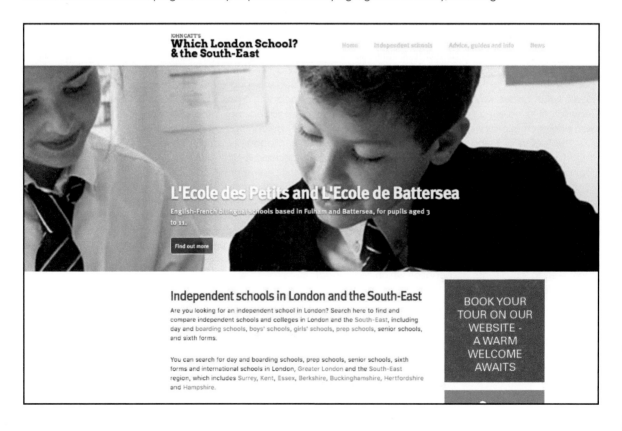

A specific school or college?
If you know the name of the school or college but are unsure of its location, simply go to the index at the back of the guide where you will find all the schools listed alphabetically. You will find that some page numbers are prefixed with the letter D, this denotes that the school appears in the directory section. Schools with page numbers not prefixed by the letter D are those that have chosen to include a fuller school profile, which will provide you with much more extensive information.

Maps?
See pp 39, 71 and 79 for maps of London, Greater London, and the South-East. There are also maps within the directory sections on D105 (Central London), D125 (Greater London) and D131 (South-East).

More information on relevant educational organisations and examinations?
Look in the examinations and qualifications section and the useful organisations section, both located towards the back of the guide.

Key to directory

County — **Wherefordshire**

Name of school or college — **College Academy**

Indicates that this school has a profile — *For further details see p. 12*

Address and contact number — Which Street, Whosville, Wherefordshire AB12 3CD
Tel: 01000 000000

Head's name — **Head Master:** Dr A Person

School type — **Type:** Coeducational day & boarding

Age range — **Age range:** 11–18

Number of pupils. B = boys G = girls — **No. of pupils:** 660 B330 G330

Fees per annum.
Day = fees for day pupils.
WB = fees for weekly boarders.
FB = fees for full boarders. — **Fees:** Day £11,000 WB £16,000 FB £20,000

Key to directory icons (abridged)

Key to symbols:
- ⚥ Boys' school
- ⚥ Coeducational school
- ⚥ Girls' school
- ⚥ International school

Schools offering:
- Ⓐ A levels
- Ⓑ Boarding accommodation
- Ⓔ Bursaries
- ⑯ Entrance at 16+

- ⒝ International Baccalaureate
- Ⓛ Learning support
- ⑯ Tutorial/sixth form college
- Ⓥ Vocational qualifications

Top 5 questions to ask a senior school

Kirsten Crossland, Director of Communications and Marketing at Marymount International School London, offers her advice and some key points to consider when choosing a senior school

When making the final decision about your child's senior school education, there are so many questions out there a parent may ask. Regardless of the type of schooling your child is entering – whether in the subsidised, private, international or state sectors – over the years, I have found these five to be the most interesting questions asked by parents. They are also the questions that will help you determine which school is the right fit for your child.

Question One: What is your education philosophy, and how does this translate into the classroom?

Many families may be drawn to a particular school for the name, the prestige or the legacy associated with it. Something which needs to be considered is whether the pedagogy aligns with your own family's values and goals.

As each student has their own unique characteristics and talents, not every school is right for every student. By asking this particular question, you will get an idea of the overall approach and how it will impact your child's educational experience and whether the fit is the right one.

Question Two: How does the school support students' mental and emotional wellbeing?

The focus on mental health has changed significantly for the better in the last several years. On the back of students receiving their education at home for extended periods of time in the last several years, a school's approach to managing and supporting emotional safety should be as important to the school as it is to parents. Ultimately, schools benefit greatly in educating students who are happy. Asking about the provision for this space is important to understanding how a school nurtures their students, and staff for that matter!

Question Three: How does the school foster inclusivity?

More recently, I have noticed a drive within schools to create a community environment. Students who have multiple stakeholders involved in their development, who know them individually, thrive. When no one is unnoticed, the security it offers allows for a warm and accepting community. As a parent, you will feel this in the way the question is answered, and it will provide you with a sense of whether the school is right for you.

Question Four: What are the school's academic standards and expectations and how do you measure student success?

Each school has its own set of academic expectations for its students. Some may have a rigorous academic focus, whilst others may have more practical skills and experiential learning models. By understanding the school's goals and measures of success, such as assessments and standardised testing which your child will be expected to meet, you will have an idea of how to gauge progress and the alignment to your own expectations.

Question Five: What additional programmes does the school offer?

Balance in learning has also started to make headway in educational institutions, particularly with non-academic enrichment. Extra-curricular activities are fundamental to support personal growth, skills development, and community involvement. A school with a strong time commitment to these activities is a school that understands the importance of the development of the whole of the student. By asking about this, you will have a sense of the breadth and depth of what is available to your child.

Asking these questions will give you a greater sense of the school as a whole. I would recommend asking these

to all the schools you are interested in before introducing them to your child. Ask these questions to many different staff at the school, too. A consistency in the answers provided will only solidify your comfort in their provision and provide valuable insights into the school's priorities, values, and culture. At the end of the day, armed with all this knowledge and a deep understanding of your child, you will instinctively know when a school is the right school for your child.

For more information about Marymount International School London, see page 78

The role of multilingualism in international schools

Simon McNaught, Head of the British Section at Lycée Français Charles de Gaulle de Londres, considers the assets of a multilingual education

The benefits of early exposure to bilingualism have been extensively documented: from cognitive development to cultural adaptability, including a possible way to slow down cerebral ageing, not to mention enhanced productivity and creativity.

Developing flexible brains and open-mindedness, the study and mastery of several languages give multilingual individuals a definite edge in the world. With this in mind, basing their curricula on scientific observation, tailored pedagogy and the diversity of their multinational communities, international schools often include a broad range of languages in their educational offer.

Host country and mother tongue
International schools generally have a main curriculum pertaining to their country of origin. Whether part of a

government-led network, such as the Agency for French Education Abroad (AEFE – Agence pour l'Enseignement Français à l'Étranger), or simply offering education based on a national curriculum, or even schools with a fully international identity, those schools tend to have a principle language of learning, teaching and communicating. This will be taught to all pupils and complemented with at least the language of the host country, if it is different from the main one. In London, for instance, there are bilingual schools in French, German, Italian, Portuguese, Spanish, and even Mandarin or Japanese, to name a few.

Bilingual early years
It all starts from early years, generally with a bilingual stream, taught by native speakers in two languages who

share either the day or the week for pupils to study all subjects alike in one language or the other. This approach simply recreates the natural circumstances in which a child acquires their parents' native tongues: by imitation. After the early stages of strictly oral practice (using songs, nursery rhymes, storytelling, poems and teacher's explanations for all games and activities), the fluency is then extended to the written word. At this point, pupils learn to read and write in both languages. At some schools, this is done simultaneously; at others, one language precedes the other by a few months. The objective is typically to make pupils equally proficient in the spoken and written word in both languages by the end of primary school. This does not exclude that certain schools can introduce a third language during primary education.

Modern languages at secondary level

Moving on to secondary education, now confidently bilingual, international school pupils will have the opportunity to learn other languages. The selection can be inspired by the school's location, for example in an area close to a border. The historical heritage of the school's environment, for example in multilingual countries, can also imbue the linguistic offer. In a globalised world, the simple goal of giving pupils an edge can encourage such schools to teach widely spoken languages (for example English, Spanish or Mandarin) and sometimes more "niche" tongues.

Multilingual school graduates

At the Lycée Français Charles de Gaulle in London for instance, pupils end up bilingual in French and English at the end of primary. When they graduate (age 18), they are also proficient in at least one of the following: Arabic, German, Italian, Spanish or Russian. The linguistic offer goes beyond modern languages and includes Ancient Greek and Latin, which pupils can add to their third language.

Some pupils follow a stream called the European Section. From Year 9, pupils can add two hours to their third language's compulsory curriculum. In these additional hours, one allows them to discover or further their knowledge of the literature produced in that language, and one is for another subject taught in the language (science, physical education, history etc.).

This year, a cohort of students is preparing a brand new qualification: the existing International French Baccalaureate (BFI, in French) with a tweak. The original curriculum of the BFI is bilingual. At the Lycée, a few students are now following a trilingual curriculum, which includes German language and literature.

A world of opportunities

From their first day at school, these pupils become extremely flexible and adaptable. Very often, their families are globetrotters. Yet international relocations are never an issue for them regarding their child's education, as they can easily transfer between such schools. Armed with a robust multilingual knowledge, international school graduates (with a French baccalaureate, an International Baccalaureate, International Abitur etc.) can attend almost any higher education institution worldwide. It is rather common for such students to prepare university degrees including at least a year abroad, or to spend their entire further studies in another country. As an example, the majority of London's Lycée Français students choose to study in the United Kingdom; others go to France, the United States, Canada or Europe.

In the same vein, for their work experience and careers, these students have a truly international and mobile profile, which is in high demand by recruiters for jobs at any level.

An international alumni network

Whatever their chosen professional field, the students will have built strong connections with their classmates, most likely in various countries. This alumni network gives them precious support for career opportunities and opens up the world for them.

At a time when the British government is addressing the decline in modern languages education, international schools present a well-tried system where pupils can really become citizens of the world.

For more information about Lycée Français Charles de Gaulle de Londres, see page 55

The benefits of a bilingual education

Suzanne Haigh, Head at Kensington Wade, shares the advantages and importance of children learning a second language

Kensington Wade is an award-winning, bilingual nursery and prep school in west London for children aged 3-11. At Kensington Wade half the lessons are taught in English and half in Chinese, providing full immersion in the two languages and giving children complete fluency in both.

We believe that our pupils benefit from a bilingual education both in the short term and for the rest of their lives. Being bilingual has a profound effect on the brain and provides many academic, economic, and social advantages.

Boosted cognitive development and memory
A large, and rapidly growing, body of research shows that learning a second language boosts brain capacity in areas such as creative thinking, pattern recognition, and problem-solving as well as the ability to multi-task.

Bilingual people are more able to sort out relevant information from irrelevant information, meaning they can focus better and be more effective thinkers and decision-makers. They tend to make less emotionally charged and more critically analysed decisions.

Children who learn multiple languages have stronger memories and are more cognitively creative. Research indicates that bilingual people are usually better at remembering names, directions etc. than those who speak one language.

Improved academic achievement
The brain of a bilingual person is regularly challenged to recognise, find meaning and communicate in multiple languages. This cognitive flexibility makes bilingual children more able to think critically and analyse complex information.

Studies indicate that pupils who have a bilingual education show greater achievements than their monolingual peers, especially in maths, reading and vocabulary, and that they often do better at standardised tests than those who know one language. Young learners also develop greater linguistic awareness, a better understanding of their native language and increased self-esteem.

Enhanced social skills and perspectives

Bilingual pupils are adept at shifting their perspective and understanding the world from others' points of view. This interpersonal agility and openness encourage a more compassionate and considered approach to the world.

Economic opportunities

There is a growing need for a multilingual workforce and the ability to conduct business in more than one language is becoming more critical. Looking ahead to your child's future career, bilingual people often hold higher positions and earn better incomes than monolinguals in the same industry.

Having the ability to communicate with customers in more than one market is a clear advantage and opens doors for those who wish to move and work abroad.

Cultural understanding

Exposure to two languages helps develop an appreciation for differences in cultures. Bilingual people can engage with languages through stories, songs, and other sources of information without requiring translation. They can also talk directly with locals or fellow travellers which all leads to more meaningful cultural understanding.

At Kensington Wade our classes are also a great opportunity to teach children about diversity and promote equality which leads to greater tolerance as children become adults. We believe that those who have a second language give themselves the best chance to embrace the world that awaits them.

Further language acquisition

Being bilingual from childhood, particularly where two languages are given equal prominence in an education setting, significantly enhances a person's ability to acquire fluency in additional languages at any stage in life.

So, why do we think at Kensington Wade that Chinese is an important language to learn? It is the most widely spoken language on earth and is becoming increasingly influential due to China's growing economic, political, and cultural power.

Cognitive benefits

Learning Chinese also has cognitive benefits because, unlike most other languages, Chinese stimulates and activates the development of both sides of the brain (Wellcome Trust UK, 2003). This is especially true if children learn how to both read and write it.

Chinese writing develops shape recognition and spatial awareness as children need to make sure that each character is the same size, no matter how many strokes are required.

Children who study Chinese learn to recognize the difference between the sound and substance particles of various characters to establish their meaning and pronunciation. This process stimulates the development of excellent problem-solving skills.

Psychologists also suggest that children are open to better and easier learning of Chinese as it is a tonal language and they have the sensitivity to pick up nuances of tone and sound, making it easier for children to grasp Chinese pronunciation. The tonal associations of Chinese can also enhance musical ability.

Looking to the future

At Kensington Wade we believe that knowing Chinese will give our pupils an extra edge in the increasingly global economy. Business leaders and international corporations are looking for people who can speak the language and operate successfully in a Chinese cultural context. Governments also need Chinese specialists to deal with diplomatic affairs related to China.

Broadening cultural horizons

Learning Chinese opens a window into a fascinating history and culture and an immense store of literature and art. China is publishing more books than any other country and is making more and more contributions to scientific, technological, and philosophical studies. The writings of Chinese policy makers, administrators, economists, and business leaders will also become increasingly mainstream.

Come and visit us to find out more about our unique nursery and school. Please visit www.kensingtonwade.com

For more information about Kensington Wade School, see page 49

Embracing mistakes in the classroom

Miss Antonia Beary, Headmistress at Mayfield School, on why making mistakes is an important learning tool for students

Our role, as parents and teachers, is to give our young people the skills and the confidence to be the best version of themselves. Nobody achieves success (however, you may choose to define it) without making mistakes, but the pressure on our young people to be perfect, particularly from social media and wider societal influences and expectations, not least those imposed by the spectre of GCSE and A Levels, often clouds their perspective. Education should not simply be about what we learn, but how we learn. What happens in the school environment, therefore, is key, and how we address these challenges of fundamental importance.

Creating an environment where individuals are able to make their own mistakes, and learn from them, should be a priority for us all. An environment where students are not always right, but mistakes will not scar for life. I would like to suggest that expecting every piece of work to be an A* throughout a child's career, aways being in the first team or playing the leading protagonist, is not going to create the resilient individuals we need to respond to the needs of the age in which we find ourselves.

This is where creative and performing arts and team sports have a fundamental role to play. Our foundress at Mayfield was ahead of her time in placing creativity at the heart of our curriculum and encouraging an appreciation of interdisciplinary approaches when she established the school over 150 years ago. To be a good scientist you need to be creative; to be a fine artist you need discipline, structure and perspective. Some skills take on greater importance in some subjects than others, of course. Much maligned and often seen as the poor relations, creative subjects, along with sport, are the first to be squeezed out of the curriculum. This is at best short-sighted, and I am convinced has the potential to destroy independent thinking and stifle creativity and teamwork in all sectors of the economy.

In art, as in life, there is seldom just one right answer, one interpretation, one correct approach. It is not possible to play an instrument, recite a speech, draw or sculpt an object perfectly the first time you try. In fact, to create something impressive, you need to put in a considerable amount of time and effort. Creative art does not produce itself – even if you are a genius. Writing a poem or a novel will require many drafts, discarded lines, paragraphs, sentiments before it is completed. This is why studying these creative subjects is so important. You cannot stay within your comfort zone: you have to make mistakes, adapt, revise and learn to make progress.

To say 'you can't make an omelette without breaking eggs' may be a cliche, but it is also true. (nb being able to make a tasty omelette is a useful accomplishment, and harder to do well than it might seem, yet is a practical life skill which features on few curricula). You need to take risks, step beyond the safe and secure, to achieve something new and interesting, or make your own mark. We need to be educating girls and boys to make mistakes and take calculated risks not simply to improve and broaden their horizons, but to ensure they are able to function and contribute constructively to the society in which they live, and which we want them to be defining and leading.

To do well at GCSE and A Level, you need to learn the answers that the examiner wants you to give, and use the precise terminology required to get the marks. Now, as teachers of course we have a responsibility to provide our students with the information and tools with which to achieve the best possible grades. It is true that to discern what someone wants, and to provide them with information they need in the form they require is a useful skill, so this is an important element of education. But it is not the only one, and sadly it takes on a disproportionate importance in the current education system, overshadowing other more practical skills and talents. If you have good teachers and work hard you can

do very well, without necessarily having to think outside the box, or challenge any conventions. However, even if you understand complex concepts, think originally and independently, you won't necessarily be rewarded with an A*.

Frequently it takes different approaches to encourage making mistakes and learning from them in boys than in girls. Creating an environment where girls feel comfortable to get things wrong and reflect on why things didn't work out as they expected, then on how to improve, without panicking, stressing or losing confidence in themselves and their ability, is an art. It is frequently a different environment, using predominantly different approaches from those which help boys flourish. Not better, just different, and of course there are some similarities and shared approaches which need to be employed.

One size does not fit all. We want to be educating a generation who can recognise fake news, who won't be short-sighted and who will challenge the conventions of contemporary society when it is needed, rather than simply conforming to the values – or lack thereof – of the current hierarchy. If we are going to stop this generation making the mistakes we have made, then they need to begin to make their own, and sooner, rather than later. The best place for this, is in school.

For more information about Mayfield School, see page 93

The importance of play and creativity in a primary setting

Philippa Ireton on why creative play is essential to child development and how Dallington School embraces a play-based learning approach

"Creative people are curious, flexible, persistent, and independent with a tremendous spirit of adventure and a love of play." – Henri Matisse

In a world of highly competitive schooling, where tests and homework are the norm, it is worth remembering these words of Henri Matisse.

So often creativity and play get squeezed out of the equation when schools are against the clock, preparing their young charges for the next stage of schooling. 'Getting ready to sit down and learn' is one of those phrases still heard in schools – somehow managing to suck all the potential joy out of learning. It is sometimes forgotten how important play is to children's natural development.

We know fundamentally that play is essential to healthy brain development, as well as improving the physical, social, and emotional wellbeing of children and young people. Through play, children learn about the world and themselves, build self-confidence, and learn skills that they can use in tackling schoolwork.

Frequent daily play can help reduce anxiety, stress, and irritability, as well as helping to boost sheer joy and self-esteem. We also know that play improves literacy; children are born with the ability to learn language, and from birth, language and literacy skills are built through play and interactions. Singing and learning poems help children develop listening skills and learn about the sounds in words.

At Dallington School we know how important it is to allow time for unstructured play – not just in the Early Years but also as children progress through school. They need time to direct their own activities, without being led by an adult. Many children have their lives filled with after school activities, violin lessons, extra maths, and have no time to be bored, and therefore have no time for creative play, nor the ability to create their own play. The United Nations lists play as one of the basic rights of every child.

Imagine the scene: a group of year 3 children have been discussing weather patterns as part of a geography lesson. It stemmed from their cross curricular topic last term about the Stone Age. Wondering how Stone Age people managed to live with adverse weather, and how they might have predicted when it was going to be really wet, or very cold, the discussion turned to how the children themselves might replicate the lives of Stone Age people. They decided they needed to take their investigation outside to the local park, and thus began an outdoor exploration of den building, weather watching and recording, and creating a receptacle to catch the rain.

Another chance discussion in year 2 about the effect plastic has on the health of our seas has led to an extraordinary learning journey, with children campaigning for the replacement of single-use cups in the school, writing heart-felt letters to the council, creating awareness posters and leading a whole school assembly about the issue. This is what play-based education can look like, led by children's curiosity and where the educator is in turn led. The children brought together all sorts of different skills, presentation, art, writing; all inspired by a discussion that started with one question.

In most schools these opportunities become ever-decreasing once children reach the age of five. Perceived expectations of progress and whole-class teaching take the place of child-led endeavour. It takes skilled staff to recognise in the moment those fascinations that excite children, and to follow their lead.

This is what a regular day at Dallington School can look like. We believe that it is important to ensure that every day is exciting and fun, and to allow children's natural learning to take off in different directions. Allowing a certain fluidity in the timetable enables the teacher to give children this wonderful gift of time and freedom. An enquiry topic-based curriculum is an ideal way to help children become the architects of their own learning; the very cross curricular nature brings together so many different lines of enquiry and throws up new questions

and interests. Children have the time to work through the process of planning, problem solving, and discussing how to present their work. Home learning projects, usually model-making, are kept out on display so that children can return to them at different times during the school day, and can explain to each other (and visiting adults) the details of what they have created.

This type of approach is not necessarily easy, it takes a lot of planning time to ensure that this provision is maintained, but we have shown that learning through play can be one of the most effective ways to do this and is the best possible way for children to embrace their learning and take ownership of it. The most important thing we educators can teach our children is 'how to be a learner'. It gives children the all-important transferable skills they need to continue to be successful learners in the future.

Finally, let us all allow children to enjoy their childhood!

For more information about Dallington School, see page 44

Supporting children's emotional development

Knightsbridge School's pioneering partnership with Place2Be has helped its students build emotional resilience

Knightsbridge School was the first private day school in the UK to develop a partnership with the children's mental health charity Place2Be.

Magoo Giles, the Founder and Principal of Knightsbridge School, signed the school up with Place2Be in 2014. Magoo served on the front line with the armed forces in Bosnia in the mid-Nineties and insisted on having independent, specialist experts at the school to help students and teachers navigate an increasingly complex and changing world.

His actions were remarkably prescient. The work of Place2Be in schools has become ever more vital in recent years. The Covid pandemic, the war in Ukraine and subsequent economic crisis have been a huge challenge for many young people and their families, as well as a worrying spike in children presenting with poor mental health in all UK schools.

The war in Ukraine in particular, has felt very close to home at Knightsbridge School (KS), which offers a British education with an international flavour by dint of its central London location.

"Knightsbridge School, like other non-denominational organisations, can be a melting pot," says Magoo. "World events affect our children and families. Amongst our school population, we have a wonderfully diverse and cultural group which includes

Russians and Ukrainians. The last few months have been far from easy, but Place2Be has been crucial in creating understanding and giving children the language they need to communicate their emotions on this difficult subject".

At Knightsbridge School (KS), the charity's one-to-one and group counselling, plus expert training for staff, has become an integral part of the school's excellent pastoral support. KS is still one of only a few independent schools who work with the charity, but the school's leaders are keen to spread the word about its immense benefits.

"We are a progressive school and saw the increasing need to have a service that was impartial yet professional and supportive, in an ever-adapting landscape," reflects Magoo. *"Creating a safe, confidential, impartial space for children to visit and work through their problems is critical for their development. We cannot expect to experience everything our young people go through, so it is crucial they have the support they need and we can draw from the immense experience that Place2Be can offer."*

Soon after joining, Place2Be became an established part of the school system, embedded inside and outside the classroom. Making full use of Place2Be's whole-school approach allowed the school to serve children who were at different stages of their emotional development, including those who were more reluctant to seek help.

Shona Colaço, Head of KS, says, *"We have children here from completely differing backgrounds, cultures, and experiences. Some are comfortable to use specialist services, whereas for others, the idea of seeking counselling is completely alien. Over the years, Place2Be has integrated seamlessly with our curriculum and existing pastoral care programme, allowing us to reach each child at the stage they most need it."*

And it's not just the bigger world issues that children can struggle with. Academic pressure, performance anxiety, family dynamics, friendship and self-esteem issues can all affect children's mental health.

Place2Be School's Project Manager Paula Losch, explains, *"Many issues will resonate across both the independent and state sector, such as anxiety, which has been a big theme for us. A lot is demanded of children and having to respond to these demands can create pressure. Other issues are more specific to us as a school with such a diverse and international school community – we support children whose parents have recently relocated, who are learning English for the first time, who are forming friendships in new contexts."*

Many children were anxious about returning to school during Covid, or were worried about missing out, says Losch. They were concerned on how absence would affect their performance and their friendships. Would they miss something critical? Would everything be different when they got back? *"Just knowing that Place2Be is there provides comfort and continuity."*

She adds, *"When children are overwhelmed by loneliness, sadness, grief, or anxiety, they can't focus on learning and enjoying life with friends and family. The school recognises this and that's why Place2Be is such an essential service here. They know that for children to grow academically, they must be well."*

Place2Be at KS runs drop-in sessions through Place2Talk and involves parents, providing guidance and a listening ear, to ensure there is a wraparound approach to each child's development.

"Though many people assume we are just providing one-to-one counselling sessions, it is so much more. We lead in-class circle times, hold coffee mornings, and invite mental health professionals to the school to speak on topics which are of most concern to students. Students also know that they can knock on the Place2Be door at any time, leave a slip in a box, and we are here. We also offer a space for staff to come and discuss issues and support parents, too – this includes partnering with the school's parent groups (specifically the Knowledge Society). We are here for the whole school community," says Losch.

Since working with Place2Be, the school has spread the word within the independent sector and helped broker critical relationships with other schools. KS has also helped fundraise for Place2Be's community outreach programmes.

What advice would Magoo give other schools interested in Place2Be?

"I would say go for it and go for it early. Early intervention is crucial. It helps to create the right culture right from the start, which develops young people in all kinds of ways. Place2Be has seriously opened the eyes of our young people to better mental health and helped to grow the empathy in our school community alongside our community values The KS Code. We owe it to our children to care for their mental wellbeing as well as academic progress".

For more information about Knightsbridge School, see page 50

A pathway to life ahead

Davenies School explains how their award scheme helps to enrich the learning of their pupils

As a preparatory school for boys aged 4-13, the Davenies Award Scheme (DAS) is a hugely important part of our Senior School enrichment programme. In Years 7 and 8 – the senior years at Davenies – boys take part in a range of activities, projects and experiences designed to enhance their all-round education, to strengthen their understanding of fundamental transferable skills, and teach them essential life skills. The aim is to ensure that every Davenies boy leaves us at the end of Year 8 well prepared for their life ahead; DAS sessions enable us, as a school, to provide a pathway to this, furnished with events to continue to Engage, Inspire and Challenge beyond the weekly timetable.

DAS started at Davenies as a way of teaching the things outside of the syllabi that we wanted our boys to know, all in line with our school aim to Engage, Inspire and Challenge. All boys in Years 7 and 8 have weekly DAS sessions after school, which provide the bulk of the DAS programme. These Monday night offerings include a series of activities and projects from teamwork

and leadership tasks to service in the community, from learning about the government vista to essential life skills acquisition such as ironing and car maintenance. As part of our Senior School Enrichment Programme, boys in Years 7 and 8 take part in projects aligned in their objectives to introduce many aspects of entrepreneurship in preparation for life after Davenies, and beyond.

The Endeavour Project challenges our senior boys to research and create a multi-sensory presentation (in groups) about a topic of their choice; they then deliver short face-to face-talks, in a Science Fair-style, to judges, parents, peers and siblings. In Year 8, boys take part in the Dragons' Den Project, introducing them to product development, marketing and advertising, culminating in a Dragons' Den-style presentation to a panel of investors. Following on from this, The Tenner Challenge invites boys to use £20 as seed money (formerly £10 for a number of years but increased due to ever rising costs!) to develop a micro-business in which they design, produce and sell a product, in order to raise money for charity. In doing these projects, boys at Davenies obtain a head start in the areas of project management, sales and marketing, collaborative working and presenting before moving into Year 9, and further ahead, to the GSCE and A level years, potentially planting the seeds of inspiration that could grow and develop into future careers as entrepreneurs.

The biggest benefits of these projects as part of DAS are seen through observations of the boys. Their ability to work together cooperatively and productively is evident year on year. In preparation for the workplace, boys are able to disagree and debate the merits of different ideas without falling out or taking it personally – there is a collective understanding that it is all for the benefit of the project/team. As a project, it provides the opportunity to all boys, regardless of academic profile, to develop their understanding and shine in a task that they find engaging and exciting. This is borne out in their presentations, which see them thrive whilst being pushed out of their comfort zones, and shows the boys that when they go the extra mile in preparing and developing a project, they can achieve outstanding outcomes. As a result, a number of boys who find presenting a challenge thrive in these projects and their self-confidence and sense of self-efficacy is boosted exponentially. Feedback received from parents about the projects and what their sons get from them are 100% positive every year, as is the reaction received from the boys when reviewing the projects. Their only complaint is that they cannot keep selling and developing their business and profits in school time!

Further strands of DAS include global understanding, cultural experiences, leadership through service and life skills. Drawing on the expertise and experience of leaders in their fields, boys in Years 7 and 8 regularly welcome a variety of guest speakers for short talks followed by a Q&A with time for discussion afterwards. Speakers range from a government advisor talking about Global Issues and

the UK's position in COP26, to a Hollywood Stunt Actor and Coordinator providing an insight into the fascinating, and sometimes dangerous world of filmmaking. Such talks, which are commonplace in senior schools and universities, inform and inspire our boys as they begin to look ahead to future career options.

Cultural experiences via our Whacky Weekends are a series of optional trips available to both Years 7 and 8. They encompass a range of different visits and activities including theatre outings, adventure trips, meals out and movie nights at school. Although trips vary from term to term, they remain fixed in their fundamental aim of providing a wide range of engaging and cultural experiences for the boys to enjoy, both individually and collectively. By doing things outside of the normal school day, Whacky Weekends form an integral part of the Senior School enrichment programme, providing the chance for boys to strengthen their bonds with each other and the staff, whilst introducing them to new and exciting experiences.

A rite of passage for all Davenies Year 8 boys, the post-exam Leavers' Programme is founded on the tenets of DAS. The final few weeks of Year 8 life at Davenies are spent off-timetable as the boys enjoy an engaging, stimulating and challenging mix of trips, speakers and activities. As such, the Davenies Award Scheme is viewed as an essential part of a boy's Davenies education, not merely an add on. The 'award' element, therefore, allows for the recognition, reward and celebration of the boys' engagement, application and achievement as they progress through the multiple strands. Culminating in the award of a Bronze, Silver, Gold or Platinum Certificate, a presentation is made of their overall DAS contributions. In this way, we ensure that each boy's effort, achievement and experience is recognised formally at the end of their time at Davenies, providing a springboard to success at their next school.

For more information about Davenies School, see page 86

Choosing a school – what to consider

However much a school may appeal at first sight, you still need sound information to form your judgement

Schools attract pupils by their reputations, so most go to considerable lengths to ensure that parents are presented with an attractive image. Modern marketing techniques try to promote good points and play down (without totally obscuring) bad ones. But every Head knows that, however good the school prospectus is, it only serves to attract parents through the school gates. Thereafter the decision depends on what they see and hear. Research we have carried out over the years suggests that in many cases the most important factor in choosing a school is the impression given by the Head. As well as finding out what goes on in a school, parents need to be reassured by the aura of confidence that they expect from a Head. How they judge the latter may help them form their opinion of the former. In other

words, how a Head answers questions is important in itself and, to get you started, we have drawn up a list of points that you may like to consider. Some can be posed as questions and some are points you'll only want to check in your mind. They are not listed in any particular order and their significance will vary from family to family, but they should be useful in helping you to form an opinion.

Before visiting and asking questions, **check the facts** – such as which association the school belongs to, how big it is, how many staff *etc*. Is there any form of financial pie chart showing how the school's resources are used? The answers to questions like these should be in the promotional material you've been sent. If they aren't, you've already got a good question to ask!

Hendon Prep School - see editorial on page 5

Check the website. Is it up-to-date? Look at the school's social media feeds and videos. What type of tone do they set? That first impression is very important.

When you get to the school you will want to judge the overall atmosphere and decide whether it will suit you and your child. Are any other members of the family going to help to pay the fees? If so, their views are important and the school's attitude towards them may be instructive.

When you make it to the inner sanctum, **what do you make of the Head as a person?** Age? Family? Staying? Moving on? Retiring? Busted flush? Accessible to children, parents and staff? If you never get to see the Head, but deal with an admissions person of some sort, it may not mean you should rule the school out, but it certainly tells you something about the school's view of pupil recruitment.

Academic priorities – attitude towards league tables? This is a forked question. If the answer is 'We're most concerned with doing the best for the child', you pitch them a late-developer; if the answer is, 'Well, frankly, we have a very high entry threshold', then you say 'So we have to give you a foolproof academic winner, do we?'

Supplementary questions:

- What is the ratio of teachers to pupils?
- What are the professional qualifications of the teaching staff?
- What is the school's retention rate? In prep schools this means how many pupils do they lose at 11 when the school goes on to 13.
- How long is the school day – and week?
- What are the school's exam results?
- What are the criteria for presenting them?
- Were they consistent over the years?
- Is progress accelerated for the academically bright?
- How does the school cope with pupils who do not work?
- Where do pupils go when they leave?
- How important and well resourced are sports, extra-curricular and after school activities, music and drama?
- What cultural or other visits are arranged away from the school?

Other topics to cover:

- What is the school's mission?
- What is its attitude to religion?
- How well is the school integrated into the local community?
- How have they responded to the Charities Act initiatives?
- What are the responsibilities and obligations at weekends for parents, pupils and the school?
- Does the school keep a watching brief or reserve the option to get involved after a weekend incident?
- What is the school's attitude to discipline?
- Have there been problems with drugs, drink or sex? How have they been dealt with?
- What is the school's policy on bullying?
- How does the school cope with pupils' problems?
- What sort of academic and pastoral advice is available?
- What positive steps are taken to encourage good manners, behaviour and sportsmanship?
- What is the uniform?
- What steps are taken to ensure that pupils take pride in their personal appearance?
- How often does the school communicate with parents through reports, parent/teacher meetings or other visits?
- What level of parental involvement is encouraged both in terms of keeping in touch with staff about your own child and more generally, *eg* a Parents' Association?

And finally – and perhaps most importantly – what does your child make of the school, the adults met, the other children met, pupils at the school in other contexts, and the website?

Initial advice

Educational institutions often belong to organisations that encourage high standards. Here we give a brief guide to what some of the initials mean.

BSA

The Boarding Schools' Association

Since its foundation in 1965-6, the Boarding Schools' Association (BSA) has promoted boarding education and the development of quality boarding through high standards of pastoral care and boarding accommodation. So parents and prospective pupils choosing a boarding school can be assured that more than 600 member schools in nearly 40 countries worldwide are committed to providing the best possible boarding environment for their pupils.

A UK boarding school can only be a full member of the BSA if it is also a member of one of the Independent Schools Council (ISC) constituent associations, or in membership of the BSA State Boarding Forum (SBF). These two bodies require member schools to be regularly inspected by the Independent Schools' Inspectorate (ISI) or Ofsted. Other boarding schools who are not members of these organisations can apply to be affiliate members. Similar arrangements are in place for overseas members. Boarding inspection of ISC-accredited independent schools has been conducted by ISI since September 2012. Ofsted retains responsibility for the inspection of boarding in state schools and non-association independent schools.

Boarding inspections must be conducted every three years. Boarding in England is judged against the National Minimum Standards for Boarding Schools which have been newly updated for September 2022.

Relationship with government

BSA is in regular communication with the Department for Education (DfE) on all boarding matters in England and also with devolved governments for other parts of the UK. The Children Act (1989) and the Care Standards Act (2001) require boarding schools in England to conform to national legislation. The promotion of this legislation and the training required to carry it out are matters on which the DfE and BSA work together. BSA worked especially closely with the DfE and other government departments during the coronavirus pandemic, supporting the safety and continuity of education for its member schools' pupils and staff.

Boarding training

BSA delivers the world's largest professional development programme for boarding staff. It offers:

- Two-year courses for graduate and non-graduate boarding staff – these involve eight study days and two assignments, each about 4,000 words long. This is the flagship training opportunity for staff seriously interested in boarding excellence
- A Diploma course for senior experienced boarding staff, involving three study days and two assignments spread between March and October
- A broad range of day seminars and webinars on topics of particular interest to boarding/pastoral staff – e.g. Essentials of Boarding, Leading a Boarding Team,
- Meeting the Needs of Overseas Boarders
- Specialists one or two-day conferences for Boarding Staff, Heads, Health & Wellbeing staff**, Marketing and Admissions staff* and State Boarding Schools staff and Safeguarding Leads**
- Basic training online, for those very new to boarding.

*With SACPA (Safeguarding and Child Protection Association), part of the BSA Group
**With HIEDA (Heath in Education Association) part of the BSA Group
**With BAISIS (British Association of Independent Schools with International Students), part of the BSA Group
In 2022, BSA Group also launched a new association, The Institute of Boarding (TIOB), which aims to be the world's first professional association for boarding school staff.

State Boarding Forum (SBF)

BSA issues information regards its state boarding school members and BSA should be contacted for details of these schools. In these schools, parents pay for

boarding but not for education, so fees are substantially lower than in an independent boarding school.

Chief Executive: Robin Fletcher
Deputy Chief Executive and Chief Operating Officer: Aileen Kane

Boarding Schools' Association
Unit 11/12, Manor Farm
Cliddesden, Basingstoke
Hants, RG25 2JB
Tel: 020 7798 1580
Email: bsa@boarding.org.uk
Website: www.boarding.org.uk

GSA

The Girls' Schools Association, to which Heads of independent girls' schools belong

The Girls' Schools Association helps girls and their teachers to flourish. It represents the Heads of a diverse range of independent UK girls' schools (day & boarding), among which are some of the top-performing schools in the country.

The GSA encourages high standards of education and promotes the benefits of being taught in a largely girls-only environment. GSA schools are internationally respected and have a global reputation for excellence. Their innovative practice and academic rigour attract pupils from around the world. Students at GSA schools enjoy abundant extra- and co-curricular opportunities. Academically, they thrive in the humanities and do disproportionately well in 'difficult' modern languages and STEM (science, technology, engineering, maths) subjects. A high percentage – 93% – progress to higher education.

GSA schools share experience, specialisms, opportunities and facilities with state sector schools in a wide range of partnerships. Many also provide means-tested bursaries for families of limited financial means.

The GSA is also committed to research projects which unite both state and independent girls' schools.

Twenty first century girls' schools come in many different shapes and sizes. Some cater for 100% girls, others provide a predominantly girls-only environment with boys in the nursery and/or sixth form. Some follow a diamond model, with equal numbers of boys but separate classrooms between the ages of 11 to 16. Educational provision across the Association offers a choice of day, boarding, weekly, and flexi-boarding education. Schools range in type from large urban schools of 1000 pupils to small rural schools of around 200. Many schools have junior and pre-prep departments, and can offer a complete education from age 3/4 to 18. Some also have religious affiliations. Heads of schools in the Girls' Day School Trust (GDST) are members of the GSA.

The Association aims to inform and influence national and international educational debate and is a powerful and well-respected voice within the educational establishment, advising and lobbying educational policy makers on core education issues as well as those relating to girls' schools and the education of girls. The Association has strong links with the Department for Education, OFQUAL, Awarding Bodies and Higher Education institutions.

The GSA also provides its members and their staff with professional development courses, conferences, advice and opportunities to debate and share best practice, ensuring that they have every opportunity to remain fully up-to-date with all aspects of their profession.

As the GSA is one of the constituent bodies that make up the Independent Schools' Council (ISC), its schools are required to undergo a regular cycle of inspections to ensure that these rigorous standards are being maintained. Most GSA schools also belong to the Association of Governing Bodies of Independent Schools, and Heads must be in membership of the Association of School and College Leaders (ASCL) or the National Association of Headteachers (NAHT). Early Career Teachers take part in the Induction Programme overseen by ISTIP.

The Association's secretariat is based in Leicester.

Suite 105, 108 New Walk, Leicester LE1 7EA
Tel: 0116 254 1619
Email: office@gsa.uk.com
Website: www.gsa.uk.com
Twitter: @GSAUK

President 2022/3: Heather Hanbury, LEH
President 2023/4: Marina Gardiner Legge, Oxford High School for Girls
Chief Executive: Donna Stevens

HMC

The Heads' Conference, to which the Heads of leading independent schools belong

Founded in 1869 the HMC exists to enable members to discuss matters of common interest and to influence important developments in education. It looks after the professional interests of members, central to which is their wish to provide the best possible educational opportunities for their pupils.

The Heads of some 296 leading independent schools are members of The Headmasters' and Headmistresses' Conference, whose membership now includes Heads of boys', girls' and coeducational schools. International membership includes the Heads of around 56 schools throughout the world.

The great variety of these schools is one of the strengths of HMC but all must exhibit high quality in the education provided. While day schools are the largest group, about a quarter of HMC schools consist mainly of boarders and others have a smaller boarding element including weekly and flexible boarders.

All schools are noted for their academic excellence and achieve good results, including those with pupils from a broad ability band. Members believe that good education consists of more than academic results and schools provide pupils with a wide range of educational co-curricular activities and with strong pastoral support.

Only those schools that meet with the rigorous membership criteria are admitted and this helps ensure that HMC is synonymous with high quality in education. There is a set of membership requirements and a Code of Practice to which members must subscribe. Those who want the intimate atmosphere of a small school will find some with around 350 pupils. Others who want a wide range of facilities and specialisations will find these offered in large day or boarding schools. Many have over 1000 pupils. 32 schools are for boys only, others are coeducational throughout or only in the sixth form. The first girls-only schools joined HMC in 2006. There are now 39 girls-only schools.

Within HMC there are schools with continuous histories as long as any in the world and many others trace their origins to Tudor times, but HMC continues to admit to membership recently-founded schools that have achieved great success. The facilities in all HMC schools will be good but some have magnificent buildings and grounds that are the result of the generosity of benefactors over many years. Some have attractive rural settings, others are sited in the centres of cities.

Pupils come from all sorts of backgrounds. Bursaries and scholarships provided by the schools give about a third of the 240,000 pupils in HMC schools help with their fees. These average about £35,000 per annum for boarding schools and £15,000 for day schools. About 190,000 are day pupils and 45,000 boarders.

Entry into some schools is highly selective but others are well-suited to a wide ability range. Senior boarding schools usually admit pupils after the Common Entrance examination taken when they are 13.

Most day schools select their pupils by 11+ examination. Many HMC schools have junior schools, some with nursery and pre-prep departments. The growing number of boarders from overseas is evidence of the high reputation of the schools worldwide.

The independent sector has always been fortunate in attracting very good teachers. Higher salary scales, excellent conditions of employment, exciting educational opportunities and good pupil/teacher ratios bring rewards commensurate with the demanding expectations. Schools expect teachers to have a good education culminating in a good honours degree and a professional qualification, though some do not insist on the latter especially if relevant experience is offered. Willingness to participate in the whole life of the school is essential.

Parents expect the school to provide not only good teaching that helps their children achieve the best possible examination results, but also the dedicated pastoral care and valuable educational experiences outside the classroom in music, drama, games, outdoor pursuits and community service. Over 89% of pupils go on to higher education, many of them winning places on the most highly-subscribed university courses.

All members attend the Annual Conference, usually held in a large conference centre in September/October. There are ten divisions covering England, Wales, Scotland

Leading
Independent
Schools

HMC

and Ireland where members meet once a term on a regional basis, and a distinctive international division.

The chair and committee, with the advice of the general secretary and membership secretary, make decisions on matters referred by membership-led sub-committees, steering groups and working parties. Close links are maintained with other professional associations in membership of the Independent Schools Council and with the Association of School and College Leaders.

Membership Secretary: Dr Simon Hyde
Tel: 01858 469059

12 The Point
Rockingham Road
Market Harborough
Leicestershire LE16 7QU
Email: office@hmc.org.uk
Website: www.hmc.org.uk

IAPS

The Independent Association of Prep Schools (IAPS) is a membership association representing leading headteachers and their prep schools in the UK and overseas

With around 660 members, IAPS schools represent a multi-billion pound enterprise, educating more than 170,000 children and employing more than 15,000 staff. As the voice of independent prep school education, IAPS actively defends and promotes the interests of its members.

IAPS schools must reach a very high standard to be eligible for membership, with strict criteria on teaching a broad curriculum, maintain excellent standards of pastoral care and keeping staff members' professional development training up-to-date. The head must be suitably qualified and schools must be accredited through a satisfactory inspection. IAPS offers its members and their staff a comprehensive and up-to-date programme of professional development courses to ensure that these high professional standards are maintained.

Member schools offer an all-round, values-led broad education which produces confident, adaptable, motivated children with a passion for learning. The targets of the National Curriculum are regarded as a basic foundation which is greatly extended by the wider programmes of study offered. Specialist teaching begins at an early age and pupils are offered a range of cultural and sporting opportunities.

IAPS organises a successful sports programme where member schools compete against each other in a variety of sports. In 2019-20, over 17,000 competitors took part in 119 events across 7 sports.

Our schools are spread throughout cities, towns and the countryside and offer pupils the choice of day, boarding, weekly and flexible boarding, in both singe sex and co-educational schools. Most schools are charitable trusts, some are limited companies and a few are proprietary. There are also junior schools attached to senior schools, choir schools, those with a particular religious affiliation and those that offer specialist provision as well as some schools with an age range extending to age 16 or above.

Although each member school is independent and has its own ethos, they are all committed to delivering an excellent, well-rounded education to the pupils in their care, preparing them for their future.

IAPS
Bishop's House
Artemis Drive
Tachbrook Park
CV34 6UD
Tel: 01926 887833
Email: iaps@iaps.uk
Website: iaps.uk

ISA

The Independent Schools Association (ISA) is a family of over 590 Headteachers who represent the diverse range of independent education practised across the UK and overseas

The Independent Schools Association (ISA), established in 1878, is one of the oldest of the Headteachers' Associations for schools that make up the Independent Schools Council (ISC).

ISA exists to provide professional support, fellowship and opportunity to their 595 Members who nurture and develop over 120,000 pupils within their schools. Promoting best practice and fellowship remains at the core of the ISA, as it did when it began over 140 years ago.

ISA celebrates a wide-ranging membership, not confined to any one type of school, but including all: nursery, pre-preparatory, junior and senior, all-through schools, coeducational, single-sex, boarding, day, as well as performing arts and specialist provision schools.

As well as the support and specialist professional development opportunities for ISA's Members through their programme of courses and conferences, pupils in ISA schools benefit from their Head's membership with access to the extensive ISA Sport and Arts programmes.

ISA Sport champions inclusion in physical activity through positive experiences for young people across a programme of 58 national (and over 140 regional) events at venues such as St George's Park.

ISA Arts helps schools inspire creativity, expression and individuality across the arts through both virtual and in-person events.

Membership is open to any Head or Proprietor, provided they meet the necessary accreditation criteria, including inspection of their school by a government-approved inspectorate.

The ISA President, Lord Lexden, represents the Association in the House of Lords and seeks to join discussions of education when they take place and welcomes further collaboration between the independent and maintained sectors.

ISA is supported by a number of committees, comprised of serving Heads and Honorary Members, who meet regularly to consider the issues that affect independent education. Some committee areas include education, monitoring developments in education and formulating responses to Government, and EDI, developing and promoting the principles of inclusion within the Association and supporting Members in promoting Equality, Diversity and Inclusion (EDI) in their schools.

President: Lord Lexden
Chief Executive: Rudolf Eliott Lockhart

ISA House, 5-7 Great Chesterford Court, Great Chesterford, Essex CB10 1PF
Tel: 01799 523619
Email: isa@isaschools.org.uk
Website: www.isaschools.org.uk

ISA celebrates a wide-ranging membership, not confined to any one type of school, but including all: nursery, pre-preparatory, junior and senior, all-through schools, coeducational, single-sex, boarding, day and performing arts and special schools

The Society of Heads

The Society is an Association of Heads of just over 130 well-established independent schools

The Society is an Association of Heads of just over 130 well-established independent schools. It was founded in 1961 when a group of Heads decided they needed a forum in which to share ideas and experience. Since then the Society has grown substantially in size, reputation and effectiveness and represents a vibrant community of independent schools throughout England and Wales with some additional overseas members.

The Society's policy is to maintain high standards in member schools, to promote independent education, to provide an opportunity for the sharing of ideas and common concerns, to foster links with the wider sphere of higher education and to strengthen relations with the maintained sector by promoting partnerships.

Within the membership there is a wide variety of educational experience. Some schools are young, some have evolved from older foundations, some have behind them a long tradition of pioneer and specialist education; a number are at the leading edge of education in music, dance and the arts; and several are well known for their effective support for those with specific learning difficulties. The great majority are co-educational but we also have some all-boys and all-girls schools. Many have a strong boarding element; others are day only. All offer a stimulating sixth-form experience and give a sound and balanced education to pupils of widely varying abilities and interests.

The Society is one of the constituent Associations of the Independent Schools Council. Every Full Member school has been accredited through inspection by the Independent Schools Inspectorate (or Estyn in Wales and HMIE in Scotland) and is subject to regular visits to monitor standards and ensure that good practice and sound academic results are maintained. The Society is also represented on many other educational bodies.

All members are in membership of the Association of School and College Leaders (ASCL) or other union for school leaders and Full Member schools belong to AGBIS or an equivalent professional body supporting governance.

There are also categories of Alliance and Alliance Overseas Membership to which Heads are elected whose schools do not fulfil all the criteria for Full Membership but whose personal contribution to the Society is judged to be invaluable.

> The Society has grown substantially in size, reputation and effectiveness and represents a vibrant community of independent schools throughout England and Wales with some additional overseas members.

The Society hosts the autumn meeting, summer meeting and the annual conference for members. The Society also provides an extensive professional development programme.

The Society of Heads Office,
Office 101B, Harborough Grow-On Centre, Compass Point Business Park, Market Harborough, Leicestershire LE16 9HW
Tel: 01858 433760
Email: info@thesocietyofheads.org.uk
Website: www.thesocietyofheads.org.uk

The Independent Schools Council

The Independent Schools Council (ISC) works with its members to promote and preserve the quality, diversity and excellence of UK independent education both at home and abroad

What is the ISC?

The ISC brings together seven associations of independent schools, their heads, bursars and governors. Through our member associations we represent approximately 1,400 independent schools in the UK and overseas, which educate more than half a million children.

The ISC's work is carried out by a small team of dedicated professionals in central London. We are assisted by contributions from expert advisory groups in specialist areas. Our priorities are set by the board of directors led by our chairman, Barnaby Lenon.

ISC schools

Schools in membership of the ISC's constituent associations offer a high quality, rounded education. Whilst our schools are very academically successful, their strength also lies in the extra-curricular activities offered, helping to nurture pupils' soft skills. There are independent schools to suit every need, whether you want a day or boarding school, single-sex or co-education, a large or a small school, or schools offering specialisms, such as in the arts.

Our schools are very diverse: some are selective and highly academic, while others have very strong drama or music departments full of creative opportunities. For children with special needs there are many outstanding independent schools that offer some of the best provision in the country.

Many schools have high levels of achievement in sport, offering a wide range of facilities and excellent coaches. Independent schools excel at traditional sports like football and rugby, but also offer more unusual sports like rowing and fencing.

There is also a wealth of co-curricular opportunities available. Whether your child is into debating, sailing, or the Model United Nations, most schools offer numerous clubs and activities.

Academic results

Typically, the ISC publishes a sector-wide analysis of Year 11 and Year 13 exam results for independent schools every August. However, due to the ongoing impact of the pandemic on grading, the ISC did not conduct an external analysis of member schools' results in 2022. There was no sector-wide ISC publication of results in 2020 or 2021 because exams were temporarily replaced by different assessment processes created in response to the crisis.

Looking back to 2019, 45.7% of Year 13 exam entries at independent schools were graded A*/A, compared to the national average of 25.5%. That year 95.6% of Year 11 exams at independent schools were graded C/4 or higher, compared to the national average of 67.3%.

Fee assistance

Schools take affordability very seriously and are acutely aware of the sacrifices families make when choosing an independent education. Schools work hard to remain competitive whilst facing pressures on salaries, pensions and maintenance and utility costs. They are strongly committed to widening access and many schools have extended their bursary provision – this year, the amount of means-tested fee assistance has risen to a total of £480m. Over 180,000 pupils currently benefit from reduced fees, representing over a third of pupils at our schools.

Our schools are very diverse: some are selective and highly academic, while others have very strong drama or music departments full of creative opportunities.

School partnerships

Independent and state schools have been engaged in partnership activity for many years, with the majority of ISC schools currently involved in important cross-sector initiatives. These collaborations involve the sharing of expertise, best practice and facilities, and unlock exciting new opportunities for all involved. To learn more about these valuable partnerships, visit the Schools Together website: https://www.schoolstogether.org/

ISC Associations

There are seven member associations of the ISC, each with a distinctive ethos in their respective entrance criteria and quality assurance:
Girls' Schools Association (GSA)
Headmasters' and Headmistresses' Conference (HMC)
Independent Association of Prep Schools (IAPS)
Independent Schools Association (ISA)
The Society of Heads
Association of Governing Bodies of Independent Schools (AGBIS) – www.agbis.org
Independent Schools' Bursars Association (ISBA) – www.isba.org.uk

Further organisations who are affiliated to the ISC:
Boarding Schools Association (BSA), Council of British International Schools (COBIS), Scottish Council of Independent Schools (SCIS) and Welsh Independent Schools Council (WISC).

The Independent Schools Council can be contacted at:
First Floor,
27 Queen Anne's Gate,
London,
SW1H 9BU
Telephone: 020 7766 7070
Website: www.isc.co.uk

independent
schools
council

Help in finding the fees

Chris Procter, joint managing director of SFIA, outlines a planned approach to funding your child's school fees

Despite the challenges of the Covid-19 pandemic and, more recently, the conflict between Russia and Ukraine the independent education sector remains resilient, according to the latest Independent Schools Council (ISC) survey, conducted in January 2022. The number of pupils in ISC schools stood at 544,316, a new record high.

Average school fee increases were 3% between the 2020/21 and 2021/22 school years, the second lowest annual rise ever recorded in the ISC Census. The average day school fees were £5,218 which is an increase of 3.1%. The average boarding school fees were £12,344 per term, an increase of 2.9%.

Fees charged by schools vary by region – for example, the average day school fees per term ranged from £4,500 in the North West to £6,250 in London.

Over £1.2bn of fee assistance was provided in the 2021/22 school year, of which £960m came from schools themselves. Over a third of pupils in ISC schools received at least one type of fee support.

£480m of means-tested fee assistance was provided, an increase of £25m on the previous year. The average means-tested bursary stood at over £10,840. Nearly half of all pupils on means-tested bursaries had more than half of their fees remitted.

The overall cost of school fees (including university fees) might seem daunting: the cost of educating one child privately could well be very similar to that of buying a house but, as with house buying, the school fees commitment for the majority of parents can be made possible by spreading it over a long period rather than funding it all from current resources.

It is vital that parents do their financial homework, plan ahead and start to save early. Grandparents who have access to capital could help out; by contributing to school fees they could also help to reduce any potential future inheritance tax liability.

Parents would be well-advised to consult a specialist financial adviser as early as possible, since a long-term plan for the payment of fees – possibly university as well – can prove very advantageous from a financial point of view and offer greater peace of mind. Funding fees is neither science, nor magic, nor is there any panacea. It is quite simply a question of planning and using whatever resources are available, such as income, capital, or tax planning opportunities.

The fundamental point to recognise is that you, your circumstances and your wishes or ambitions, for your children, or grandchildren are unique. They might well appear similar to those of other people but they will still be uniquely different. There will be no single solution to your problem. In fact, after a review of all your circumstances, there might not be a problem at all.

So, what are the reasons for seeking advice about education expenses?

- To reduce the overall cost
- To get some tax benefit
- To reduce your cash outflow
- To invest capital to ensure that future fees are paid
- To set aside money now for future fees
- To provide protection for school fees
- Or just to make sure that, as well as educating your children, you can still have a life

Any, some, or all of the above – or others not listed – could be on your agenda, the important thing is to develop a strategy.

At this stage, it really does not help to get hung up on which financial 'product' is the most suitable. The composition of a school fees plan will differ for each family depending on a number of factors. That is why there is no one school fees plan on offer.

The simplest strategy but in most cases, the most expensive option, is to write out a cheque for the whole bill when it arrives and post it back to the school. Like most simple plans, that can work well, if you have the money. Even if you do have the money, is that really the best way of doing things? Do you know that to fund £1,000 of school fees as a higher rate taxpayer paying 40% income tax, you currently need to earn £1,667, this rises to £1,818 if you are an additional rate taxpayer where the rate is 45%.

How then do you start to develop your strategy? As with most things in life, if you can define your objective, then you will know what you are aiming at. Your objective in this case will be to determine how much money is needed and when.

You need to draw up a school fees schedule or what others may term a cash flow forecast. So, you need to identify:

- How many children?
- Which schools and therefore what are the fees? (or you could use an average school fee)
- When are they due?
- Any special educational needs?
- Inflation estimate?
- Include university costs?

With this basic information, the school fees schedule/cash flow forecast can be prepared and you will have defined what it is you are trying to achieve.

Remember though, that senior school fees are typically more than prep school fees – this needs to be factored in. Also, be aware that the cost of university is not restricted to the fees alone; there are a lot of maintenance and other costs involved: accommodation, books, food, to name a few. Don't forget to build in inflation, I refer you back to the data at the beginning of this article.

You now have one element of the equation, the relatively simple element. The other side is the resources you have available to achieve the objective. This also needs to be identified, but this is a much more difficult exercise. The reason that it is more difficult, of course, is that school fees are not the only drain on your resources. You probably have a mortgage, you want to have holidays, you need to buy food and clothes, you may be concerned that you should be funding a pension.

This is a key area of expertise, since your financial commitments are unique. A specialist in the area of school fees planning can help identify these commitments, to record them and help you to distribute your resources according to your priorities.

The options open to you as parents depend completely upon your adviser's knowledge of these complex personal financial issues. (Did I forget to mention your tax position, capital gains tax allowance, other tax allowances, including those of your children and a lower or zero rate tax paying spouse or partner? These could well be used to your advantage.)

A typical school fees plan can incorporate many elements to fund short, medium and long-term fees. Each plan is designed according to individual circumstances and usually there is a special emphasis on what parents are looking to achieve, for example, to maximise overall savings and to minimise the outflow of cash.

Additionally, it is possible to protect the payment of the fees in the event of unforeseen circumstances that could lead to a significant or total loss of earnings.

Short-term fees

Short-term fees are typically the termly amounts needed within five years: these are usually funded from such things as guaranteed investments, liquid capital, loan plans (if no savings are available) or maturing insurance policies, investments etc. Alternatively, they can be funded from disposable income.

Medium-term fees

Once the short-term plan expires, the medium-term funding is invoked to fund the education costs for a further five to ten years. Monthly amounts can be invested in a low-risk, regular premium investment ranging from a building society account to a friendly society savings plan to equity ISAs. It is important to understand the pattern of the future fees and to be aware of the timing of withdrawals.

Long-term fees

Longer term funding can incorporate a higher element of risk (as long as this is acceptable to the investor), which will offer higher potential returns. Investing in UK and overseas equities could be considered. Solutions may be the same as those for medium-term fees, but will have the flexibility to utilise investments that may have an increased 'equity based' content.

Finally, it is important to remember that most investments, or financial products either mature with a single payment or provide for regular withdrawals; rarely do they provide timed termly payments.

Additionally, the overall risk profile of the portfolio should lean towards the side of caution (for obvious reasons).

There are any number of advisers in the country, but few who specialise in the area of planning to meet school and university fees. SFIA is the largest organisation specialising in school fees planning in the UK.

This article has been contributed by SFIA and edited by Chris Procter, Managing Director.

Chris can be contacted at:
SFIA, 27 Moorbridge Road,
Maidenhead,
Berkshire, SL6 8LT
Tel: 01628 566777
Email: enquiries@sfia.co.uk
Web: www.sfia.co.uk

Profiles

Schools in Central London

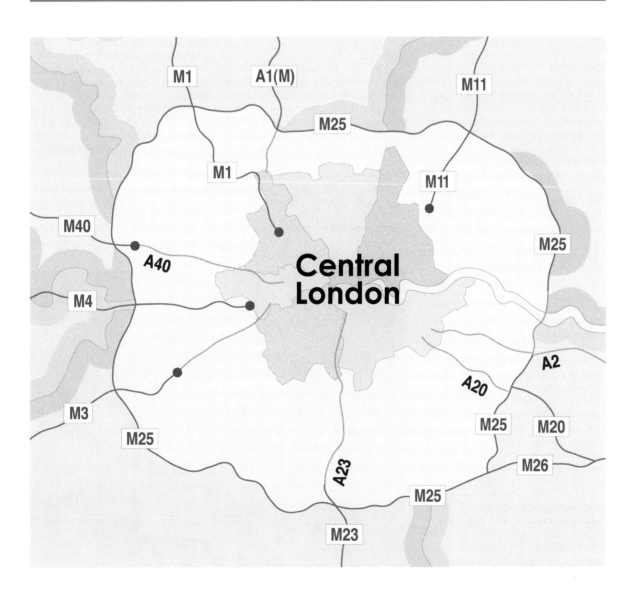

Broomwood Prep, Boys

26 Bolingbroke Grove, London, SW11 6EL

Tel: 020 8682 8888
Tel: 020 8682 8830 (Admissions)
Email: admissions@broomwood.com
Website: www.broomwood.com
Head (and Group Principal):
Mr Kevin Doble
School type: Boys' Day Preparatory

Religious Denomination: Church of England, all denominations welcome
Age range of boys: 7–13 years
No. of pupils enrolled as at 01/01/2023: 200
Fees as at 01/01/2023:
Day: £7,535 per term
Average class size: Av 17

ABOUT US: BROOMWOOD inspires and equips children aged 3-13 to #BeYourBEST. We offer a joyful co-educational pre-prep education at Broomwood Pre-Prep and Little Broomwood, followed by two single-sex, yet highly collaborative prep schools, Broomwood Prep, Boys and Broomwood Prep, Girls which prepare for both 11+ and 13+ exits. Whilst the schools have their own traditions and unique characteristics, we are united by what drives us: a bespoke, dynamic, and rich journey where pupils develop their own passions and talents, as well as being stretched in new directions, so they become the best version of themselves.

THE CURRICULUM: Boys thrive in our busy yet friendly school which provides outstanding teaching that stimulates, stretches, nurtures, and develops individual strengths to prepare boys for entry to top secondary schools at 11 and 13 – both in and out of London, whilst retaining a friendly and collaborative relationship with Broomwood Prep, Girls.

GAMES & THE ARTS: Our sports team includes FA, RFU, and ECB qualified staff with a wealth of experience of playing sport to a high level who aim to inspire boys to enjoy and work hard in all sports, offering a high quality and wide varied sporting programme. All boys play matches in the major sports and teams are very competitive even against much bigger schools. A wide-ranging club's programme includes karate, coding, and spy-club. Thriving and vibrant music, drama, and art departments with ambitious projects, multiple ensembles, and exciting performances.

PASTORAL CARE: Our tutor system ensures that each boy has someone looking out for him over and above the care he receives from every staff member. The small and friendly community enables staff and boys to get to know each other well. Parent partnership is actively encouraged, and the Headmaster's door is always open.

ENTRANCE & EXIT: Automatic entry for boys from our pre-prep school if it's the right school for them. Around 6-10 places a year for external candidate at 7 and some at 11. Exit to a broad mix of London day and out of town boarding at 11 & 13 including Bradfield, Dulwich, Harrow, Tonbridge, Marlborough, Wellington, Epsom, Emanuel, Trinity, Whitgift, Charterhouse, Sherborne, Cranleigh and Eton. Strong record in scholarships across all areas including academic, music, DT, drama, and sport.

HEAD TEACHER'S PHILOSOPHY: 'The whole child is the whole point': academic rigour, a focus on traditional manners, outstanding extra-curricular opportunities, holistic pastoral care and most importantly, running a school that allows the boys to be happy so that they fulfil their academic potential.

OUTSTANDING CHARACTERISTICS: Broomwood equips and inspires boys and girls aged 3-13 to #BeYourBEST by giving them the very best of all worlds: a joyful co-educational start to education at the age of 3 or 4 in a bespoke, specialist Early Years centre within a wider school setting. This is followed by a seamless transition to single-sex, yet highly collaborative, prep schools at the age of 7, before departing for some of the best schools in the country at the age of 11 or 13 – both day, boarding, co-ed and single-sex.

Broomwood is part of the wider Dukes Education family. Together we're extraordinary.

Broomwood Prep, Girls

68-74 Nightingale Lane, London, SW12 8NR

Tel: 020 8682 8810
Tel: 020 8682 8830 (Admissions)
Email: admissions@broomwood.com
Website: www.broomwood.com
Head: Mrs Louisa McCafferty
Group Principal: Mr Kevin Doble
School type: Girls' Day Preparatory

Religious Denomination: Church of England, all denominations welcome
Age range of girls: 7–13 years
No. of pupils enrolled as at 01/01/2023: 200
Fees as at 01/01/2023:
Day: £7,535 per term
Average class size: Av 17

ABOUT US: BROOMWOOD inspires and equips children aged 3-13 to #BeYourBEST. We offer a joyful co-educational pre-prep education at Broomwood Pre-Prep and Little Broomwood, followed by two single-sex, yet highly collaborative prep schools, Broomwood Prep, Boys and Broomwood Prep, Girls which prepare for both 11+ and 13+ exits. Whilst the schools have their own traditions and unique characteristics, we are united by what drives us: a bespoke, dynamic, and rich journey where pupils develop their own passions and talents, as well as being stretched in new directions, so they become the best version of themselves.

Broomwood Prep, Girls prepares for both 11+ & 13+ exits which offers an excellent and rounded education that nurtures and stretches in equal measure. Our winning combination of traditional values and innovative teaching coupled with an exciting enrichment programme challenges and stimulates both breadth and depth of learning. Broomwood girls are happy, confident, rounded individuals who are well prepared for future success.

THE CURRICULUM: A broad and stimulating mastery approach, with technology used at every level fosters a love of learning, bolsters self-confidence, creativity, and critical thinking, helping girls to maximise their potential whilst retaining a friendly and collaborative relationship with Broomwood Prep, Boys.

GAMES & THE ARTS: Sport and the arts are an important part of our curriculum, and we offer a surprisingly wide variety. We place great value on creativity with exceptionally strong music, art, and drama departments. New Art and DT block. On-site cookery school for Years 6 & 7.

PASTORAL CARE: We know that happy children thrive academically. With small class sizes, an excellent tutor system and mindfulness and wellbeing programmes built into the curriculum, we pride ourselves on nurturing the whole child and developing individual strengths so that when girls leave us at 11 or 13, they are confident, happy, well-rounded individuals with a strong sense of purpose.

ADMISSIONS & EXIT: Automatic entry for girls from our pre-prep school if it's the right school for them. Around 6-10 places a year for external candidate at 7 and some at 11. We take pride in the breadth of our curriculum and get wonderful results in all areas with girls regularly winning awards and scholarships at both 11 and 13, in all subjects, to some of the country's best schools, both day and boarding including Alleyn's, Benenden, Emanuel, Marlborough, Bradfield, JAGS, Streatham & Clapham High, Woldingham, Wellington, Cranleigh and King's, Canterbury. On average, around 25 per cent of leavers win awards across all areas: academic, art, music, drama, and sport.

HEAD'S PHILOSOPHY: We prepare for life, not just the next school. Our focus on the essential skills of creativity, critical thinking, resilience, independence and confidence, provides girls with the benefits of a holistic education where everything is important, and each girl is supported and enabled to be and do her best and is prepared for an exciting future.

OUTSTANDING CHARACTERISTICS: Broomwood equips and inspires boys and girls aged 3-13 to #BeYourBEST by giving them the very best of all worlds: a joyful co-educational start to education at the age of 3 or 4 in a bespoke, specialist Early Years centre within a wider school setting. This is followed by a seamless transition to single-sex, yet highly collaborative, prep schools at the age of 7, before departing for some of the best schools in the country at the age of 11 or 13 – both day, boarding, co-ed and single-sex.

Broomwood is part of the wider Dukes Education family. Together we're extraordinary.

Broomwood Pre-Prep and Little Broomwood

192 Ramsden Road, London, SW12 8RQ

Tel: 020 8682 8840
Tel: 020 8682 8830 (Admissions)
Email: admissions@broomwood.com
Website: www.broomwood.com
Head: Mrs Caron Mackay
Group Principal: Mr Kevin Doble
School type: Co-educational Day Pre-Preparatory & Nursery

Religious Denomination: Church of England, all denominations welcome
Age range of pupils: 3–7 years
No. of pupils enrolled as at 01/01/2023: 300
Fees as at 01/01/2023:
Little Broomwood: £3,000–£5,250 per term (see website for details)
Pre-Prep: £6,140 per term

ABOUT US: Broomwood Pre-Prep and Little Broomwood is the co-educational pre-prep school and pre-school class of BROOMWOOD in Wandsworth, South West London that inspires and equips children aged 3-13 to #BeYourBEST. We offer a broad, modern, and innovative curriculum designed to provide mastery of the building blocks of education, delivered in an inclusive, exciting and enjoyable way, harnessing curiosity and creating a desire to learn. All children have specialist teaching in arts, sport, music and French. Maths mastery is a speciality.

MOTTO: 'To do your best, to #BeYourBEST' exemplifies our ethos. We help each child to develop to the best of their individual ability and believe that a supportive but focused environment, without undue stress or 'hot housing', is the best way to enable them to fulfil their potential, both inside and outside the classroom.

GAMES & THE ARTS: All children take part in PE and Games for at least five periods per week and progress from learning basic skills to playing in competitive matches in the Prep Schools. Great emphasis on building confidence through art, drama, and musical performance. A multitude of clubs from Reception onwards include karate, coding, art, and cookery.

PASTORAL CARE: The school is split between two buildings a short walk from each other. Each site is small enough, and intimate enough, for all children to be well known to all staff. We have a strong pastoral team which includes learning support, a full time school nurse and a qualified school counsellor.

ADMISSIONS: *Little Broomwood:* Register and visit ASAP. In the September following a child's first birthday, parents are invited to express interest. Offers are then made in the order of the expressions of interest. Deposit secures place.
Broomwood Pre-Prep – Reception: Automatic entry for Little Broomwood and priority children (siblings & Dukes Education nurseries). All others should register and visit 18 months before entry. Random ballot in March/April to ensure equal mix of boys and girls and a good spread of birthdays. Entry at other ages: subject to current school reference and satisfactory school report. Children from the Pre-Prep progress automatically to the Prep Schools at the age of 7 providing these are the right schools for them.

HEAD TEACHER'S PHILOSOPHY: Children only have one chance to get a great education, so it's important to get it right from the start – and we do. Our focus is on creating a love of learning and to build the core skills that will enable children to succeed in the future. Our pupils love coming to school. We embrace different tools to ensure that our children are well prepared for the future: the power of the Yeti (it's ok not to be able to do something YET); the five Learning Powers of Curiosity, Communication, Creativity, Independence and Resilience. Plus, maths mastery and Thematic learning that immerses children into a subject. Above all, our focus is on the individual child and throughout their time with us they are supported, guided, stimulated, and stretched to be their BEST, before leaving us for the prep schools, brimming with confidence and ready for the next stage.

Broomwood is part of the wider Dukes Education family. Together we're extraordinary.

Dolphin School
(incorporating Noah's Ark Nursery Schools)

(Founded 1986)

106 Northcote Road, London, SW11 6QW

Tel: 020 7924 3472

Email: admissions@dolphinschool.org.uk

Website: www.dolphinschool.org.uk

Head Teacher: Mr S Gosden

Appointed: September 2021

School type: Co-educational Day Preparatory & Nursery

Age range of pupils: 2–11 years

No. of pupils enrolled as at 01/01/2023: 162

Fees as at 01/01/2023:

Day: £13,395–£14,670 per annum

Average class size:

18 in school: 8 in Nursery

Teacher/pupil ratio: 1:8 Nursery, 1:9 (Lower School), 1:18 (Upper School)

Curriculum
Our small class sizes enable us to get to know your child extremely well so that we can not only set specific individualised academic targets, but also discover how he or she learns best. We give priority to English and maths as well as hands-on science, colourful geography, history (with outings to the real thing) and whole-school Spanish.

Games and the arts
We train pupils in the arts with fantastic specialist teaching and a plethora of performing and exhibiting opportunities. We also coach children in a wide range of sports through dynamic teaching and a superb fixture list.

Pastoral care
We are committed to giving both time and care to grow your child's character on his or her journey from Reception to Year 6. Our Christian ethos leads us to believe that personal growth ultimately matters more than anything. So while we are thrilled that our leavers win academic or sporting scholarships to a range of excellent secondary schools, we are even more excited about who they are – and pleased that they enjoyed the journey.

Entry requirements
Reception class: appointment with the Head Teacher. Years 1-6: assessment day and past school reports.

Head Teacher's philosophy
If we want children to be the best they can be, academically, artistically, in sport or as people, we must start by valuing them for who they are.

Outstanding characteristics
The combination of nurture and dynamism. The passionate commitment of the staff. A fantastic all-round education.

Examinations offered
11+ entry examinations.

Senior exit schools: Alleyns, Box Hill, Caterham, Christs Hospital, Dulwich College, Emanuel, Epsom College, Francis Holland, Frensham Heights, Hurstpierpoint, Ibstock Place, JAG's, Kew House, Kings College, Streatham & Clapham High, Reeds, Royal Russell, St John's Leatherhead, Sydenham High, Thames Christian School, Trinity, Tudor Hall, Whitgift, Woldingham, Worth.

Dolphin School Trust is a registered charity (No. 1145113) and exists to promote a high quality of education for all its children based upon Christian principles.

Dallington School

(Founded 1978)

8 Dallington Street, Islington,
London, EC1V 0BW
Tel: 020 7251 2284
Email: admin@dallingtonschool.co.uk
Website: www.dallingtonschool.co.uk
Head of School: Mr James Griffiths
Appointed: September 2022

School type: Co-educational Day
Preparatory & Nursery
Age range of pupils: 3–11 years
No. of pupils enrolled as at 01/01/2023: 81
Boys: 58 **Girls:** 23
Fees as at 01/01/2023:
Day: £12,450–£15,660 per annum
Teacher/pupil ratio: 1:8 (with full time TA)

The original and only alternative, progressive family-run school in the heart of London, welcoming children from 3 to 11. *"The joy and reward of lifelong learning takes time. That time is called childhood, spent with people who understand and value it, in a stimulating environment that promotes it."* – Mogg Hercules MBE

These are the words of our founder, and we are proud to uphold her philosophy and aims to this day.

Dallington School was founded in 1978 to offer an alternative, holistic and progressive education to the mainstream on offer at the time. Our philosophy and ideas focus on nurturing children's development and broadening their learning experiences; encouraging children to become independent and curious learners; we encourage children to learn to think for themselves and we give them the opportunities to explore their interests, develop exceptional collaborative and social skills and debate intelligently. Dallington children are kind, self-aware and aware of others. We want school to be fun; for children to love coming to school; for every day to be a surprise, and most of all for children to feel that they are valued, being listened to and that their contribution is valid.

Situated in Clerkenwell, a stone's throw from the City of London, St Paul's and the Barbican, Dallington prides itself on being very different from many independent day schools. Offering a vibrant oasis of creativity, offering a rich and diverse curriculum, we celebrate childhood, embrace the individuality of every child and allow our children to flourish at their own pace in a relaxed and supportive 'family' environment. We offer a child-centred, creative, holistic and ambitious experience, designed to develop the whole, unique child and to prepare them for their onward educational journey.

Experiential learning is an important part of a Dallington education. Through enquiry topics and projects, science, geography and history are brought together in a meaningful, linked way. By integrating the different disciplines, we aim to give children a sense of the interrelatedness of the curriculum. Project

work allows children to make important connections in their thinking and develop key skills through sustained shared thinking and collaborative group work and provides the perfect opportunity for children to develop their ability to manage and extend themselves.

Projects are explored from many different perspectives, and will draw in creative writing skills, painting and model-making. Curricular-related trips to museums, galleries, theatres and the zoo serve to embellish and enrich their learning and understanding of the topic being studied.

Mathematics and Literacy are core subjects taught to a very high standard. In all classrooms teachers offer personalised teaching, so that every child can progress at their own pace and receive the support they need. This allows children who are developing their skills more quickly, to be suitably challenged and not grow bored. Dallington children have high literacy skills and often read well above their reading age. Weekly visits to the local library help develop their love of books and reading for pleasure.

Music and the performing arts ripple through everything we do. The chance to sing and learn rhythm through drum playing, as well as learning the ukulele, and other instruments, is a joyful experience for children. Learning about music from around the world, with visiting musicians, enriches their understanding of the different cultures of the world.

Outdoor learning – Forest school – is embedded into the curriculum and children spend lots of time outside, enjoying nature and learning about the world around them. We consider this to be a vital part of their development; a chance to spread their wings and have contact with the earth.

Life after Dallington

Our Head knows every child well and will start preparation for entry into secondary school in Year 5 with discussions with children and their parents about which schools might suit them. We don't put any unnecessary pressure on children by spending hours on exam papers, but offer a carefully designed model combining adaptive questioning, mindful practices, creative writing and public speaking, all of which provide the children with transferrable lifelong skills, incorporating our core values of relationships, empathy, creativity, individuality, play and enjoying the journey.

Our children move on to secondary school with a real sense of purpose, armed with self-confidence and an ability to adapt to new situations and new relationships. The school motto 'Value your own worth and understand the differences in others' serves them well for

the future.

In the words of a former Dallington parent: *"Dallington has a special something. It's very hard to put your finger on it, but it's absolutely there. It comes from a deep understanding of children, letting them enjoy their childhood, and learn who they really are."*

Faraday Prep School

Old Gate House, 7 Trinity Buoy Wharf,
London, E14 0JW
Tel: 020 8965 7374
Email: info@newmodelschool.co.uk
Website: www.faradayschool.co.uk
Head Teacher: Lucas Motion

School type: Co-educational Day
Preparatory
Age range of pupils: 4–11 years
No. of pupils enrolled as at 01/01/2023: 100
Fees as at 01/01/2023:
Day: £4,320 per term
Average class size: 14

Founded in 2009, Faraday Prep School, judged 'excellent' in all areas by the Independent Schools Inspectorate in November 2022, offers inspirational learning in an inspirational setting. A happy, vibrant and diverse independent primary school in East London, the school's historic and artistic riverside location, provides a magical environment and access to a stimulating, creative community that offers exciting learning opportunities.

We give every child a first-class education rooted in a creative curriculum, with small classes, quality teaching and a personal approach in a caring and kind environment.

In these formative years our aim is to inspire a love of learning and that the desire to explore, grow and create will stay with our pupils for life. We place a strong focus on literacy and numeracy, with a targeted approach that enables each child to progress at their own level.

Our lessons stretch, challenge and engage pupils of all abilities and interests. We present children with the great literature, music and works of art to help them acquire an increased understanding of the world in which they live and build a thorough understanding of knowledge in each subject. As such, our curriculum is broad, balanced and stimulating, and includes specialist teaching in Art, French, Music, Drama and Physical Education.

Children join our Reception class in their fifth year and leave for senior school at the age of eleven. The school day runs from 8.45 am until 3.30 pm, with our private buses running before and after school from a range of East London locations. We support busy parents by welcoming children from 8.15 am and by offering after-school care until 5.30 pm each day, with a wide range of extra-curricular activities on offer from gardening to robotics.

Our setting beside the River Thames, opposite the iconic O2 arena and beside the Trinity Lighthouse, gives our pupils an inspirational location in which to learn. We are fortunate enough to be surrounded by creative industries and frequently collaborate with them through workshops to enrich children's learning and also make the most of all that London has to offer, with regular trips to museums, historic attractions and galleries.

Entry into Reception is non-selective and based on the date the completed registration form is returned to our Registrar, with siblings given priority. Entry higher up the school is by interview and informal assessment in the classroom. We offer regular open days and welcome private tours.

Fulham School

(Founded 1996)

1-3 Chesilton Road, London, SW6 5AA
Tel: 020 8154 6751
Email: senioradmin@fulham.school
Website: fulham.school
Executive Head of Fulham: Bex Tear
School type: Co-educational Day Preparatory & Senior, Nursery & Sixth Form

Religious Denomination:
Non-denominational
Age range of pupils: 3–18 years
No. of pupils enrolled as at 01/01/2023: 650
Fees as at 01/01/2023:
Day: £19,158–£22,431 per annum
Average class size: 18

About Fulham

School Fulham School is independent and co-educational, providing a rich and diverse curriculum to boys and girls from age 3 to age 18. Situated in the heart of Fulham, the three school sites, Nursery & Pre-Prep, Prep and Senior, are ideally located to take advantage of London and the endless opportunities it offers to enhance education. For over 25 years Fulham School has believed in co-education in its broadest sense: not just girls and boys learning together but learners of all abilities understanding that they have much to offer each other, and teachers as keen to learn and evolve as their students. Specialist teachers and support staff inspire pupils to work to the limits of their potential, so they are prepared for the next steps in life while learning more about themselves and developing a broad range of interests.

Personalised Learning

Combining the best of tradition with innovative skills and methods Fulham School celebrates diverse abilities across academic, creative, and sporting pursuits. Teachers encourage the development of creative, problem-solving individuals who have tenacity, kindness, and self-worth. From the most academic to the most creative, the most driven to the most supportive, Fulham School wants each pupil to delight in what they do as they discover personal interests, gifts, and talents. *"Our close-knit, global community celebrates individuality, kindness, and initiative and works together to achieve more."* Bex Tear – Executive Head of Fulham School

Support

Fulham School supports the highest of academic high-flyers to achieve the scholarships and university places that will challenge them most alongside pupils whose chief passions and interests are expressed in practice and rehearsal rooms or on the sports field. All pupils are encouraged to make contributions where their strengths lie and recognise the contributions of others.

Hendon Prep School

(Founded 1873)

20 Tenterden Grove, Hendon,
London, NW4 1TD
Tel: 020 8203 7727
Email: admissions@hendonprep.co.uk
Website: www.hendonprep.co.uk
Headteacher: Mrs Tushi Gorasia
Appointed: October 2020

School type: Co-educational Day
Preparatory & Nursery
Age range of pupils: 3–11 years
No. of pupils enrolled as at 01/01/2023: 170
Fees as at 01/01/2023:
Full Time Preschool to Year 6:
£13,680–£17,550 per annum

Rated Excellent in all areas by the ISI in January 2023, Hendon Prep is a small independent school for girls and boys from 3-11 years old.

With a long-standing reputation for providing a holistic education, Hendon Prep is a school which prides itself on valuing well-being and academic attainment equally and has created an environment which celebrates diversity and inclusion.

This strong focus on belonging and wellbeing leads to great academic progress and outcomes, with children moving onto some of the most selective senior schools in the country at 11+, often with scholarships.

In their recent inspection report the ISI noted that *"Pupils of all ages and abilities achieve well and make excellent progress from their varied starting points, well above the national averages."*

Classes are small, and Hendon Prep offers a truly personalised approach to leaning, ensuring that pupils are stretched and challenged daily to ensure they meet their own unique potential, and ultimately develop a lifelong love of learning.

The ISI inspectors noted that *"Pupils demonstrate an excellent attitude to learning from an early age and throughout the school, in response to teaching which encourages initiative and independence."*

From the very start of their educational journey in the Preschool class, children benefit from subject specialist teaching in music, French and PE. The curriculum is further enriched at each stage with the addition of Art as a specialist subject in Reception, Spanish from Year 1, verbal and non-verbal reasoning from Year 2, and from Year 3 upwards the children are taught by subject specialist teachers across the board.

The school provides a fantastic range of facilities to enhance pupils' learning and experience. They have bright and well-resourced classrooms, complete with an ICT suite, dedicated Art and Design studio, music room, library, and a fully equipped science laboratory. A large playground and outside classroom give pupils much needed space for play and outdoor learning. With a planting area, amphitheatre, Astroturf football and netball pitch and giant chess board, playtimes are full of fun at Hendon Prep.

Kensington Wade School

Fulham Palace Road, London, W6 9ER
Tel: 020 3096 2888
Email: office@kensingtonwade.com
Website: www.kensingtonwade.com
Head: Mrs Suzanne Haigh

School type: Co-educational Day Preparatory & Nursery
Age range of pupils: 3–11 years
No. of pupils enrolled as at 01/01/2023: 108
Fees as at 01/01/2023:
Day: £6,560 per term

Kensington Wade is an award-winning, bilingual nursery and prep school in west London for children aged 3-11. At Kensington Wade half the lessons are taught in English and half in Chinese, giving children complete fluency in both languages, and thus a lifelong advantage for a global future.

Our child-centred approach creates a happy, stimulating environment with strong academic achievement and exceptional preparation for 11+ assessments for progression to top senior schools. Our results are consistently outstanding, and are a testament to the excellence of our dual language provision.

We offer specialist teaching from the very start with all children enjoying music lessons and, as they travel up the school, swimming, sports, computing, Spanish and science. We also provide an extensive co-curricular programme with activities designed to challenge the children intellectually, physically and creatively.

At Kensington Wade the happiness of our pupils is a huge priority, and we work closely with all our families to make sure that their children feel safe and loved by every member of our staff.

Our pupils come from a wide range of backgrounds. Many of the families at Kensington Wade do not speak Chinese at home. They may speak another language but what all our families share is an understanding of the considerable benefits of bilingualism, and the value of learning a language from an early age in an immersive setting – particularly Chinese.

Within weeks of joining Kensington Wade, all children are greeting each other, singing, counting and playing in Chinese. This fluency and ease in both languages is developed throughout their time with us, and they rapidly develop the ability to converse at a high level on any subject, and to read and write in Chinese using traditional characters.

Our innovative curriculum really engages and excites the children whilst also giving them a lifelong skill and advantage for the future.

Knightsbridge School

KNIGHTSBRIDGE
SCHOOL
(Founded 2006)

67 Pont Street, Knightsbridge,
London, SW1X 0BD
Tel: +44 (0)20 7590 9000
Email: office@knightsbridgeschool.com
Website: www.knightsbridgeschool.com
Head: Miss Shona Colaço
Appointed: 2015

School type: Co-educational Day
Preparatory, Senior & Nursery
Age range of pupils: 3–16 years
No. of pupils enrolled as at 01/01/2023: 400
Fees as at 01/01/2023:
Day: £7,452 per term
Average class size: 18
Teacher/pupil ratio: 1:12

At Knightsbridge School we believe in the power of community. Of being connected as a family within our school and being part of the community outside. At KS, as our school is known, we aim to be an unashamedly happy and vibrant school. Our ethos is based on human values – known as the KS Code – a set of shared beliefs centred on caring for each other and fulfilling our individual potential every day.

Our school has an amazing atmosphere where children can be themselves, where they can discover their many strengths and challenge their weaknesses, supported by an unbelievably dedicated team of teachers and staff. We are a 'joined-up' community at KS – each and every member of staff is connected with every child.

KS has real academic rigour; our children excel across the curriculum, but we are not, and never will be, an academic hothouse. Instead, we provide an enriching and truly rounded education; we have more than 70 extra-curricular clubs at the school. A strong spirit of can-do attitude runs throughout the school from children to staff to our wonderful parents who support us every step of the way.

KS is deeply involved with the local community, it has meaningful partnerships with two local primary schools, Ashburnham Community School (ACS) and Marlborough Primary School (MPS). We raise funds for both schools and support Place2Be (in-house counselling service) activities in the schools, as well as providing access to co-curricular clubs and offering staff training.

Children learn best when they are happy. And we believe much of human happiness comes from being part of a community so we do everything we can to create a warm, vibrant community both inside and outside our school.

Come and see for yourself by booking a school tour.

Lloyd Williamson School Foundation

LLOYD WILLIAMSON
SCHOOLS

12 Telford Road, London, W10 5SH

Tel: 020 8962 0345
Email: admin@lws.org.uk
Website: www.lloydwilliamson.co.uk
Co-Principals: Ms Lucy Meyer &
Mr Aaron Williams
Appointed: December 1999
School type: Co-educational Day

Preparatory, Senior & Nursery
Age range of pupils: 4 months–16 years
Fees as at 01/01/2023:
Day: £18,000 per annum
Nursery: £100 per day
Average class size: 12-16
Teacher/pupil ratio: 1:12

Over the past twenty-three years, Lloyd Williamson Schools have built an excellent reputation for high academic standards, personalised learning for individual children and a friendly, happy environment in which to learn. CAS visas can be offered. We are pleased to offer parents important extras:

- Breakfast and after-school club at no extra cost (the school and nurseries are open 7.30am – 6pm).
- Holiday clubs (we are open 50 weeks of the year).
- Small classes (max 16 to Year 6, max 18 in Secondary).
- Sensible fees.
- Home-cooked meals freshly prepared every day by our in-house chefs.

We boast excellent facilities, a homely atmosphere with school pets, and dedicated teachers who support the children to be focused, positive and enthusiastic. Ofsted say: *"Staff are ambitious for pupils and make sure that pupils feel valued"*; *"The curriculum is ambitious and well planned"* and *"There is a focus on kindness, listening to others and on pupils finding and following their passion".*

In the words of our children: *"I'm really happy here – the teachers really listen and if I get stuck they help!" "There is always someone who listens to me." "I like the way the big children look after the little children."* And the parents: *"You always know a Lloyd Williamson child – they're so polite!" "I think the school is, beyond doubt, the best I could wish for." "The best kept secret in London!"*

To visit the school or nurseries, please contact the school admin team on 020 8962 0345 or admissions@lws.org.uk.

L'Ecole de Battersea

(Founded 2005)
Trott Street, Battersea, London, SW11 3DS

Tel: 020 7371 8350
Email: admin@lecoledespetits.co.uk
Website: www.lecoledebattersea.co.uk
Principal: Mrs F Brisset
Head: Mr L Balerdi
Founder: Mrs M Otten
School type: Independent Bilingual Pre-Primary and Primary (Partenaire AEFE)

Religious Denomination:
All denominations welcome
Age range of pupils: 3–11 years
No. of pupils enrolled as at 01/01/2023: 250
Fees as at 01/01/2023:
Day: £5,075 per term
Average class size: 18 (max 21)

L'Ecole de Battersea opened in 2005 following on the success of its sister school, L'Ecole des Petits. The school combines the best elements of the English and French systems, with highly qualified teachers who provide a truly bilingual and rich cultural education from age three through to age eleven. Immersed in both languages and cultures on a daily basis, the pupils develop enquiring minds, strong self-confidence and a profound sense of understanding and tolerance of others.

The school community is very closely knit together, and offers strong support to a diverse range of over 32 nationalities. The aim is for pupils to reach oral, written and written fluency in both English and French by the time they leave the school at age 11. The teaching emphasis throughout the school is fundamentally based on the French system, into which aspects of the English curriculum and methodology are integrated.

The highly motivated bilingual team of teachers is qualified in both the English and French educational systems. This bilingual facility enables children and parents to choose to progress on to either the English private school system or to the French Lycée system, and is also ideal for the increasingly popular International Baccalaureate.

The school welcomes pupils from a range of cultures, and so aims to generate a truly international atmosphere. Partnership with the family is paramount in the school's ethos, and the school successfully seeks to develop confident and balanced children with experience of a wide range of activities, an appreciation of artistic and cultural heritage and a thoughtful and considerate attitude towards others.

L'Ecole de Battersea is also committed to maintaining the safest environment possible with the installation of high-performance air purification equipment in all classrooms, and other common areas, reducing pollution and the risk of infection.

The school is only a five-minute drive from Chelsea and operates a twice daily school bus service between South Kensington and Battersea, as well as a link to its sister school in Fulham.

L'Ecole de Battersea is inspected by both the French Inspectorate and Ofsted and achieves excellent academic results. OFSTED 2022 report qualified the school as *"Outstanding in all categories"*.

L'Ecole des Petits

(Founded 1977)
2 Hazlebury Road, Fulham, London, SW6 2NB

Tel: 020 7371 8350
Email: admin@lecoledespetits.co.uk
Website: www.lecoledespetits.co.uk
Principal: Mrs F Brisset
Head: Miss E Mesnage
Founder: Mrs M Otten
School type: Independent Bilingual Pre-Primary (Partenaire AEFE)

Religious Denomination: All denominations welcome
Age range of pupils: 3–6 years
No. of pupils enrolled as at 01/01/2023: 120
Fees as at 01/01/2023:
Day: £4,935 per term
Average class size: 14 (max 18)

L'Ecole des Petits is a flourishing pre-primary school situated in Fulham, just ten minutes from Chelsea, with easy access by public transport. The school also runs its own daily morning and afternoon bus service between South Kensington and Fulham, and between its sister school in Battersea.

The school was founded in 1977 to cater for English and French families who wanted their children to grow up in a bilingual environment. By combining the English Early Years curriculum with the French National curriculum, the school provides all aspects of education in both French and English.

Children are taught by qualified and highly-motivated bilingual teachers. The school aims to provide an education that enhances early learning skills in the controlled environment of small classes in a warm and friendly atmosphere, which encourages children to express themselves whilst following the structured bilingual curriculum.

We consider maintaining traditional family values a very important aspect of our approach. Our philosophy is to develop confident and happy children by providing the best possible all-round education and care, with an abundance of sports, drama, clubs, school outings and events as well as academic lessons. Our pupils are prepared to move onto both English and French schools, and many continue their primary education at our sister school, L'Ecole de Battersea.

According to one of our parents, L'Ecole des Petits is *"the best possible place for our daughter. Safe, friendly and caring environment where she is eager to go to learn. The team is fabulous and the school is perfect. It produces well rounded confident children."*

L'Ecole des Petits is inspected by both the French Inspectorate and Ofsted and achieves excellent academic results. OFSTED 2020 report qualified the school as *"Outstanding in all categories"*.

London Park School, Clapham

LONDON PARK SCHOOL
Clapham

7-11 Nightingale Lane, Clapham South, London, SW4 9AH

Tel: 020 8161 0301
Email: admissions@londonparkschools.com
Website: www.londonparkschools.com
Head: Mr Paul Vanni
Group Principal: Mrs Suzie Longstaff
School type: Co-educational Day Senior & Sixth Form

Religious Denomination: Church of England, all denominations welcome
Age range of pupils: 11–16 (plus 16-18 in standalone Sixth Form)
No. of pupils enrolled as at 01/01/2023: 250
Fees as at 01/01/2023:
Day: £7,535 per term
Average class size: Av 17-20

ABOUT US: London Park School Clapham is the cornerstone of an exciting new family of schools offering an outstanding, innovative, and personal education for students aged 11-16 (with the option to move on to our sixth form in Belgravia afterwards).

Each LPS school will be relatively small, with its own Head, its own staff and own identity, but sharing common values and benefitting from some exciting and innovative shared activities and initiatives.

THE CURRICULUM: Transformative teaching lies at the heart of our modern, stimulating curriculum, which is designed to provide an outstanding, rounded education that prepares students for tomorrow's world. It combines student wellbeing, academic excellence and a broad base of community, leadership, and entrepreneurial skills. We support and stretch and our thematic approach in Years 7-9 helps to develop higher-order thinking skills, strong teamwork, and motivated students with the analytical and problem solving skills that pay dividends in examinations and stand them in good stead for the future.

GAMES & THE ARTS: We offer both the more traditional sports such as football and netball, as well as exploring other, more alternative sports too. Our proximity to Clapham Common and other local sports grounds is a bonus. We strongly encourage creativity and have seen some great emerging talent in Art, DT, drama, and film club and have an annual whole school production and a Year 7 film which they write/film and edit.

PASTORAL CARE: Our students' wellbeing informs everything we do. We offer outstanding pastoral care to help each student develop the skills required for the challenges of modern life. Wellbeing is built into the weekly timetable and our tutorial system and thematic learning approach ensures that every student is well known, with all staff invested in the success and happiness of each child.

ENTRANCE AND EXIT: Main entrance in Year 7 (two classes) with an additional intake of one class in Year 9. Assessment via a combination of digital testing data, written and group task activities plus Head's interview. Students move on to LPS Sixth Form for A-Levels.

HEAD TEACHER'S PHILOSOPHY: Education should be modern, relevant, and prepare children for the ever-changing world in which we live. London Park Schools draws on the best of current practices in education with one eye firmly on the future with committed, innovative teachers who can transform the educational experience of our students so that they can move on to the next stage of their education with confidence.

OUTSTANDING CHARACTERISTICS: London Park School Clapham offers the best of both worlds: the care and support of a small school, with the opportunities and facilities of a larger one. A school that offers every student an outstanding, rounded education that prepares them for tomorrow's world. A school where character, collaboration, resilience, and entrepreneurship are taught and valued.

London Park Schools is part of the wider Dukes Education family. Together we're extraordinary.

Lycée Français Charles de Gaulle de Londres

LYCÉE FRANÇAIS
CHARLES DE GAULLE
DE LONDRES

(Founded 1915)
35 Cromwell Road, London, SW7 2DG
Tel: 020 7584 6322
Email: inscription@lyceefrancais.org.uk
Website: www.lyceefrancais.org.uk
Head of School: TBC

School type: Co-educational Day Preparatory & Senior, Nursery & Sixth Form
Age range of pupils: 3–18 years
No. of pupils enrolled as at 01/01/2023: 3450
Fees as at 01/01/2023:
Day: £7,631–£15,965 per annum

The Lycée Français Charles de Gaulle de Londres is governed by the AEFE (*Agence de l'Enseignement Français à l'Etranger*, a vast network with over 500 French schools in about 140 countries). 3,450 pupils are taught, spread over the main site in South Kensington and the three locations of its primary schools: Ecole Marie d'Orliac (Fulham), Ecole de Wix (Clapham) and Ecole André Malraux (Ealing).

Since its inception in 1915, the school has evolved and more than forty nationalities now make up its community. One thing has not changed though: its ability to develop educational practices whilst never losing sight of its tradition of excellence. Whichever section it be, British, International, Bilingual, Multilingual or French – this balance of tradition with modernity provides our pupils with a unique experience in an exceptional environment.

Delivering first-class education, this centennial institution offers various curricula leading towards public examinations (French *brevet* and *baccalauréat*, GCSEs, A-Levels) with consistent outstanding results. Typical success rates are 99.6% for the *Brevet* with over 82% "*Très bien*" honours and over 99% for the *Baccalauréat* (over 64% "*Très bien*" honours); in the British section, 100% for A-levels (over 62% A*/A) and 100% for GCSEs with 78% 9-7 grades.

The school makes a simple and honest commitment: to offer each child the best conditions to realise their academic potential, to be able to develop and thrive in a peaceful environment and achieve the level of excellence required to access their desired course even at the most competitive universities and higher education institutions worldwide.

The Headteacher confirms: "*We nurture each individual with care and help them build self-confidence – this remains our pledge to our families as much today as it has been for over a century.*"

Maida Vale School

(Founded 2020)
18 Saltram Crescent, London, W9 3HR
Tel: 020 4511 6000
Email: admissions@maidavaleschool.com
Website: www.maidavaleschool.com
Headmaster: Mr Magnus Bashaarat

School type: Co-educational Day Senior & Sixth Form
Age range of pupils: 11–18 years
No. of pupils enrolled as at 01/01/2023: 160
Fees as at 01/01/2023:
Day: £8,073 per term

Maida Vale School is a co-educational, independent senior school for pupils aged 11-18 years. Owned by the Gardener Schools Group, a family founded company set up in 1991, Maida Vale is the sister school to Ravenscourt Park Preparatory School, Kew Green Preparatory School and Kew House Senior School.

Maida Vale School takes a modern and pioneering approach to every aspect of school life, selecting each year group as a cohort of students who will encourage and inspire each other. The school welcomes pupils with varying academic profiles, encouraging the individual abilities of each child, and placing emphasis on confidence, self-esteem and creativity. We believe this approach produces high levels of academic and personal achievement for each pupil.

We operate a true 'Open Door' policy, welcoming parents and members of the wider community to become a part of school life. Our school seeks to cultivate the feeling of a family and social hub that offers emotional support and security for all students and employees.

With a broad curriculum, a vast enrichment programme and an extended school day, Maida Vale School has the variety and flexibility to enable pupils to develop their individual talents and fulfil their potential. Our small teaching and tutor groups, combined with the importance we place on communication between home and school, allow us to provide the highest level of pastoral care.

Maida Vale School takes a fresh approach to all areas of school life and is not bound by current conventions and practices which no longer seem useful. Whilst retaining the core traditional values established in our schools, we will continue to make decisions about the curriculum, timetabling and the length and shape of the school day and term which reflect this.

Maida Vale School is a beautiful Victorian building that was once a former college. The Victorians believed in light-filled classrooms with high ceilings and large windows, and we have built on this, taking the school into the 21st Century by fitting it with cutting edge facilities and equipment.

Maple Walk Prep School

MAPLE WALK
PREP SCHOOL

62A Crownhill Road, London, NW10 4EB
Tel: 020 8963 3890

Email: admin@maplewalkschool.co.uk
Website: www.maplewalkschool.co.uk
Head Teacher: Claire Murdoch
School type: Co-educational Day
Preparatory

Age range of pupils: 4–11 years
No. of pupils enrolled as at 01/01/2023: 170
Fees as at 01/01/2023:
Day: £4,194 per term
Average class size: 15

Maple Walk, judged excellent in all areas by the Independent Schools Inspectorate, is a happy, vibrant, exceptional value prep school for boys and girls aged 4-11 in north west London, nurturing children's wellbeing and academic best through fun, kindness and respect for one another.

We provide a safe, supportive and stimulating environment with small class sizes for outstanding learning and personal development where children flourish, developing self-confidence, self-esteem and social awareness.

Cultivating a growth mindset, Maple Walk's innovative, creative curriculum underpinned by academic rigour instils a love of learning and resilience ensuring each child is well prepared for whatever the future holds. The numerous opportunities outside the classroom are fundamental to the school day. Through sporting activities, first class music, art and drama, we encourage every child to find their own particular strength with many gaining scholarships at top independent secondary schools. We are proud pupils receive secondary offers of their choice and often with multiple offers!

Our enriching selection of after school clubs allows pupils to explore a diverse range of activities beyond the school day including sports, science, gymnastics, animation, robotics and plenty more.

Known as 'the small school with a big heart', we have a great school community and that strong community spirit goes beyond the school gates connecting and building relationships with the local community. Roundwood Park, a 5 minute walk away, is also a key part of the school day where we do a lot of our sports and have our Forest School.

We are housed in purpose-built accommodation and comes with a host of eco credentials, including a ground source heat pump for our heating and hot water, solar PV panels for electricity and a growing sedum roof to attract local wildlife.

Entry into Reception is non-selective and based on the date the completed registration form is returned to our Registrar, with siblings given priority. Entry higher up the school is by interview and informal assessment in the classroom.

Mander Portman Woodward – MPW London

M|P|W

(Founded 1973)

90-92 Queen's Gate, London, SW7 5AB

Tel: 020 7835 1355
Email: london@mpw.ac.uk
Website: www.mpw.ac.uk
Principal: Mr Steve Boyes BA, MSc, PGCE
Appointed: January 2023
School type: Co-educational Day & Boarding Senior & Sixth Form

Age range of pupils: 14–19 years
No. of pupils enrolled as at 01/01/2023: 600
Fees as at 01/01/2023:
Day: £10,765 per term
Average class size: 6
Teacher/pupil ratio: 1:6

Tailored, not uniform: when it comes to a good education, one size does not necessarily fit all.

Founded in 1973, MPW London is one of the UK's leading Sixth Form colleges, offering a distinctive alternative to traditional schools. Situated in the heart of one of the capital's most exclusive and vibrant locations, the college offers a socially relaxed yet highly academically disciplined environment.

A bespoke approach

Our model is based around a strong focus on exam preparation and equipping students with the skills, attitude and confidence to succeed at the country's top universities.

Students choose their own unique paths with GCSEs and A levels offered in over 40 subjects and in any combination. Whichever combination they choose, each student has a Director of Studies, who provides them with tailored academic and pastoral support. The teaching method has been devised with a focus on individual attention too – teaching is in small Oxbridge-style tutorial groups, each with fewer than 10 students.

But it's not just in the academic realm where students can express themselves. Walk over the threshold of an MPW college and you will immediately sense the relaxed, yet focused atmosphere. Students are treated like the young adults that they are; there is no school uniform, they are on first-name terms with their tutors, they are not patronised by allowing low expectations of behaviour or attainment and they are encouraged to take responsibility for themselves.

Strong results and progression

Despite having a non-selective admissions policy and a wide variety of courses targeted at students of different academic abilities, our students achieve outstanding overall results year after year. In particular, our 'value-added' score (the progress students make from GCSE to A level) is exceptional.

In 2022, over two-thirds of A level grades were A*/B. These results unlock the doors to some of the UK's best universities – in the last three years, two-thirds of our students progressed to top tier universities (Russell Group, University of London and specialist institutions).

Learning to secure those prestigious university places is also a key element of the MPW experience. Students are given unrivalled support in completing UCAS applications by the same experts who put together the renowned *Getting into* series of books, which offers invaluable advice and guidance on how to secure that coveted place at a first-choice university.

Stunning location

MPW London is located in South Kensington (Zone 1), one of the most exclusive and affluent parts of the capital. It is just a few minutes' walk from Hyde Park, Imperial College and many world-famous museums, including the Science Museum, the Natural History Museum and the Victoria & Albert Museum.

Rated Excellent by ISI

In our last Independent School Inspectorate (ISI) report, we received the highest rating of 'Excellent', prompting the inspectors to report, "The quality of the students' spiritual, moral, social and cultural development is excellent. In line with the aims of the college, students are encouraged to develop confidence, self-belief and self-discipline."

More House School

MORE HOUSE SCHOOL
KNIGHTSBRIDGE

(Founded 1952)

22-24 Pont Street, Knightsbridge, London, SW1X 0AA
Tel: 020 7235 2855
Email: registrar@morehousemail.org.uk
Website: www.morehouse.org.uk
Head: Ms Faith Hagerty
Appointed: April 2021

School type: Independent Girls' Day
Religious Denomination: Catholic
Age range of girls: 11–18 years
No. of pupils enrolled as at 01/01/2023: 145
Fees as at 01/01/2023:
Day: £7,750 per term
Average class size: 16
Teacher/pupil ratio: 1:4

More House is a small school that means big business. Having taught girls since 1952, we know how girls learn best. Our pupils skip up our steps as 11-year-old children and leave us at 18, as accomplished and emotionally intelligent young women, ready to go out and change the world.

As a school, we embrace a number of juxtapositions. Inside our historic building, we deliver a progressive Catholic education. Our lessons start in Knightsbridge but extend to the wider world. Our small class sizes engage our pupils in big thinking.

We are preparing our pupils for the juggling act of adulthood. Our core values of commitment, integrity and compassion are evident in the students' academic and co-curricular achievements, their relationships with others and through initiatives such as our More Green sustainability group and Faith in Action programme. Our outstanding pastoral care enables our girls to flourish in a nurturing environment that recognises and cherishes the whole person.

More House is committed to the expression of the Catholic faith, both explicitly and – perhaps more importantly – in our daily life together. Our girls are passionate and thoughtful global citizens, who act with integrity, honesty, and a sense of justice. While we are a Catholic school, we warmly welcome children of all faiths or none.

Our central London location provides a launchpad for access to London's best sporting venues, galleries, museums and theatres.

As a school, we are innovative and encourage creativity right across the curriculum. What the world needs at this very moment is versatile and ethical leaders who are driven by more than the traditional measures of success.

It is the nurturing of the individual at More House that cultivates young women who are confident and creative enough to channel their strengths and be agents of change. We are proud to be a greenhouse, not a hothouse.

North Bridge House

North Bridge House

(Founded 1939)

65 Rosslyn Hill, London, NW3 5UD

Tel: 020 7428 1520

Email: admissionsenquiries@
northbridgehouse.com

Website: www.northbridgehouse.com

Executive Headteacher: Brendan Pavey

Heads of Nursery & Pre-Prep Schools:
Nishi Kapoor, Michelle Blaber & Eilish Sleator

Head of Prep School: Tom Le Tissier

Heads of Senior Schools:
Christopher Jones &
Charlotte Tassell-Dent

School type: Co-educational Day
Preparatory & Senior, Nursery & Sixth Form

Age range of pupils: 2–18 years

No. of pupils enrolled as at 01/01/2023: 1430

Fees as at 01/01/2023:

Nursery: £8,676 (half days)–£17,334 (full time)

Pre-Reception & Reception:
£18,174 –£20,193 per annum

Years 1-2: £20,943 per annum

Years 3-11: £21,855 per annum

Years 12-13: £23,148 per annum

Average class size: 20

Founded in 1939, North Bridge House shares a warm, family atmosphere across six North London school sites, providing a unique and personalised education for pupils aged 2 to 18 years. Shaped by centuries-old heritage and boasting many modern facilities, our schools provide an inspiring learning environment at the heart of the Capital. Children benefit from educational partnerships with the likes of the Zoological Society of London and the Estorick Collection of Modern Italian Art, while specialist, individualised teaching prepares pupils for every milestone of their school career.

At North Bridge House, we are on a constant journey of getting to know and understand every learner as a unique and rounded individual, fostering academic excellence while cultivating character and promoting wellbeing. Happy children learn best and our pupils are notably high-achieving. Reception and Key Stage 1 children outperform national averages in English and maths by 20-30%. Our Prep School is renowned for first-class results in boys' and girls' senior school entrance examinations, with many pupils awarded highly competitive scholarship places. NBH Senior Schools also celebrate outstanding exam results, with GCSE students achieving top grades in STEM subjects and Sixth Formers gaining places at Russell Group and Oxbridge destinations.

We empower our young people to thrive in everything they do, providing much more than a simply academic education. In our curricular design we have embedded timetabled enrichment opportunities, which together with our broad range of extra-curricular activities, are key to our character education programme. Forest School, residential and day trips, LAMDA, Duke of Edinburgh and our Inspiring Futures programme also enhance the whole school experience, while specialist pastoral care and the school's wellbeing charter further empower our children to find and realise their true personal potential. Furthermore, North Bridge House provides 1-2-1 devices for all pupils in Year 3 and above, facilitating their learning both in school and at home.

Pupils also enjoy a wide range of sports during weekly PE and Games sessions, which make the most of both on site facilities and the school's prime north London location. From our Regent's Park home ground to Allianz Park, Hampstead Heath, Highbury Fields, Lee Valley White Water Centre and local leisure centres, students frequent the best facilities for track and field, outdoor adventure and water sports, as well as yoga, martial arts and fitness classes.

At the heart of the school is a highly qualified team of specialist teachers, dedicated to setting every child on their own individual path to success – so that they fulfil their time at North Bridge House and beyond. From the fundamental foundations that are established in the early years of education to the expert UCAS and careers advice that is provided at A-Level, North Bridge House prepares confident and determined boys and girls for the challenges and rewards of real life.

Our schools

North Bridge House Nursery Hampstead
33 Fitzjohn's Avenue, London NW3 5JY

North Bridge House Pre-Prep Hampstead
8 Netherhall Gardens, London NW3 5RR

North Bridge Nursery & Pre-Prep West Hampstead
85-87 Fordwych Road, London NW2 3TL

North Bridge House Prep Regent's Park
1 Gloucester Avenue, London NW1 7AB

North Bridge House Senior Hampstead
65 Rosslyn Hill, London NW3 5UD

North Bridge House Senior Canonbury
6-9 Canonbury Place, London N1 2NQ

Ravenscourt Park Preparatory School

(Founded 1991)

16 Ravenscourt Avenue, London, W6 0SL
Tel: 020 8846 9153
Email: admissions@rpps.co.uk
Website: www.rpps.co.uk
Headmaster: Mr Carl Howes MA
(Cantab), PGCE (Exeter)
Appointed: September 2015

School type:
Co-educational Day Preparatory
Age range of pupils: 4–11 years
No. of pupils enrolled as at 01/01/2023: 418
Fees as at 01/01/2023:
Day: £6,632 per term
Average class size: 20

Ravenscourt Park Preparatory School (RPPS) is a lively, co-educational, independent school for children aged 4 to 11 in West London. Owned by the Gardener Schools Group, a family founded company set up in 1991, RPPS was the first of four schools to open, followed by Kew Green Preparatory School, Kew House Senior School and Maida Vale School.

There is a palpable sense of community at RPPS, and visitors often comment on the warm and happy atmosphere, and the family feel that they notice around the school.

Our school is situated next to Ravenscourt Park, a twenty-acre park which provides the setting for the majority of PE and Games lessons. RPPS has specialist on-site facilities such as a multi-purpose Auditorium, Library, Music Suite, Art Studio and Science Laboratory. Additional facilities include a designated gymnasium, ICT suite and large outdoor playground space.

RPPS provides an education of the highest quality with an engaging curriculum that is varied, exciting and forward-looking, whilst also preparing pupils for transfer at the end of Year 6 to London Day Schools and 11+ boarding schools. Additionally, RPPS offers pupils the opportunity to attend either one of its sister senior schools, Kew House or Maida Vale, via an automatic through route thus enabling them to remain with us until they are 18.

Our pupils engage in the excitement of learning and develop the confidence to question, analyse and express their opinions. We encourage children to develop a Growth Mindset so that they become resourceful, resilient, reflective and enthusiastic learners who are able to learn from their mistakes and build on their successes.

We form strong and trusting partnerships with our parents and we operate an 'Open Door' policy, where parents' comments, views, contributions and suggestions are valued.

The Independent Schools Inspectorate (ISI) visited RPPS in 2021 and we were delighted to have received the judgement of 'excellent' in both of the report's key outcomes.

Sarum Hall School

(Founded 1929)
15 Eton Avenue, London, NW3 3EL
Tel: 020 7794 2261
Email: admissions@sarumhallschool.co.uk
Website: www.sarumhallschool.co.uk
Headmistress: Miss Karen Coles BEd
(Hons), Exon

School type: Girls' Day Preparatory &
Nursery
Age range of girls: 3–11 years
No. of pupils enrolled as at 01/01/2023: 185
Fees as at 01/01/2023:
£5,450 (Nursery)
£5,900 (Reception – Year 6) per term

Sarum Hall School is a modern and successful school located in the heart of Belsize Park, in which pupils are motivated to learn, inspired to fulfil their potential, and encouraged to achieve excellence. Our motto of *spirit, happiness, success* underpins our philosophy of individuality, inclusivity and positivity. The Golden Values of kindness, courage, respect, honesty, fairness and resilience ensure that every girl develops as an individual with a strong sense of purpose and moral compass both in the school community and society beyond. We encourage children to engage with their future and understand their role in shaping the world in which they will live and work.

Our modern facilities were purpose built in 1995 and the girls benefit from spacious classrooms which promote creativity and curiosity in their learning. The girls have a wonderful variety of lessons with specialist teachers in which high standards are set and an emphasis on practical activities and the application of information is nurtured. We are proud of our outdoor space which boasts a floodlit netball court and 4 short tennis courts, garden, pond and our iconic treehouse and beach huts, which allow us to house a wealth of activities both in the curriculum and as part of our extensive clubs programme. In addition, our dedicated Science Lab, Art Room, Food Studio, Library, ICT suite and separate Music and Drama classrooms provide cross-curricular learning opportunities and enable us to deliver a broad and engaging curriculum.

Our main entry point is at 3+ and we are non-selective as we advocate an individual approach to each child's educational journey; we feed to the most selective senior schools in the area and beyond. We believe in teaching the girls a set of transferrable skills, which they will use and apply in all aspects of life, establishing them as strong, confident and independent young women with a zest for life and a thirst for knowledge.

St Benedict's School

(Founded 1902)

54 Eaton Rise, Ealing, London, W5 2ES

Tel: 020 8862 2000
Email: admissions@stbenedicts.org.uk
Website: www.stbenedicts.org.uk
Headmaster: Mr A Johnson BA
Appointed: September 2016
Headmaster from September 2023:
Mr Joe Smith
School type: Co-educational Day
Preparatory & Senior, Nursery & Sixth Form

Religious Denomination: Catholic
Age range of pupils: 3–18 years
No. of pupils enrolled as at 01/01/2023: 1083
Boys: 716 **Girls:** 367 **Sixth Form:** 185
Fees as at 01/01/2023:
Day: £14,940–£19,575 per annum
Average class size: Junior School: 17;
Senior School: 17; Sixth Form: 18
Teacher/pupil ratio: 1:10

St Benedict's is London's leading independent Catholic coeducational school, in leafy Ealing. Within a caring, happy community, St Benedict's has strong academic standards. The Junior School and Nursery offer a holistic education for children aged 3 to 11, which continues through the Senior School and Sixth Form. St Benedict's, which welcomes children of other faiths and of no faith, is committed to supporting all children develop their full potential.

Inspirational teaching and exceptional pastoral care are at the heart of the education we offer.

The Junior School and Nursery provide a supportive, friendly and vibrant coeducational environment in which to learn. In the Nursery a carefully planned and child-centred programme enables and extends learning and development. The Junior School provides a broad and balanced curriculum based on a rigorous academic core. Sharing excellent facilities with the Senior School, and participating in a programme of cross-curricular activities, helps ease the transition at 11+ to the Senior School, which is on the same site.

There are extensive opportunities in music, art, sport and drama. St Benedict's has a proud sporting tradition, which promotes the highest sporting aspirations while encouraging everyone to enjoy sport, fitness and teamwork. Music is excellent, with several choirs and many instrumental ensembles. A wide range of co-curricular activities is offered, and an after-school club is available at the Junior School.

There has been huge investment in building and facilities at St Benedict's. Having opened our new Sixth Form Centre and Art Department in 2015, a new Nursery and Pre-Prep Department opened in September 2017, providing our youngest pupils with a first-rate learning environment.

St Benedict's School is unique. Come and visit and see what we have to offer. You can be sure of a warm Benedictine welcome.

St John's Wood Pre-Preparatory School

(Founded 1982)
St Johns Hall, Lords Roundabout,
London, NW8 7NE
Tel: 020 7722 7149
Email: info@sjwpre-prep.org.uk
Website: www.sjwpre-prep.org.uk

Principal: Adrian Ellis
School type: Co-educational Day Pre-Preparatory & Nursery
Age range of pupils: 3–7 years
Average class size: 16
Teacher/pupil ratio: 1:8

Happiness is at the heart of the philosophy at St Johns' Wood Pre-Prep School, and it works. This small school, described by owner and Principal, Adrian Ellis, as feeling more like a private members' club, is a 7+ specialist school. Year 2 pupils regularly receive offers from schools including: Belmont; City of London School; Highgate; Pembridge Hall, Queen's College Prep, South Hampstead High School; St Paul's Juniors; UCS Junior School and Westminster Under School.

With a friendly and caring environment as its strength for three-to seven-year-old boys and girls, Mr Ellis believes that the excellent ratio of staff to pupils allows each child to reach their full potential. *"Of course, together with parents, we look to establish each child's unique qualities and particular talents and aim to develop them as fully as possible,"* said Mr Ellis.

Parents have high expectations of the school. Mr Ellis points out this is a two way street, *"Equally, we have high expectations of our parents. This combination is the recipe for success."*

Following this year's excellent results, St John's Wood Pre-Prep remains a recommended 'feeder' to many of London's top prep schools.

One parent wrote: *"There are private schools and then there is St. John's Wood Pre-Prep."* Mrs R, whose first child attended the school in 2016 and who went on to study at City of London School for Girls added, *"We've been with Adrian and his staff pre Covid, during the pandemic and now post Covid and they have been very supportive, making sure that they have kept the community atmosphere throughout. It's one of the reasons my husband and I wanted our son to start his educational journey here."*

St Mary's School Hampstead

ST MARY'S SCHOOL HAMPSTEAD

(Founded 1871)

47 Fitzjohn's Avenue, Hampstead,
London, NW3 6PG

Tel: 020 7435 1868
Email: office@stmh.co.uk
Website: www.stmh.co.uk
Headteacher: Miss Charlotte Owen
Appointed: September 2023
School type: Girls' Day Preparatory &
Nursery
Religious Denomination: CISC

Age range of girls:
2 years 9 months–11 years
No. of pupils enrolled as at 01/01/2023: 300
Fees as at 01/01/2023:
Day: £9,330–£17,250 per annum
Average class size: Max 20
Teacher/pupil ratio: 1:9.5

St Mary's School Hampstead provides an outstanding and inspirational Catholic education to girls from 3-11 years.

St Mary's School celebrates the uniqueness of every pupil and their achievements. The rigorous, challenging curriculum places a strong emphasis on high academic achievement within a culture of care and support.

The School aims to instil four key habits of learning in their pupils. The children are encouraged to be risk takers, not only in their play, but also in their learning. They are also taught to be resilient and not to fall at the first hurdle. Staff ask the children to make mistakes because in the process of challenging themselves, they make more academic progress. The girls at St Mary's School are respectful, not just of each other, but of themselves. Finally, pupils are encouraged to be reflective, of their behaviour and their academic work.

An extensive refurbishment programme has been completed to deliver the most enriching and stimulating learning environments. The Global Learning Centre is a cutting-edge space that includes an Engineering and Robotics Lab, Virtual Reality Launch Pad, Art and Design Studio as well as a Green Room. This technology is used to support and enhance all curriculum areas and learning every day from Nursery to Year 6.

The focus on technology is equally balanced with an emphasis on creative and physical development.

Music, drama, art and sports are an essential part of school life and involve everyone. St Mary's School is a leafy oasis in the heart of Hampstead. The extensive and self-contained outside space includes climbing equipment and the full-size netball court has been upgraded enabling football, rugby, cricket and tennis to be enjoyed.

Used together – the integrated technology and the broad curriculum – the girls at St Mary's are flourishing. They are adopting habits of learning and making independent choices that they can take forward into their secondary education.

Leavers achieve impressive results, gaining offers and Academic Scholarships from schools including City of London School for Girls, Francis Holland School, Highgate School, North London Collegiate, South Hampstead High School, St Mary's Ascot and St Paul's Girls' School.

St Mary's School Hampstead offers an outstanding and inspirational Catholic education for girls 3-11 years. Find out more about this remarkable school at: www.stmh.co.uk

St Paul's Cathedral School

ST PAUL'S
CATHEDRAL
SCHOOL

(Founded 12th Century or earlier)

2 New Change, London, EC4M 9AD

Tel: 020 7248 5156

Email: admissions@spcs.london.sch.uk

Website: www.spcslondon.com

Headmaster: Simon Larter-Evans BA (Hons), PGCE, FRSA

Appointed: September 2016

School type: Co-educational Pre-Prep, Day Prep & Boarding Choir School

Religious Denomination: Church of England, admits pupils of all faiths

Age range of pupils: 4–13 years

No. of pupils enrolled as at 01/01/2023: 270

Boys: 165 **Girls:** 105

Fees as at 01/01/2023:

Day: £16,044–£17,277 per annum

Full Boarding: £9,706 per annum

Average class size: 15-20

Teacher/pupil ratio: 1:10

Curriculum

A broad curriculum, including the International Primary Curriculum, prepares all pupils for 11+, 13+, scholarship and Common Entrance examinations. There is a strong musical tradition and choristers' Cathedral choral training is outstanding. A wide variety of games and other activities is offered. At the latest ISI inspection in May 2017, the school was rated 'Excellent'.

Entry requirements

Entry at 4+, 7+ and 11+ years: Pre-prep and day pupils interview and short test; Choristers voice trials and tests held throughout the year for boys between 6-8 years. Scholarships available at 11+ years.

St Paul's Cathedral School is a registered charity (No. 312718), which exists to provide education for the choristers of St Paul's Cathedral and for children living in the local area.

The Roche School

The
Roche
School

(Founded 1988)

11 Frogmore, London, SW18 1HW
Tel: 020 8877 0823
Email: office@therocheschool.com
Website: www.therocheschool.com
Headmistress: Mrs Vania Adams BA(Hons),
PGCE, MA
Appointed: September 2010
School type: Co-educational Day
Preparatory & Nursery

Religious Denomination:
Non-denominational
Age range of pupils: 2–11 years
No. of pupils enrolled as at 01/01/2023: 270
Boys: 130 **Girls:** 140
Fees as at 01/01/2023:
Day: £16,470–£17,190 per annum
Average class size: 18
Teacher/pupil ratio: 1:9

The Roche School is a vibrant, aspirational, family-run nursery and primary school in South West London. It is committed to developing pupils intellectually, creatively and in sporting terms, within the context of a warm and friendly culture.

Core subjects are grouped according to focus so that pupils are challenged appropriately and everyone receives a high level of attention. The school seeks continually to build on its fine academic reputation which sees children placed at a wide range of top London schools after the 11+ examinations, with many achieving scholarships.

Parents favour local secondary schools. King's College Wimbledon, Wimbledon High, Dulwich College, Tiffin, Hampton and Whitgift feature prominently.

The new Year 6 Centre ensures that pupils make the move to senior school with the requisite academic, social and emotional strength.

The Roche School is delighted to be offering an additional Spanish Bilingual Stream class in Reception, alongside the respected provision of their traditional English Reception class. Mornings in the Spanish Bilingual Stream consist of the same high-quality curriculum in English as the English Reception. Afternoons involve English curriculum-based lessons delivered in Spanish by a qualified teacher with in-depth Spanish fluency.

The host of specialist teachers in music and sport provide further enrichment to the children's learning.

The school has a strong focus on personal happiness and respect for oneself and others. It is values-based, using The Roche Approach as a cohesive strategy in this respect. There is a commitment to diversity and to the significance of equal opportunities, with pupils accessing non-gender bias initiatives in sport, growth mindset programmes and Philosophy 4 Children. Expressive arts are strong and the emphasis on holistic development reaps dividends in terms of confidence and individuality.

Schools in Greater London

Babington House School

(Founded 1887)

Grange Drive, Chislehurst, Kent BR7 5ES

Tel: 020 8467 5537

Email: sjames@babingtonhouse.com

Website: www.babingtonhouse.com

Headmaster: Mr Tim Lello MA, FRSA, NPQH

Appointed: 2013

School type: Co-educational Day Preparatory & Senior, Nursery & Sixth Form

Age range of pupils: 3–18 years

No. of pupils enrolled as at 23/03/2022: 466

Fees as at 23/03/2023:

Nursery: £4,477 per term (inclusive of lunches) based on 12 week term

Preparatory (Reception to Year 6): £5,255 per term (inclusive of lunches)

Seniors & Sixth Form (11 to 18): £6,550 per term (inclusive of lunches)

Teacher/pupil ratio: 1:20

Inspiring Teachers, Inspiring Children

Over the past four years, Babington pupils have achieved 80% A* to B grades at A Level.

It is an excellent school achieving amazing results and inspiring pupils from the Sixth Form right down to the Nursery.

The school is an independent coeducational day school, situated in a beautiful group of buildings on Grange Drive in Chislehurst, near Bromley. It has 466 pupils from age 3 to 18.

Being a small school has BIG advantages. It has high standards of behaviour, dress and conduct, benefiting from no more than 20 pupils in a class and a strong sense of community.

Babington is an academic school. The School is committed to outstanding music, drama, sport and the arts in their broadest sense and offers a wealth of extracurricular opportunities. Our academic, social and sporting endeavours are underpinned by core Christian values.

The co-educational Senior School is academically selective with an Entrance Examination for Year 7 entry. In Sixth Form, the focus is very much on A-level study in small sets with the opportunity for work experience, which helps university applications stand out and provides great self-confidence.

Headmaster, Tim Lello comments *"Our commitment to provide an academic and well-rounded education with small class sizes, tailored to the needs of our pupils is really paying off, our pupils and parents are happy and we are achieving excellent results."*

See for yourself –

www.babingtonhouse.com

Hampton Court House

(Founded 2000)
Hampton Court Road, Richmond upon Thames, London, Surrey KT8 9BS
Tel: 020 8614 0865
Email: reception@hchnet.co.uk
Website: www.hamptoncourthouse.co.uk
Headteacher: Katherine Vintiner

School type: Co-educational Day Preparatory & Senior, Nursery & Sixth Form
Age range of pupils: 2–18 years
No. of pupils enrolled as at 01/01/2023: 300
Fees as at 01/01/2023:
Day: £15,075–£22,044 per annum
Average class size: 20
Teacher/pupil ratio: 1:5

Hampton Court House is an award-winning all-through school nestled in Bushy Park on the Southwest London and Surrey borders, embodying Achievement With Heart.

We are an independent co-educational day school for ages 2 – 18, educating children in our Pre-Prep School, *The Little Courtiers*, to students in Year 13. The majority of our pupils elect to stay on to complete their full education with us, enjoying great success in their GCSEs and A Levels. With over 70% A*/A grades at A Level, Hampton Court House was in 2022 ranked in the top 50 independent schools nationwide (The Telegraph) and in the top 10 independent schools in London (School Owl).

We strive to lay the foundations of a lifelong love of learning, and it is important to us that children enjoy being here and look forward to coming to school. In keeping with our ethos, we believe that children need some guided freedom in order to develop their independence and confidence to use their voice. Our non-uniform parkland campus environment, in which staff and pupils alike are addressed on a first-name basis, cultivates an energy where our pupils can explore their individuality and style with taste and discretion.

Our programmes offer an extraordinary education. From the Forest School in Pre-Prep, to the award-winning LabelFrancÉducation accredited French bilingual programme in Prep and the Nebula Future Researcher's Programme© in our Sixth Form, Hampton Court House pupils get a headstart every step of the way.

Open Mornings are held weekly during term-time

Chigwell School

Chigwell School

AUT VIAM INVENIAM AUT FACIAM

(Founded 1629)

High Road, Chigwell, Essex IG7 6QF

Tel: 020 8501 5700
Email: admissions@chigwell-school.org
Website: www.chigwell-school.org
Head Teacher: Mr Damian King
School type: Co-educational Day & Boarding Preparatory, Senior & Sixth Form
Religious Denomination: Anglican
Age range of pupils: 4–18 years

No. of pupils enrolled as at 01/01/2023: 1057
Boys: 566 **Girls:** 491
No. of boarders: 27
Fees as at 01/01/2023:
Reception to Year 4: £4,895–£5,245 per term
Year 5 to Year 13: £5,795–£6,945 per term
Full Boarding: £11,995 per term

Welcome

Nestled in the outskirts of London in leafy Essex, Chigwell is a co-educational school for 4 to 18-year-olds with boarding available at Sixth Form. The school was founded in 1629 and for nearly four centuries we have been preparing pupils to go out into the world. Clearly that world has evolved a great deal since then and, whilst we are conscious of our long heritage, we are always looking to innovate so that Chigwellians are well prepared to contribute positively, to inspire change for the better and to continue learning throughout their lives.

Facilities

We benefit from a unique blend of listed historic buildings, modern facilities and extensive 100-acre grounds. We have a dedicated Drama Centre for those aspiring thespians, Music school that houses many ensembles and our prestigious Choir. We have dedicated buildings for Art, Science, Modern Foreign Languages, English, maths and even a self-contained Junior School building with it's own library for our Year 3 to Year 6 pupils. Our Swallow library, situated in the oldest part of the school has some wonderful architectural features and is of historical significance.

Our dedicated Pre-prep school was built ten years ago to house Reception, Year 1 and Year 2 pupils. It benefits from its own library, multipurpose hall and dining room, an ICT suite, science, music rooms, spacious playgrounds, a woodland classroom, a fairy garden and an adventure play area.

The school's more recent addition is the Sixth Form Centre which is home to our A Level pupils. It has six classrooms, study, and social spaces and a centre for careers and university advice, as well as a coffee shop and a large seating area.

Our sporting facilities are second to none and we are about six months away from completing our new sports centre this September. It will be home to a six-lane 25-meter swimming pool, five-court multipurpose sports hall, gym, individual studios, and a café.

Boarding

Our boarding provision and care have been classified as excellent by ISI. Our four boarding houses are homes from home for approximately 30 sixth-form international pupils, who come from a range of countries both within Europe and overseas. Our boarders benefit from a homely close-knit and caring support network of houseparents.

Entry Requirements

At 4+ the assessment consists of pupil participation in a range of activities based around numeracy, literacy, listening and responding to stories/songs and joining in with a range of activities centred on the EYFS curriculum. At 7+ and 11+ one can expect an interview followed by an English and a Maths paper. At 13+ candidates will sit an English and Maths paper as well as a modern foreign language of their choice, followed by an interview for successful

candidates. Entrance to Sixth Form typically require 8s and 9s in the subjects being studied at A-Level along with an interview and a school report.

Path to Success

Chigwell School is a happy, mutually supportive, family-orientated community in which parents and staff work in partnership to help pupils reach their full potential and where friendships formed often last a lifetime. You will find that we are a busy school where pupils of all ages work closely with each other and their teachers. In Chigwell pupils we look for academic ambition and a genuine eagerness to be involved in all that the

school has to offer. Through the curriculum and the wide range of opportunities available to them beyond the classroom, each becomes the very best they can be: independent in spirit, adventurous in approach and empathetic in how they treat others. Ultimately, we aim that each and every pupil will forge their own path to success, true to our motto: Find a way or make a way.

There is a special warmth about the nurturing Chigwell community, with excellent facilities set in a beautiful open site of 100-acres, within view of the City of London.

Kew Green Preparatory School

(Founded 2004)

Layton House, Ferry Lane, Kew Green, Richmond, Surrey TW9 3AF
Tel: 020 8948 5999
Email: admissions@kgps.co.uk
Website: www.kgps.co.uk
Headteacher: Mrs Sasha Davies
Appointed: September 2022

School type: Co-educational Day Preparatory & Nursery
Age range of pupils: 2–11 years
No. of pupils enrolled as at 01/01/2023: 275
Fees as at 01/01/2023:
Day: £6,632 per term
Average class size: 20
Teacher/pupil ratio: 1:6.4

Kew Green Preparatory School (KGPS) is a co-educational, independent school for children aged 2 to 11, nestled in a peaceful corner of Kew Green near Kew Gardens in Richmond. Owned by the Gardener Schools Group, a family founded company, KGPS is the sister school to Ravenscourt Park Preparatory School, Kew House Senior School and Maida Vale Senior School. KGPS recently expanded, opening Kew Green Nursery in September 2022. Kew Green Nursery is located at a new site close to the main Prep school. Kew Green Nursery children receive an automatic place in Reception at the Prep school. Consequently, children can attend KGPS from ages 2 to 11, and, if desired, ages 2-18 within the Gardener Schools Group.

KGPS is housed in an attractive building, with an abundance of outside space and surrounded by trees and the river Thames. Amidst its countryside setting for a London Prep school, KGPS provides an education of the highest quality, with high expectations and ambition set for all pupils.

We provide an engaging, broad and forward-thinking curriculum where all pupils are challenged within their learning. We prepare pupils for 11+, receiving offers and scholarships from a range of independent London day schools and 11+ boarding schools. Additionally, KGPS offers pupils the opportunity to attend either one of its sister Senior Schools, Kew House or Maida Vale, through a guaranteed place for Year 7.

In addition to the core lessons, specialist teaching is timetabled for Art & DT, Music, PE & Games, Swimming, French, Spanish and Computing. Our school calendar is full of enrichment opportunities, including a full trip, residential and workshop schedule as well as a wide-ranging specialist extra-curricular club provision for all pupils. We also have a healthy competitive side when it comes to sporting fixtures.

At KGPS, we champion curiosity, creativity, confidence and collaboration in all areas of school life and learning. Importantly, we enable our children to succeed, be recognised and feel valued. We continue to look ahead, aiming to ensure our education is purposeful and relevant. We strive to mould young citizens and future adults who are resilient, adaptable, articulate and active learners. Importantly, we prioritise the development of strong self-esteem alongside academic progress.

In addition to scheduled parent and school events, we have an 'Open Door' policy for our parents, and this further strengthens the excellent partnership between school and our families.

Kew House School

Kew House, 6 Capital Interchange Way,
London, Middlesex TW8 0EX

Tel: 0208 742 2038
Email: admissions@kewhouseschool.com
Website: www.kewhouseschool.com
Headmaster: Mr Will Williams
School type: Co-educational Day Senior
& Sixth Form

Age range of pupils: 11–18 years
No. of pupils enrolled as at 01/01/2023: 595
Fees as at 01/01/2023:
Day: £8,073 per term
Average class size: 22

Located in West London, Kew House School is a co-educational, independent senior school for pupils aged 11-18 years. Owned by the Gardener Schools Group, a family founded company set up in 1991, Kew House is the sister school to Ravenscourt Park Preparatory School, Kew Green Preparatory School and Maida Vale Senior School.

Kew House School takes a modern and pioneering approach to every aspect of school life, selecting each year group as a cohort of students who will encourage and inspire each other. The school recognises and enhances the individual abilities of each child, placing emphasis on confidence, self-esteem and creativity. We believe this approach produces high levels of academic and personal achievement for each pupil.

By operating a true 'Open Door' policy that welcomes parents and members of the wider community to become a part of school life, Kew House has developed the feeling of a family and social hub that provides emotional support and security for all pupils and employees.

Sport is an important part of the curriculum and Kew House pupils achieve success at both regional and national levels. Pupils benefit from using state of the art facilities at sporting locations just a stone's throw away from the school, including professional tennis courts and cricket grounds. Just a short walk from the River Thames, rowing is also part of the curriculum.

In September 2017, Kew House opened a brand new Sixth Form Centre which benefits from a beautifully designed independent learning centre on the ground floor. Facilities include a Sixth Form Cafe, library, roof terrace, audio-visual suite, recording studio and Sixth Form seminar rooms.

Following an inspection in April 2022 by the Independent Schools Inspectorate (ISI), the judges rated Kew House 'excellent' in both key outcomes. An outstanding set of results for GCSE pupils in 2022, exceeding the success rates of the previous two years of examinations: 98.9% of grades were a 9-4.

Marymount International School London

George Road, Kingston upon Thames, Surrey KT2 7PE

Tel: +44 (0)20 8949 0571
Email: admissions@marymountlondon.com
Website: www.marymountlondon.com
Headmistress: Mrs Margaret Giblin
School type: Girls' Day & Boarding Senior & Sixth Form
Age range of girls: 11–18 years

No. of pupils enrolled as at 01/04/2023: 248
Fees as at 01/09/2023:
Day: £28,830 per annum
Weekly Boarding: £46,740 per annum
Full Boarding: £48,810 per annum
Average class size: 12
Teacher/pupil ratio: 1:5

Marymount International School London is an independent, day and boarding school for girls which nurtures the limitless potential of curious, motivated students (ages 11 to 18) of diverse faiths and backgrounds. Founded in 1955 through the charism of the Religious of the Sacred Heart of Mary (RSHM), we proudly stand as the first all girls' school in the United Kingdom to adopt the International Baccalaureate curriculum (IB MYP and Diploma), where girls are inspired to learn in a creative, collaborative, interdisciplinary, and exploratory environment.

Students are empowered to build their confidence, leadership skills, and sense of self on a seven-acre garden campus conveniently located just twelve miles from Central London. The campus offers outstanding facilities, including a STEAM Hub, sports hall, dance studio, modern dining hall, tennis courts and an All-Weather Pitch. The School's challenging academic program is based on the International Baccalaureate curricula:

- The Middle Years Programme (MYP),offered in Grades 6 to 10, encourages students to draw meaningful connections between eight broad and varied subject groups. With a central focus on the development of conceptual understanding and effective approaches to learning (ATL) skills, the MYP is a student-centred, inquiry-based programme rooted in interdisciplinary learning.
- The International Baccalaureate Diploma Programme (DP) for Grades 11 and 12 builds on the strong foundation of the MYP, leading to independent research opportunities as well as exceptional university placement within the UK and around the world.
- Our Independent School Inspectorate rated the school 'Excellent' from their November 2022 inspection.

The School provides a bespoke, student-centred college counselling programme which leads to successful placements in top universities in the UK and around the world.

Marymount's holistic approach to learning delivers a well-rounded education that encourages critical thinking, intercultural understanding, and participation in a wide array of interesting extracurricular offerings. Robust transport service from London/surrounding areas and boarding options (full, weekly, and flexi) are available.

Marymount offers year-round rolling admission as space allows. The admissions section of the website, featuring an online application portal, provides all of the information necessary to get started. Applicant families are encouraged to learn more about the School's strong tradition of excellence by exploring the website, making contact by phone/email, and scheduling a campus/virtual tour.

Schools in the South-East

The following unitary authorities are also within the councils listed

Bracknell Forest, Reading, Slough, Windsor & Maidenhead and Wokingham

Brighton & Hove
Medway
Milton Keynes

Peterborough
Portsmouth & Southampton
Thurrock and Southend-on-Sea

Aberdour School

Aberdour
floret qui laborat

(Founded 1928)

Brighton Road, Burgh Heath, Tadworth, Surrey KT20 6AJ
Tel: +44 (0)1737 354119
Email: enquiries@aberdourschool.co.uk
Website: www.aberdourschool.co.uk
Headmaster: Mr S. D. Collins

School type: Co-educational Day Preparatory & Nursery
Age range of pupils: 2–11 years
No. of pupils enrolled as at 01/01/2023: 335
Fees as at 01/01/2023:
Day: £4,920–£17,070 per annum

Finding the brilliance in every child
Enquire now for September 2023
Independent day school for girls and boys aged 2-11 years

Every child has the potential to shine. At Aberdour, we aim to find the brilliance in every child, by providing an individual tailored education that identifies their potential and maximises their opportunities to learn, grow and succeed.

Founded in 1928 Aberdour is a thriving and extremely successful preparatory school for girls and boys aged 2-11 years. Set in 12 acres of beautiful Surrey parkland, Aberdour is truly a hidden gem, providing a safe and happy haven for your child. With our many purpose-built facilities for learning, sport and play, your child can develop his or her talents and skills whilst experiencing an exceptional breadth of opportunity both inside and outside the classroom.

Opening September 2023, a new purpose built Pre-Prep will allow children and staff to learn in an innovative, creative and dynamic environment.

Aberdour developed Personalised Achievement Learning® in 2007, providing a truly personalised education with breadth and flexibility. We have supported P.A.L® with major investments in our staff, our systems, our buildings, our IT and our resources, and the combination of a child-focused education. Through P.A.L®, we believe that every child will fulfil their individual potential if we nurture the talent that is within them, whatever that talent may be. Genuinely innovative teaching has made a real difference to the children's skills, achievements and enjoyment of life. We invite you to come see for yourself.

Please visit our website for information on our Admissions process and to contact our Registrar.

Belmont School

(Founded 1880)
Pasturewood Road, Holmbury St Mary,
Dorking, Surrey RH5 6LQ

Tel: 01306 730852
Email: admissions@belmont-school.org
Website: www.belmont-school.org
Headteacher: Mrs Helen Skrine BA, PGCE, NPQH, FRSA
Headteacher (from August 2023):
Mr Marc Broughton
School type: Co-educational Day & Weekly Boarding

Age range of pupils: 3–16 years
No. of pupils enrolled as at 01/01/2023: 190
Fees as at 01/01/2023:
Reception: £3,790 per term
Year 3: £5,880 per term
Year 7: £6,380 per term
Year 9: £6,810 per term

At Belmont School, we believe that the happiness and well-being of every pupil is of paramount importance and lies at the heart of a successful education.

Founded in 1880, Belmont School is nestled in the Surrey Hills on its own private estate in Holmbury St Mary and is an independent school for boys and girls from Early Years to GCSE. Pupils have 65 acres of wooded parkland to explore for activities such as Forest School, cross-country and mountain biking, including the School's own mountain biking academy and bespoke MTB bike trails.

From the age of three, pupils receive specialist teaching in Music, Performing Arts, French, Forest School, Art, IT and PE as well as the option to learn Ballet. Throughout their time at Belmont, pupils encounter a broad and challenging curriculum in small class sizes and each child is stretched or supported to reach their personal best.

Belmont's aim is for each pupil to leave as a well-rounded individual and so the academic curriculum is enriched by sport, performing arts, visual arts and other cultural and creative opportunities.

Alongside the facilities and academic provision at Belmont, every pupil is given excellent pastoral care and a family feel permeates throughout. The children's wellbeing is given equal priority alongside their achievements as encapsulated in the School's strapline, 'Achievement through Happiness'.

Belmont seeks to oil the wheels of family life and parents can drop children off for breakfast at 7.30am. In the evenings, pupils may stay for after school clubs or day board until 8pm. Pupils from as young as seven can board and many look forward to a night's flexi boarding enjoying activities like Nerf battles, swimming, film and pizza nights.

To find out more about Belmont School, please visit the website: www.belmont-school.org, where you can arrange to visit in person or take a virtual tour.

Bede's Senior School

BEDE'S COURAGEOUS

Upper Dicker, Hailsham,
East Sussex BN27 3QH
Tel: 01323 356609
Email: admissions@bedes.org
Website: www.bedes.org/senior
Head: Mr Peter Goodyer
School type: Co-educational Day &
Boarding Senior & Sixth Form

Age range of pupils:
13–18 years (boarding from 13)
No. of pupils enrolled as at 01/01/2023: 832
Day: 491 **No. of boarders:** 341
Fees as at 01/01/2023:
Day: £8,300 per term
Weekly Boarding: £12,240 per term
Full Boarding: £12,990 per term

Bede's Senior School is an independent, co-educational school for pupils from the age of 13 to 18, offering both day and boarding places. Bede's is located in the heart of the beautiful Sussex countryside, in the rural village of Upper Dicker in East Sussex, just over an hour from London.

At Bede's, we believe that every child is unique, each possessing individual and sometimes hidden talents. Bede's fosters a community of curiosity which encourages every individual to find and develop their passions, seek new horizons, develop lasting friendships and achieve their potential.

The school champions choice at every turn. Each Bedian is nurtured to find joy in their pursuit of brilliance, to develop a genuine love of learning. This culture of compassion and conscientiousness enables Bede's to nurture inquisitive minds and, in combination with the opportunities its campus provides, create unforgettable memories.

Bede's is a truly unique place to be – it has its very own zoo, caring for over 70 different species. It is also home to Legat Dance Academy – a school of dance whereby pupils align the dual demands of dance training alongside a high quality academic programme. Bede's also boasts a year round sports programme that provides pupils the choice to focus on their favourite sports all year round rather than seasonally.

Bede's is a place where every pupil is truly treated as an individual and where they are enriched in a holistic way – enabling them to flourish in all aspects of life.

Pastoral

Our exceptional pastoral care is evidenced as happy pupils who are engaged in their learning and actively involved in the wider life of the school embracing every opportunity provided to them. Pupils who are kind to themselves and each other and are gracious about success and failure.

At the Senior School, the House system, which sees pupils from all year groups integrated into a family unit, ensures that each pupil feels familiar and grounded from day one. The Housemaster or Housemistress is supported by their team of House Tutors as well as House Prefects.

Tutors typically oversee 10-12 tutees and meet with them daily, either in their tutor groups or one to one. This regular contact time ensures that tutors get to know their tutees quickly, supporting them in all aspects of their life at Bede's Senior School.

Academic

As no two pupils are the same, Bede's is geared towards enabling everyone to identify their personal passions and then acquire expertise in their specific areas of interest. Bede's offers a considered and diverse array of high quality courses both within the academic timetable and as part of a unique co-curricular programme.

In Year 10, all pupils study English and Maths GCSE along with a Science GCSE/BTEC, and most pupils study at least one language. Bede's offers a carefully curated range of GCSE and BTEC options in a wide variety of subjects including Business, Ceramics, Computer Science, Performing Arts and many more. The Fifth Form years are full of personal growth and development as pupils seek real areas of specialisation. They will emerge, at the end of two years' study, ready to face the challenges of the Sixth Form and life beyond.

Bede's offers an exciting curriculum of 35 subjects at A Level/BTEC, designed to educate, engage and enthuse. There is a supportive Sixth Form, Universities and Careers team to help pupils in their transition to higher education and the world beyond studying. The Sixth Form provides an exciting time for pupils, who can flourish in subjects that they have chosen. Sixth Form subjects include BTEC Dance, Economics, BTEC Animal Management and BTEC Production Arts.

Co-Curricular

Bede's provides a holistic approach to education. It is our strong belief that learning takes place beyond the confines of the classroom. With this in mind, Bede's places creativity, service and action at the heart of the pupil experience.

Bede's pupils pick from a wide array of over 100 clubs and activities that include climbing, e-sports, downland walking, mixed martial arts, debating and music. Activities slots occur three times a week and allow pupils to explore a range of interests. Every pupil is able to pursue their talents via our specialist staff, unbeatable facilities and an innovative timetable.

Boarding

Bede's Senior School offers full and weekly boarding options as well as day boarding by which day pupils are attached to a boarding house and stay at school for prep and supper until 7.15pm when they take the late bus home.

Bede's boasts five stunning boarding houses, one of which opened in just September 2022. It is a beautiful development with modern facilities, a 170 square metre atrium, meeting spaces, offices, and kitchen facilities. Each boarding house is made up of approximately 70-80 pupils who are organised into smaller groups of 10, spanning the year groups, who all look out for each other.

On Saturday mornings, boarders are typically involved in either sport (including matches), academic enrichment activities, drama, music or art. There are many activity sessions running, trips to local towns and cultural centres every Saturday afternoon and on Sundays, there are lots of informal on-site opportunities for recreation.

Houses all frequently plan low key or School-wide social and charity events on Saturday nights, from casino nights and formal dinners to silent discos. There are plenty of activities to get involved with that change throughout the year.

Sport

Sport plays a fundamental part of life at Bede's. With a nationally recognised programme, world class facilities and specialist, ex professional coaches, opportunity, drive and participation is at the heart of what we do. Whether pursuing sport as a career or a hobby, Bede's pupils are encouraged to exceed all expectations and grow in confidence.

We have positioned our sports purposefully across the Trust, with six core sports; Hockey, Football, Cricket, Tennis, Swimming and Netball, four competitive sports; Basketball, Golf, Equestrian and Athletics, as well as a number of support sports.

For those pupils looking to convert their passion for sport into a professional career, we have extensive training programmes, fixtures schedules and expertise to enable them to perform at the highest level – and many of our success stories prove that this is consistently achieved.

Performing Arts

Bede's Senior School is home to an outstanding Performing Arts Faculty, where teachers take great pride in offering one of the most diverse and distinguished programmes for pupils who are passionate about Music, Drama and Dance in a secondary school setting.

In terms of academic courses, Bede's offers a plethora of courses for those looking to explore the Performing Arts such as BTEC Performing Arts (Dance), GCSE Drama, GCSE Music, BTEC Dance, BTEC Music Performance, Drama and Theatre A Level and Music A Level.

Bede's philosophy of teaching Performing Arts remains true to our belief in a holistic education, which provides pupils with the opportunity to grow, both academically and personally. Our aim in the faculty of Performing Arts is to provide our pupils with opportunities that would not be available to them elsewhere, so they can explore their passions, have doors opened for them in the professional world or simply discover something new.

Prep School

Bede's Prep School is an independent, co-educational school for pupils from the ages of just 3 months (Nursery) to 13, offering both day and boarding places.

Our Prep School is based in Eastbourne with easy travel links to London. The School borders the South Downs National Park and is nestled on a cliff top above Beachy Head with stunning views of the sea. Our unique location provides our pupils with many opportunities to take their learning outdoors and connect with nature.

Bede's Prep is a vibrant, energetic and forward-thinking school, which focuses on promoting learning, personal growth and development. Pupils are valued as individuals and enjoy a broad range of opportunities inside and outside the classroom to suit their interests and passions.

Berkhamsted School

(Founded 1541)
Overton House, 131 High Street,
Berkhamsted, Hertfordshire HP4 2DJ

Tel: 01442 358001
Email: admissions@berkhamsted.com
Website: www.berkhamsted.com
Principal:
Mr Richard Backhouse MA(Cantab)
Appointed: January 2016
School type: Co-educational &
single-sex, day & boarding
Age range of pupils: 3–18 years
No. of pupils enrolled as at 01/01/2023: 1883

Sixth Form: 411
Pre-Prep/Prep: 542
Senior Boys: 518
Senior Girls: 412
Fees as at 01/01/2023:
Day: £10,110–£23,175 per annum
Weekly Boarding: £31,500 per annum
Full Boarding: £37,575 per annum
Average class size: 20

Berkhamsted offers a history dating back to 1541, an excellent reputation and a commitment to developing its pupils into remarkable people who will thrive both at school and in life beyond it. The school values of serving others, being adventurous and aiming high with integrity run through all aspects of school life, from the strong academic programme to the extensive co-curricular activities on offer to pupils.

Located 30 minutes by train from Euston station and a short drive from Junction 20 of the M25, the school offers a 'diamond' structure that combines both single-sex and co-educational teaching. Boys and girls are taught together until the age of 11,

then separately from 11-16, whilst sharing in academic trips and visits and in some co-curricular activities. They come back together again in a joint Sixth Form, which from 2024 will be housed in a brand new Sixth Form Centre.

Academic results are consistently strong. 2022 saw 90% of A-Level results at A* – B, and GCSE students achieving 75% of grades 7 and above. Meanwhile, an outstanding co-curricular programme – which includes music, sport, drama, a wide range of clubs and societies, and a vibrant outdoor education programme – seeks to enable pupils to develop skills and interests which they can utilise throughout their time at Berkhamsted and beyond.

Pupils across the school enjoy the benefits of being part of a small, supportive community, yet with access to the state-of-the art facilities of a large school; a 500-seat theatre, a six-lane 25m swimming pool and sports centre, 40 acres of playing fields, a High Ropes Course and a large art department. The school prides itself on offering outstanding levels of pastoral care and the House system is a key feature of Berkhamsted. Berkhamsted offers scholarships – academic, art, drama, music and sport – and means-tested bursaries to talented pupils on entry to the school.

Cobham Hall School

(Founded 1962)

Brewers Road, Cobham, Kent DA12 3BL
Tel: 01474 823371
Email: admissions@cobhamhall.com
Website: www.cobhamhall.com
Headteacher: Mrs Wendy Barrett
School type: Girls' Day & Boarding Senior, Co-ed Sixth Form

Age range of boys: 16–18 years
Age range of girls: 11–18 years (boarding from 11)
No. of pupils enrolled as at 01/01/2023: 150
Fees as at 01/01/2023:
Day: £7,100–£8,250 per term
Full Boarding: £11,500–£13,250 per term

Nestled in 150 acres of stunning historic parkland, Cobham Hall is an independent Round Square Boarding and Day School housed in a 16th Century Manor House. The school is set in an idyllic rural setting, yet enjoys exceptional transport links and is less than 30 minutes from London by train. We offer full, weekly and flexi-boarding, and local minibus transport is available, providing ultimate flexibility for families.

Cobham Hall students are encouraged to explore and discover their talents, attributes and strengths and we believe personal and academic success, health, wellbeing, and community go hand-in-hand. A wide range of subject options are offered at GCSE and A Level, with small class sizes ensuring students have the attention they need academically.

Cobham Hall encourages students to achieve their fullest potential, supplementing an integrated academic programme with a wide range of co-curricular activities. Our innovative, skills-based curriculum is designed specifically to develop the crucial life skills young people will need in our rapidly changing world: skills in complex problem-solving, project and time management, critical thinking and creativity; resilience, communication, determination, teamwork and compassion. Key skills lessons are timetabled throughout, culminating in our Global Perspectives GCSE course and the Extended Project Qualification.

We believe untold brilliance lies within our students, and that each has the potential to develop skills and abilities they may never have believed possible.

Our school motto, 'There's more in you than you think,' underlines this. We are committed to providing our students with the academic knowledge to flourish, and to inspiring each student to have the courage to challenge themselves and find their own path in life.

At the heart of Cobham Hall lie our core values: Trust, Respect, Honesty, Kindness and Tolerance. These, alongside the Round Square IDEALS, provide the foundation for our Personal Discovery Framework, which encourages our students to explore and discover their talents, attributes and strengths.

Cobham Hall is part of the Mill Hill School Foundation and is a school for girls aged 11 to 16, and girls and boys aged 16-18 in Sixth Form.

Davenies

DAVENIES

(Founded 1940)

Station Road, Beaconsfield,
Buckinghamshire HP9 1AA
Tel: 01494 685400
Email: office@davenies.co.uk
Website: www.davenies.co.uk
Headmaster: Mr Carl Rycroft BEd (Hons)
Appointed: September 2015

School type: Boys' Day Preparatory
Age range of boys: 4–13 years
No. of pupils enrolled as at 01/01/2023: 334
Fees as at 01/01/2023:
Day: £12,825–£19,350 per annum
Average class size: Max 20

Davenies is a thriving IAPS day school for boys aged 4-13. Our ethos and philosophy enable the boys to make the most of their preparatory years, supported by high-quality pastoral care, a broad and stimulating curriculum and numerous extra-curricular opportunities.

Davenies has its own distinct character and from their earliest years children are encouraged to relish the learning experience.

We are committed to an education both in and out of the classroom, thereby enabling the academic, artistic, musical, creative and physical potential of each child to flourish. This school is a warm, caring and happy one, where self-esteem is nurtured and grown; we believe that by fostering a wide range of interests and passions we provide the boys with every opportunity to develop in confidence. Our high-quality teachers have an excellent track record of preparing children for life at the country's leading senior schools and beyond.

Enterprises such as the unique Davenies Award Scheme and the permeation of technology in our teaching and learning ensure we offer a truly independent educational experience.

At Davenies, our outstanding facilities support us in providing a positive learning experience with our own language of learning that nurtures each boy's understanding of how he learns. Davenies' boys are polite and friendly with their own individual characters, personalities, passions and interests.

The School is owned by Beaconsfield Educational Trust Limited, a company limited by guarantee, whose registered office is at 73 Station Road, Beaconsfield, Bucks HP9 1AA. Registration No. 717500 Registered Charity No. 313120.

Earlscliffe

29 Shorncliffe Road, Folkestone,
Kent CT20 2NB
Tel: 01303 253951
Email: admissions@earlscliffe.co.uk
Website: www.earlscliffe.co.uk
Headteacher: Mr Joss Williams
School type: Co-educational Day &
Boarding Sixth Form / College

Age range of pupils: 15–19 years
No. of pupils enrolled as at 01/01/2023: 130
Fees as at 01/01/2023:
Day: £9,100 per term
Weekly Boarding: £11,745 per term
Full Boarding: £13,650 per term

Earlscliffe, an independent school that offers university preparation for 15 to 19 year olds from all over the world.

The school provides the very best of English education: the gold standard A-level programme, the one year GCSE (or "International Transition Year"), the Business Diploma and the University Foundation Year. Earlscliffe applies a very personalised approach to teaching, that consistently improves a student's average grades from the time that they arrive at Earlscliffe until their final exam results. This is achieved through a very simple educational approach that includes small class sizes, longer lesson times and weekly testing in every subject.

The entire Earlscliffe boarding school experience looks to prepare students for a life at university and beyond. Students enjoy a variety of activities whilst they are in the UK that complement and enrich classroom learning. This means that an Earlscliffe student has an enhanced portfolio of studies and life skills that give them a significant advantage in the next stages of their lives.

Earlscliffe promotes independently minded, robust and future-ready students, embracing traditional English values, that are balanced by an international, open-minded perspective.

The school prides itself on an inclusive student body, with over 30 different nationalities, and a wide diversity of cultures, talents and interests.

The Earlscliffe boarding houses are managed by House Masters who carefully monitor the students' movements and ensure that they are safe and emotionally supported. It is an "in-town" campus which provides students with a sense of independence, allowing them to walk into town, to the beach, or the local sports centre.

For more information please contact Earlscliffe directly.

King Edward's Witley

King Edward's
WITLEY
Petworth Road, Godalming,
Surrey GU8 5SG

Tel: 01428 686700
Email: admissions@kesw.org
Website: www.kesw.org
Head: Mrs Joanna Wright
School type: Co-educational Day &
Boarding Senior & Sixth Form
Religious Denomination: Christian
Age range of pupils: 11–18 years

No. of pupils enrolled as at 01/01/2023: 435
Fees as at 01/01/2023:
Day: £5,960–£7,555 per term
Weekly Boarding:
£11,195–£11,630 per term
Full Boarding:
£11,790–£12,250 per term
Average class size: 15

Pupils thrive at King Edward's. We encourage them to be the best versions of themselves because individual achievement and personal growth count for more than league tables. Our unique heritage and place among British co-educational independent schools means that we can provide the best preparation for adult life to a wider range of young people than almost any other institution.

King Edward's offers your son or daughter a school that can feel as warm and welcoming as home. A springboard to a lifelong love of learning which can nurture confidence, foster collaboration and prepare them for life in a multicultural world. Most of all it can help them discover who they are. This is a school shaped by generosity of spirit, not by background.

Academic focus
A King Edward's education is a rounded education. All academic staff are subject specialists, GCSE/IGCSE in Year 11 followed by a choice of A-level courses or the IB Diploma programme in the Sixth Form. Young people discover skills, talents and enthusiasms they never knew they had and are encouraged to set their sights high and be ambitious in their learning. Our rich co-curricular programme broadens their horizons.

Pastoral
All our pupils benefit from small class sizes and our House system with its supportive pastoral networks is at the heart of school life. Each House is committed to strong connections uniting and blending boarders and day pupils into a single team. Diversity

has been a strength since our foundation in 1553 and while most of our 420 pupils are local, we attract international pupils from more than 30 countries. They help teach us what it means to be part of the wider human family.

Boarding
King Edward's is a thriving community with four senior boys and two senior girls Houses for day, weekly and flexi boarders. Lower School pupils in Years 7 and 8 reside in Queen Mary House, an impressive family-oriented building steeped in history. In 2022, we unveiled our Upper Sixth Form House, which is home to all Upper Sixth Form pupils, both boys and girls, in their final year at King Edward's. The new House benefits from landscaped outdoor space, study and social areas and boarders have

their own study bedrooms with full ensuite facilities. Our Upper Sixth Form House provides the perfect stepping stone to university and independent living.

Hobbies and activities

On our leafy, 100-acre site amid the Surrey Hills we have space for all the sport, drama, music, hobbies, and intellectual pursuits a young mind can take. King Edward's is a wonderfully safe place for youthful adventure and curiosity.

The School creates a foundation for life both now and for the future. Our timeless education reaches far beyond the exciting and challenging academic curriculum and the broad range of opportunities in all areas of school life – sporting, artistic, social and cultural.

Pupils leave as independent free-thinkers – agile, motivated, and self-disciplined. The creative, entrepreneurial thinking they develop here gives the next generation of inventors, designers and problem-solvers the ability to grasp life with both hands.

Sport

Our ethos ensures there is ample choice for boys and girls to enjoy a wide variety of sports. Our sports programme is built on the latest research with activities that blend breadth with specific development, hence offering a vast array of Physical Education programmes.

Weekly sports matches are played on Saturdays and mid-week, and in

recent years the School is proud to have achieved regional and national success in football, tennis, basketball, table tennis, fencing, climbing and athletics. If a pupil asks to participate in a particular sport, we will find an opportunity for them to do so. If a girl or boy has an aptitude for a sport, we support them in obtaining specialist and expert coaching, join programmes and local clubs to develop their skills and compete. We help plan the pursuit of coaching qualifications for our pupils.

Music

Music flourishes inside and outside the classroom with some twenty choirs, orchestras and specialist instrumental ensembles from chamber music to rock bands. A carefully structured programme enables pupils of all abilities and aspirations

to perform from informal showcase concerts and workshops to masterclasses and large-scale concerts. Annual instrumental and vocal competitions are held for soloists and ensembles. Annual House Music competitions, 'Battle of the Bands' and 'Musician of the Year' all bring the school community together. The Music and Drama Departments regularly collaborate in school productions and, thanks to our strong link to the City of London, pupils often perform at events in the City.

We aim to inspire a love of independent learning, a wealth of lasting friendships, Christian values and hopeful vision. King Edward's is an extraordinary, distinctive, forward-thinking and global minded community. It is a wonderful place to be.

Leighton Park School

LEIGHTON PARK
FOUNDED 1890

Shinfield Road, Reading, Berkshire RG2 7ED

Tel: 0118 987 9600
Email: admissions@leightonpark.com
Website: www.leightonpark.com
Head: Mr Matthew L S Judd BA, PGCE
Appointed: September 2018
School type: Co-educational Day & Boarding Senior & Sixth Form

Religious Denomination: Quaker
Age range of pupils: 11–18 years
No. of pupils enrolled as at 01/01/2023: 550
Fees as at 01/01/2023:
£7,150–£13,895 per term
Average class size: 16
Teacher/pupil ratio: 1:7

Introduction

A vibrant learning community, our values-based education focuses on each individual – with impressive results.

At its core, a Leighton Park education offers achievement with values, character and community.

The success of our academic approach is demonstrated by the latest UK Government analysis, which recognised Leighton Park as the best performing school in Berkshire and in the top 14 boarding schools in the country for the academic progress of our leavers. Our A Level students achieved 74% A*-B last year. The Independent School Inspectorate (ISI) have awarded Leighton Park a 'double excellent' standard, the highest possible attainment for an independent school, in recognition of both the quality of pupils' personal development and the quality of their academic progress.

Academic focus

An IB World School, our emphasis on problem-solving, critical thinking and intercultural skills ensures that every student can succeed in an ever-changing, globalised world. Central to the school's approach, we have particular strengths in Science, Technology, Engineering and Maths (STEM) as well as the Creative Arts (Music, Drama, Art and Dance). Combining these strengths, our students benefit from an interdisciplinary approach, fusing analytical skills from STEM with creative and interpersonal soft skills.

Music is another particular strength of the School with a new Music and Media Centre providing students with exceptional facilities, including a Yamaha Live Lounge recording studio. Our Music departments is accredited as a Flagship Yamaha Music Education Partner, the only school in Europe to hold this status, with 50% of students studying an instrument and 27 music teachers on staff.

In Sixth Form, students can choose between the International Baccalaureate Diploma Programme (IB) or A Levels, and are offered an extensive selection of subject options, including Psychology, Politics, Economics/Business Studies, Dance, a BTEC in Digital Film and Video Production and a CTEC in Physical Education.

Pastoral

All our students benefit from small class sizes. The average is 16 students per class, going down to 7 students in Sixth Form. Our dedicated teachers are able to cater lessons to each student and ensure they are kept on track both inside and out of lessons. This allows an unparalleled level of support and also a relationship between students and teachers that allows students to feel that they can speak honestly and openly to teachers about any problems they may be facing. Leighton Park was awarded the ISA National Award for Excellence in Pupil Personal Development in 2022.

Boarding

Leighton Park has a thriving boarding community, offering full, weekly and flexible options for students. The Lower School (Years 7 and 8) offers co-educational boarding in a House with separate wings for accommodation by gender. The single-sex accommodation is arranged for Senior students in School House for boys and Reckitt House for girls. Students represent 39 countries, with strong UK representation. Day students are welcome to stay until 9pm to spend time with friends or have time and space to focus on their prep.

House parents create homely environments supported by tutors and matrons, ensuring each student feels relaxed and comfortable. With a dedicated staff and plenty of opportunity to socialise with other students, each House is very much its own community.

Hobbies and other activities

Our wrap-around provision, which welcomes day students from 7.15am to 9pm, offers all our pupils the time to discover and develop their greatest talents. Students can choose from 90 different co-curricular activities to extend their learning, increase confidence, try new things and make new friends.

Sports

Sport plays an important role in life at Leighton Park with many individual performers and teams reaching county and regional level in sports. The school's Advanced Performer Programme supports elite athletes. While the school does very well in traditional sports such as rugby, netball, boys' cricket and hockey it also has strong teams in football and girls' cricket. The school is very supportive of individual talents and interests from rowing to gymnastics.

Music & Drama

Students have so many opportunities to play or perform at Leighton Park, with the Music and Drama Departments being two of the busiest places in school. The school produces a spectacular musical show every other year with many more opportunities to perform in between regular concerts, plays and tours abroad.

Facilities

Leighton Park has the facilities you would expect of a leading independent school, including a new Music and Media Centre, an impressive library, swimming pool and a combination of high tech and historic buildings. The school's innovative use of the latest teaching and learning technologies is supported by continuous investment in technology, including Google Classroom, CleverTouch screens in classrooms and personal ChromeBook laptops for students. A stunning new Sixth Form Centre will be open by 2024/25.

School life

The quiet moments and the calm atmosphere of our 65 acre park, encourage students to collect their thoughts and reflect within a caring community, providing high academic standards, excellent pastoral care and a rich and diverse co-curricular programme of activities. All of this, and the focus on mutual respect, create a stable, unique and sustainable environment where children can live, learn and grow.

LVS Ascot

A Co-educational Day & Boarding School
for young people aged 4 - 18

ROYAL
PATRONAGE

(Founded 1803)
London Road, Ascot, Berkshire SL5 8DR

Tel: 01344 882770
Email: enquiries@lvs.ascot.sch.uk
Website: www.lvs.ascot.sch.uk
Principal: Mrs Christine Cunniffe BA
(Hons), MMus, MBA
Appointed: September 2010
School type: Co-educational Day &
Boarding Preparatory, Senior & Sixth Form

Religious Denomination:
Non-denominational
Age range of pupils: 4–18 years
No. of pupils enrolled as at 01/01/2023: 833
Fees as at 01/01/2023:
Day: £11,640–£20,985 per annum
Full Boarding: £29,760–£36,660 per annum
Average class size: 18

LVS Ascot is an award winning, all-ability, independent day and boarding school that inspires boys and girls from 4 to 18 to exceed their expectations and become independent adults, through a rounded education that delivers academic rigor alongside sporting, performing and creative opportunities.

The campus includes all Infant & Junior School, Senior School and Sixth Form Facilities as well as four Boarding Houses within a spacious 26 acre site. LVS Ascot facilities include: Infant & Junior School environmental garden, indoor swimming pool, fully equipped 250 seater theatre with state of the art light and sound, learning resource centre, astro pitch, fitness centre and wellbeing hub.

Proud of its excellent academic & pastoral care, staff across the school work together to ensure that every student's personal development is nurtured, believing that encouragement and support are essential to help young people become caring, confident citizens for the future.

Being one of three schools owned and managed by the Licensed Trade Charity, income generated by the School is re-invested in the site, to offer the highest standard of educational and co-curricular facilities and is also used to fund the work of the Charity.

Mayfield School

Mayfield

(Founded 1872)
The Old Palace, Mayfield,
East Sussex TN20 6PH

Tel: 01435 874642
Email: registrar@mayfieldgirls.org
Website: www.mayfieldgirls.org
Head: Ms Antonia Beary MA, MPhil (Cantab), PGCE
School type: Girls' Day & Boarding Senior & Sixth Form
Religious Denomination: Catholic (we accept all faiths and none)

Age range of girls: 11–18 years (boarding from 11)
No. of pupils enrolled as at 01/01/2023: 425
Fees as at 01/01/2023:
Years 7 and 8: £7,950 per term
Years 9-13: £8,375 per term
Full Boarding: £12,975 per term
Flexi Boarding from: £90 per night
Average class size: 15-17

Mayfield is a leading independent boarding and day school for girls aged 11 to 18. Founded in 1872, a Mayfield education combines academic rigour, breadth of opportunity and a strong sense of community.

Set within the beautiful Sussex Countryside, conveniently located within an hour of central London and with easy access to Gatwick and Heathrow airports, the School has an excellent academic record, exceptional pastoral care and an extensive co-curricular programme. Every girl is encouraged and supported to find her strengths and develop them in an inspiring learning environment, which encourages independent critical thinking, determination and resilience. Mayfield

girls develop a lifelong love of learning, a range of transferable skills that will prepare them for their futures and friendships that will last a lifetime.

Mayfield's ethos reflects its Catholic foundation and encourages integrity, initiative, respect and a desire to be the best you can be within a vibrant and inclusive community. One of the School's greatest strengths is its proven ability to unlock and develop the unique potential and talent of each girl in an inspiring learning environment. Small classes, exemplary pastoral care, and a happy and vibrant community, ensure girls thrive and challenge themselves both inside and outside the classroom.

Mayfield's innovative curriculum

encourages questioning, reflection, creativity and the freedom to learn from mistakes. Pupils progress to prestigious universities, including Oxford and Cambridge, and increasingly to the US and Europe to study a wide range of subjects, with a regular stream of engineers, medics, vets, lawyers, economists, designers and architects.

For the past 150 years, Mayfield has nurtured generations of enterprising, purposeful young women with the skills and confidence to make a positive difference in the world. The skills, values, aspiration and resilience instilled in the girls prepares them to respond to the opportunities and challenges of the 21st century, whatever path they choose.

Reddam House Berkshire

REDDAM HOUSE
BERKSHIRE

(Founded 2015)
Bearwood Road, Sindlesham,
Wokingham, Berkshire RG41 5BG
Tel: +44 (0)118 974 8300

Email: registrar@reddamhouse.org.uk
Website: www.reddamhouse.org.uk
Principal: Mr Rick Cross
School type: Co-educational Day &
Boarding Prep & Senior, Nursery &
Sixth Form
Religious Denomination:
Non-denominational

Age range of pupils:
3 months–18 years
No. of pupils enrolled as at 01/01/2023: 675
Fees as at 01/01/2023:
Day: £12,006–£19,248 per annum
Weekly Boarding: £29,241–£33,696 per
annum
Full Boarding: £30,855–£35,310 per annum

Reddam House Berkshire is a co-educational, independent day and boarding school for pupils aged between 3 months and 18 years old. This truly majestic school, set in 125 acres of beautiful parkland, is conveniently located near Wokingham in the English county of Berkshire, a vibrant hub with easy access to the M3, M4, Heathrow and London.

The school is committed to focusing on the individual – to giving every student the personalised support they need to be their best selves in the classroom and beyond. From the world-class campus, they offer a future-focused curriculum that blends academics and the arts to create confident, independent-minded young people who are ready to excel and make a positive contribution to the world.

A future-focused, internationally respected curriculum balances academics, sports, and arts in a way that inspires all our students. From the youngest early learners to the senior school students, they instil a love of learning that stays with them forever. The school was awarded 'Excellent' in every area in their ISI report 2022.

Exam Results

Reddam House Berkshires Exam results were outstanding in 2022 with 76% of A-level grades awarded being A*/B and 50% A*/A, while 52% of GCSE results were level 9-7. More than 90% of graduates were offered places at their first choice of university.

Boarding

Reddam House offers a range of flexible boarding options for students from the age of 11 to 18 years old, including full and weekly boarding, extended days, and ad-hoc stays.

Students who board at Reddam House can expect to be part of an inclusive, respectful, and international community where independence and self-confidence are developed and celebrated.

Beyond the Classroom

Academics is just one area in which students thrive, the diverse programme of activities encourages students to develop new competencies and build the resilience, courage, and versatility they need to thrive in life beyond school.

Roedean School

ROEDEAN

(Founded 1885)
Roedean Way, Brighton,
East Sussex BN2 5RQ

Tel: 01273 667500
Email: info@roedean.co.uk
Website: www.roedean.co.uk
Head of School: Niamh Green
School type:
Girls' Day & Boarding Senior & Sixth Form
Age range of girls:
11–18 years (boarding from 11)

No. of pupils enrolled as at 01/01/2023: 700
Fees as at 01/01/2023:
Day: £6,290–£8,220 per term
Weekly Boarding:
£11,120–£12,400 per term
Full Boarding: £12,180–£14,745 per term
Average class size: 18
Teacher/pupil ratio: 1:7

Roedean is the place to nurture your talents, spark your curiosity, develop your skills, and let your imagination run riot. This is because we believe that education is about far more than just exam results. Roedean provides an all-round education within a caring and friendly community, where girls do achieve outstanding academic grades, but also pursue passions and challenge themselves to try new things.

Roedean offers day and boarding for girls aged 11 to 18 in an inspiring cliff-top location on the South Coast that has breathtaking sea-views and is close enough to Brighton to take advantage of this cultural and dynamic city. Just 30 minutes from Gatwick by car and offering the 'Victoria Escort' – where girls are chaperoned between Brighton Station and London Victoria (53 minutes) by a member of staff on Friday and Sunday evenings – Roedean is extremely accessible.

All girls develop a love for learning at Roedean and are encouraged at all stages to pursue intellectual challenge and their own interests. Outstanding GCSE and A-Level results are evidence of the resilience, curiosity and confidence fostered by Roedean's approach to academics. Our latest results show a remarkable 71% of 9-8 grades (equal to A** and A*) at GCSE and 71% A*-A grades achieved at A Level. Typically, a third of students leaving Sixth Form pursue STEM courses at university, whilst 5-6% have accepted Oxbridge offers in recent years.

From those learning new games to elite sportswomen, Roedean offers 14 different sports, with girls representing Roedean in over 800 fixtures across the board. Roedean strongly believes that whatever the pupil's aspirations in sport that her experience should be enjoyable, rewarding, and memorable.

The Creative and Performing Arts are at the very core of Roedean's ethos; the School delights in the girls' successes on stage in our newly-refurbished 350-seat professional theatre, including Les Misérables, Six, Matilda, Cabaret, and Hairspray with further opportunities to perform in music concerts, recitals, and dance showcases throughout each term at Roedean. All lessons and performances will now be held on brand-new Steinway pianos, and we now have a new Music Technology classroom with a suite of the latest generation Apple iMac computers and software.

Representing students from over 40 countries, the School has a dynamic feel; the girls hear about different experiences and traditions each day, and this helps to develop a strong sense of community and a deep understanding of other cultures and backgrounds. Roedean has a strong social conscience, and the girls play an active role in the wider community, taking great pleasure from the weekly activities they undertake, which include Sports Leaders, Language Buddies and Reading Buddies at local primary schools, and Community Action Projects such as with our neighbours the Blind Veterans.

During our most recent ISI Inspection in November 2021, Roedean was given a perfect score in every single category, with the girls' progress, positivity and keenness to get involved all being recognised by the Inspection. Roedean offers a truly inspirational setting for girls to inhabit as they grow up, where opportunities are endless. It is this holistic educational journey that develops real independence and initiative beyond the classroom, with increased social awareness, an outward-looking approach, and a desire to make a difference in the world.

St John's Beaumont Preparatory School

**ST JOHN'S
BEAUMONT**
(Founded 1888)

Priest Hill, Old Windsor, Berkshire SL4 2JN
Tel: 01784 494 053
Email: sjb.admissions@sjb.email
Website: www.sjbwindsor.uk
Headmaster: Mr P Barr
School type: Boys' Day & Boarding
Preparatory, Co-ed Pre-Prep & Nursery

Age range of boys: 3–13 years
Age range of girls: 3–7 years
No. of pupils enrolled as at 01/01/2023: 220
Fees as at 01/01/2023:
Day: £3,788–£7,502 per term
Full Boarding: £3,807 per term (+tuition fees)

Introduction

St John's Beaumont is a very special place to learn and grow; located on a stunning 75-acre campus, adjacent to Windsor Great Park, St John's offers a high-quality academic, co-curricular and external engagement programme that propagates a myriad of talents in all our pupils, enabling them to leave as confident and resilient leaders, ready to tackle the bright futures ahead of them.

Facilities

The school is set within 75 acres of established woodland, playing fields and enjoys excellent sporting facilities. There is plenty of space for cross-country, rugby, football, cricket and more. A 25m indoor swimming pool, a rowing suite and a climbing wall are also highlights of our facilities. Of equal importance to Sport is Music, Drama, and the Arts, with many students learning an instrument and outstanding LAMDA results as well as a much-acclaimed annual drama production, with state of the art lighting and sound technology.

Philosophy

'Care for the whole person' underpins our pastoral and wellbeing programme at St John's. This means that spiritual exercise is as important as physical exercise, and learning is as important as lunch!

This passion for pupil wellbeing is responsible for the shaping of St John's students and their academic success, with our boys going to some of the top secondary schools in the country.

Leavers

Our students leave St John's aged 13 and move to some of the country's finest schools, with a third of our leavers securing academic, arts and sports scholarships or exhibitions. More importantly, they leave St John's as confident, aspirational, and resilient young individuals, aware of their own potential and their ability to leave a positive impression on the lives of others.

Boarding

Our vibrant boarding community, comprising of tailored (2 or 3 nights/week), weekly and full boarders, enjoys a full evening & weekend program. The children are making the most of the school's facilities as well as the proximity to Windsor and London for regular trips. Special activities for the boarders include a Diving (PADI) course, treasure hunts in London and trips to exciting attractions such as Thorpe Park and Liquid Leisure.

St Swithun's School

St Swithun's
WINCHESTER

(Founded 1884)
Alresford Road, Winchester,
Hampshire SO21 1HA
Tel: 01962 835700
Email: office@stswithuns.com
Website: www.stswithuns.com
Head of School:
Jane Gandee MA(Cantab)
Appointed: 2010

School type: Girls' Day & Boarding Senior & Sixth Form
Age range of girls: 11–18 years
No. of pupils enrolled as at 01/01/2023: 492
Sixth Form: 137
No. of boarders: 213
Fees as at 01/01/2023:
Day: £23,478 per annum
Full Boarding: £39,492 per annum

St Swithun's School is a renowned independent day, weekly and full-boarding school for girls set in 45 acres overlooking the Hampshire Downs on the outskirts of Winchester, yet only 50 minutes by train from central London. It offers excellent teaching, sporting and recreational facilities.

The school has a long-standing reputation for academic rigour and success. Girls are prepared for public examinations and higher education in a stimulating environment in which they develop intellectual curiosity, independence of mind and the ability to take responsibility for their own learning. They achieve almost one grade higher at GCSE than their already significant baseline ability would suggest, and approximately half a grade higher at A level. St Swithun's offers a comprehensive careers and higher education support service throughout the school years. Its Oxbridge preparation is part of a whole-school academic enrichment programme providing additional challenge and stimulation.

Whilst achieving academic excellence, girls also have the opportunity to do 'something else'. There is an extensive co-curricular programme of over 100 weekly and 50 weekend activities to choose from.

As well as academic classrooms and science laboratories, there is a magnificent performing arts centre with a 600-seat auditorium, a music school, an art and technology block, a sports hall and a full-size indoor swimming pool. There is an impressive library and ICT facility. The grounds are spacious and encompass sports fields, tennis courts and gardens.

With kindness and tolerance at the heart of its community, St Swithun's provides a civilised and caring environment in which all girls are valued for their individual gifts. By the time a girl leaves she will be courageous, compassionate, committed and self-confident with a love of learning, a moral compass and a sense of humour.

TASIS The American School in England

TASIS

THE AMERICAN SCHOOL
IN ENGLAND

(Founded 1976)

Coldharbour Lane, Thorpe, Surrey TW20 8TE

Tel: +44 (0)1932 582316

Email: ukadmissions@tasisengland.org

Website: www.tasisengland.org

Head of School: Mr Bryan Nixon

Appointed: July 2017

School type: Co-educational Day & Boarding Prep & Senior, Nursery & Sixth Form

Religious Denomination:

Non-denominational

Age range of pupils: 3–18 years (boarding from 13)

No. of pupils enrolled as at 01/01/2023: 650

Fees as at 01/01/2023:

Day: £13,280–£29,080 per annum

Full Boarding: £54,510 per annum

Average class size: 15

Teacher/pupil ratio: 1:6

TASIS The American School in England provides a truly international learning experience for children aged 3 to 18. Within our culturally diverse community, students from over 60 nations benefit from personalized attention in small classes. Our caring teachers are committed to helping each student develop a sense of individuality, realize their full potential, and take pride in who they are as they discover their passion and follow their own pathway.

The TASIS boarding program provides a safe and welcoming home-away-from-home for students. In addition, our well-developed settling-in programs reflect our extensive experience working with globally mobile families. The School's support helps students and their families overcome the challenges of moving to a new school. They feel part of the TASIS community almost immediately as they adapt to new surroundings and, in many cases, a different culture and language.

Our impressive academic offerings include Advanced Placement courses developed by the American College Board and the IB Diploma Programme. Both provide well-defined pathways to universities in the US, the UK, or anywhere in the world. A broad range of co-curricular, leadership, and service opportunities round out our students' educational experience.

Our spacious 46-acre campus is set in beautiful Surrey countryside, within 20 minutes of Heathrow and 45 minutes from London. Health and safety is a priority and we have created the most secure environment possible, upholding exemplary cleaning standards and minimizing risk by implementing many rigorous strategies in accordance with UK government advice. You can rest assured that your children are in safe hands.

Your children are stepping into a complex and interconnected world. We believe that, together, we can help nurture and create a future generation of compassionate, open-minded, principled citizens. If you would like your child to thrive academically and socially in an international, diverse, and caring community, please contact our Admissions office.

Tonbridge School

**TONBRIDGE
SCHOOL**

(Founded 1553)

High Street, Tonbridge, Kent TN9 1JP

Tel: 01732 304297

Email: admissions@tonbridge-school.org

Website: www.tonbridge-school.co.uk

Headmaster: Mr James Priory MA (Oxon)

Appointed: August 2018

School type: Boys' Day & Boarding Senior & Sixth Form

Age range of boys: 13–18 years

No. of pupils enrolled as at 01/01/2023: 795

Fees as at 01/01/2023:

Day: £35,067 per annum

Full Boarding: £46,740 per annum

Average class size: GCSE 18, A level 10

Teacher/pupil ratio: 1:8

Tonbridge School was founded in 1553. It occupies an extensive site of 150 acres in North Tonbridge, Kent – just a 40-minute train ride from London Charing Cross. There are some 800 boys in seven Boarding Houses and five Day Houses.

One of the key strengths of Tonbridge is that it blends tradition and innovation successfully, with high achieving boys wearing their gifts lightly.

In the latest Sunday Times 'Parent Power' league table, published in December 2022, Tonbridge was the 8th highest ranking independent school in the country, and the top boys' boarding school.

The School is renowned for its excellent teaching and for academic achievement. Each year exam results at GCSE and A-level are outstanding, with boys progressing to leading universities including Oxford, Cambridge and Russell Group institutions: the large majority securing their first-choice destination.

Tonbridge leavers have also recently gained places (and scholarships) at top US institutions including Harvard, Massachusetts Institute of Technology (MIT), Dartmouth, Northeastern and UC Berkeley and, worldwide, at universities in Austria, Australia, Canada, China and Hong Kong.

Pastoral care is based around an outstanding House system. Strong and positive relationships between boys, staff and parents are central to its success, and the School strives to ensure that each pupil, whether a boarder or a day boy, feels fully at home and well supported. Tonbridge was the first school in the UK to put Mindfulness on the curriculum for all Year 10 pupils.

There is also a vibrant programme of Co-Curricular breadth and depth, with a wide range of societies covering everything from Beekeeping to Ultimate Frisbee.

More than 20 sports are on offer, and boys of all abilities are encouraged to take part and to enjoy themselves. Tonbridge manages to do 'sporting excellence' and 'mass participation' equally well.

Plays, musicals and drama workshops take place in the School's own EM Forster

Theatre. Music also plays an important part in Tonbridge life: nearly half of boys learn an instrument, and about a third learn more than one. There are regular performances and concerts across all genres.

The School has a strong commitment to widening access and is striving towards doubling the number of boys who receive means-tested fee assistance to be 80 to 100 boys by 2028.

Boys at Tonbridge develop a strong sense of belonging to, and serving, both local and wider communities. More than 24,000 hours of volunteering time are given by pupils and staff in a typical year. The annual 'Sleepout' by First Years, for example, supports Porchlight, the homelessness charity. Child Action Lanka is Tonbridge's overseas partner charity: following fundraising activities, the School has been able to provide a new computer suite in the Child Action Lanka base in Kilinochchi, Sri Lanka.

'Only Connect'

The question for any family considering a school like ours should be, 'What makes any one school different from another?' The easy answer is the readily visible – the manicured cricket square, the pristine swimming pool, the timeless chapel, the world-class Barton Science Centre.

But what really makes the difference between one school and another is the people. The pupils of all kinds, the staff of all kinds, the parents of all kinds.

For sure, at Tonbridge we have some of the finest, most beautiful facilities and grounds in the country, and yet it is our people who make us stand out. Our latest Good Schools Guide report states: *"Tonbridge is a brilliant school that somehow remains totally unsnobby. Boys make the most of world-class opportunities to learn and have fun, but that is not the best bit – Tonbridge's modern, proactive approach to social responsibility and bursary funding ensures that they stay firmly grounded whilst doing so."*

Tonbridge encourages its students to make connections – connections between academic subjects, between different sports and activities, between people, between cultures: with the aim of producing fine minds and good hearts. The School's ethos is summed up in just two words: 'Only Connect'.

Directory

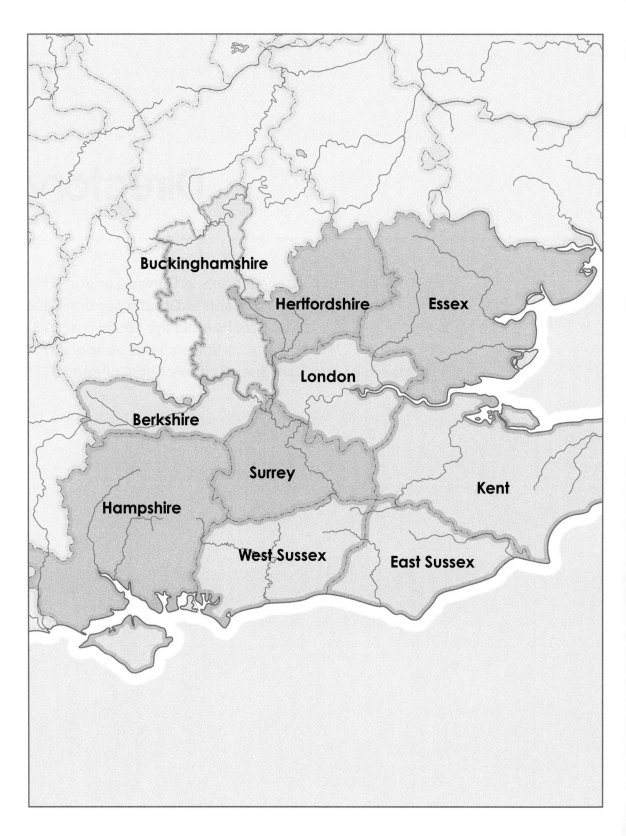

Buckinghamshire

Hertfordshire

Essex

London

Berkshire

Surrey

Kent

Hampshire

West Sussex

East Sussex

Schools and Nursery Schools in Central London

KEY TO SYMBOLS

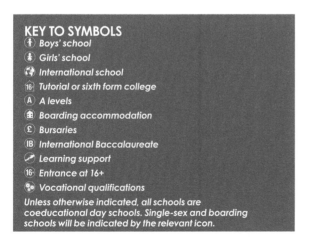

- Boys' school
- Girls' school
- International school
- Tutorial or sixth form college
- A levels
- Boarding accommodation
- Bursaries
- International Baccalaureate
- Learning support
- Entrance at 16+
- Vocational qualifications

Unless otherwise indicated, all schools are coeducational day schools. Single-sex and boarding schools will be indicated by the relevant icon.

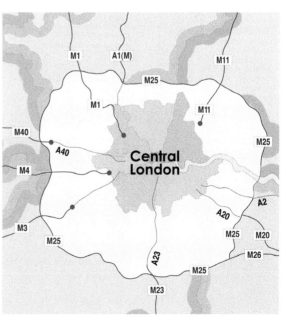

Central London

Accent London
12 Bedford Square,
London WC1B 3JA
Tel: 020 7813 7723
Head: Natasa Blecic
🔵 16⁺

Broadgate Day Nursery
21 Curtain Road, Hackney,
London EC2A 3LW
Tel: 020 7247 3491
Principal: Jacky Roberts NNEB
Age range: 0–5

Cavendish College
35-37 Alfred Place,
London WC1E 7DP
Tel: 020 7580 6043
Principal: Dr J Sanders BSc, MBA,
PhD
16⁺

Charterhouse Square School
40 Charterhouse Square,
London EC1M 6EA
Tel: 020 7600 3805
Headteacher: Mrs Caroline Lloyd
BEd (Hons)
Age range: 3–11 years

City Junior School
4 Gray's Inn Place,
London WC1R 5EY
Tel: 020 3814 3506
Head: Ms Rachel Thompson
Age range: 7–11 years

City Lit Centre & Speech Therapy
Keeley House, Keeley Street,
London WC2B 4BA
Tel: 020 7492 2600
Principal: Mr G W Horgan
16⁺

City of London School
Queen Victoria Street,
London EC4V 3AL
Tel: 020 3680 6300
Head: Mr A R Bird MSc
Age range: B10–18 years
No. of pupils: 950 VIth250
Fees: Day £21,057
🔵 Ⓐ £ 🧭 16⁺

City of London School for Girls
St Giles' Terrace, Barbican,
London EC2Y 8BB
Tel: 020 7847 5500
Headmistress: Ms Jenny Brown
Age range: G11–18 years
🔵 Ⓐ £ 🧭 16⁺

DALLINGTON SCHOOL
For further details see p. 44
8 Dallington Street, Islington,
London EC1V 0BW
Tel: 020 7251 2284
Email:
admin@dallingtonschool.co.uk
Website:
www.dallingtonschool.co.uk
Head of School: Mr James
Griffiths
Age range: 3–11 years
No. of pupils: 81
Fees: Day £12,450–£15,660

École Jeannine Manuel – London
43-45 Bedford Square,
London WC1B 3DN
Tel: 020 3829 5970
Head of School: Pauline Prévot
Age range: 3–18 years
No. of pupils: 585
Fees: Day £20,760
🔵 🟤 Ⓘ🅑

Guildhall School of Music & Drama
Barbican, London EC2Y 8DT
Tel: 020 7382 7192
Principal: Barry Ife CBE, FKC,
HonFRAM
16⁺

Guildhouse School
43-45 Bloomsbury Square,
London WC1A 2RA
Tel: +44 (0)1223 341300
Headmaster: Mr James Slocombe
Age range: 15–24 years
🔵 🟤 £ 16⁺

Italia Conti Academy of Theatre Arts
Italia Conti House, 23 Goswell
Road, London EC1M 7AJ
Tel: 020 7608 0047
Director: Chris White
Age range: 10–21 years
16⁺ Ⓐ 16⁺

Kensington College
23 Bloomsbury Square,
London WC1A 2PJ
Tel: 020 7580 1113
16⁺

London College of English & Advanced Studies Ltd
178 Goswell Road,
London EC1V 7DT
Tel: 020 7250 0610
16⁺

Royal Academy of Dramatic Art
62-64 Gower Street,
London WC1E 6ED
Tel: 020 7636 7076
Principal: Nicholas Barter MA, FRSA
16⁺

Smithfield House Children's Nursery
14 West Smithfield,
London EC1A 9HY
Tel: 020 7236 1000
Manager: Janet MacGregor
Age range: 0–5

ST PAUL'S CATHEDRAL SCHOOL
For further details see p. 68
2 New Change,
London EC4M 9AD
Tel: 020 7248 5156
Email:
admissions@spcs.london.sch.uk
Website: www.spcslondon.com
Headmaster: Simon Larter-Evans
BA (Hons), PGCE, FRSA
Age range: 4–13 years
No. of pupils: 270
Fees: Day £16,044–
£17,277 FB £9,706
🟤 £ 🧭

The Courtauld Institute of Art
Somerset House, Strand,
London WC2R 0RN
Tel: 020 7848 2777
Director: Dr Deborah Swallow
16⁺

The London Film School
24 Shelton Street,
London WC2H 9UB
Tel: 020 7836 9642
Director: Ben Gibson
16⁺

The Lyceum School
65 Worship Street,
London EC2A 2DU
Tel: +44 (0)20 7247 1588
Headmaster: Mr Mike Stanley
Age range: 4–11 years

The Method Studio London
Conway Hall, 25 Red Lion
Square, London WC1R 4RL
Tel: 020 7831 7335
16⁺

The Royal Ballet School (Covent Garden)
46 Floral Street, Covent
Garden, London WC2E 9DA
Tel: 020 7836 8899
Head of School: Mr David
Gajadharsingh
Age range: 11–19 years
(boarding from 11)
🟤

Williams College
Thavies Inn House, 5 Holborn
Circus, London EC1N 2HB
Tel: 020 7583 9222
Head: Mr Mujeeb Pathamanathan
16⁺

East London

Al-Falah Primary School
48 Kenninghall Road,
Hackney, London E5 8BY
Tel: 020 8985 1059
Headteacher: Mr M A Hussain
Age range: 5–11 years

Al-Mizan School
46 Whitechapel Road,
London E1 1JX
Tel: 020 7650 3070
Headteacher: Mr Mohammed Badr
Age range: B7–11 years

Alphabet House Day (Montessori) Nursery
Methodist Church, Windmill
Lane, Stratford, London E15 1PG
Tel: 020 8519 2023
Principal: Ms Kemi Balogun

Alphabet House Nursery School
23 Harold Road, Upton
Park, London E13 0SQ
Tel: 020 8548 9466
Principal: Ms Kemi Balogun

Ann Tayler Children's Centre
1-13 Triangle Road (off Westgate
Street), Hackney, London E8 3RP
Tel: 020 7275 6022
Fees: Day £10

Azhar Academy Girls School
235a Romford Road, Forest
Gate, London E7 9HL
Tel: 020 8534 5959
Executive Head Teacher:
Rookshana Adam
Age range: G11–16 years
🚶

Azhar Academy Primary School
470 High Road, Leytonstone,
London E11 3HN
Tel: 020 3327 1150
Headteacher: Ms Saima Ahmed
Age range: 3–11 years

Beis Trana Girls' School
186 Upper Clapton Road,
London E5 9DH
Tel: 020 8815 8000
Age range: G3–16 years
🚶

Bethnal Green Montessori School
68 Warner Place, Bethnal
Green, London E2 7DA
Tel: 020 7739 4343
Head: Sidonie Winter
Age range: 2–6

Building Crafts College
Kennard Road, Stratford,
London E15 1AH
Tel: 020 8522 1705
Principal: Mr John Taylor
16⁺ 🌐

Busy Bees at Chingford
2 Larkswood Leisure Park, 175 New Road, Chingford, London E4 9EY
Tel: 020 8524 7063
Nursery Manager: Natalie Keyes
Age range: 3 months–5 years

Busy Bees in London ExCel
5 Western Gateway, Royal Victoria Docks, London E16 1XL
Tel: 020 7474 7487
Nursery Manager: Rebecca Davy
Age range: 0–5

Buttercup Primary School
181 Cannon Street Road, London E1 2LX
Tel: 020 3759 7408
Headteacher: Ms Rena Begum
Age range: 3–11 years

Chingford House Nursery
22 Marlborough Road, Waltham Forest, London E4 9AL
Tel: 02085 272902
Age range: 6 months–5 years

City of London College
71 Whitechapel High Street, London E1 7PL
Tel: 020 7247 2166
Head: Mr David Nixon
16

Darul Hadis Latifiah
1 Cornwall Avenue, Bethnal Green, London E2 0HW
Tel: 020 8980 2673
Principal: Mr Maulana Muhammad Hasan Chowdhury
Age range: B11–18 years

East End Computing & Business College
149 Commercial Road, London E1 1PX
Tel: 020 7247 8447
Head: Anthony Wilkinson
16

FARADAY PREP SCHOOL
For further details see p. 46
Old Gate House, 7 Trinity Buoy Wharf, London E14 0JW
Tel: 020 8965 7374
Email: info@newmodelschool.co.uk
Website: www.faradayschool.co.uk
Head Teacher: Lucas Motion
Age range: 4–11 years
No. of pupils: 100
Fees: Day £4,320
£

Forest School
College Place, Snaresbrook, London E17 3PY
Tel: 020 8520 1744
Warden: Mr Marcus Cliff Hodges
Age range: 4–18 years
A £ 16

Gatehouse School
Sewardstone Road, Victoria Park, London E2 9JG
Tel: 020 8980 2978
Headteacher: Mrs Sevda Korbay
Age range: 3–11 years

Grangewood Independent School
Chester Road, Forest Gate, London E7 8QT
Tel: 020 8472 3552
Headteacher: Mrs Beverley Roberts
Age range: 2–11 years

Hafs Academy
26 Maryland Road, Stratford, London E15 1JW
Tel: 020 8555 4260
Head of School: Mr Kazi Hussain
Age range: B7–16 years

Happy Faces at Wisdom Kids Nursery
524 High Street, London E12 6QN
Tel: 020 8478 2805

Independent Place Nursery
26/27 Independent Place, Shacklewell Lane, Hackney, London E8 2HD
Tel: 020 7275 7755
Head: Ms Dawn Pennington
Age range: 0–5
No. of pupils: 43

Jamiatul Ummah School
56 Bigland Street, London E1 2ND
Tel: 020 7790 7878
Principal: Mr Nojarul Islam
Age range: B11–16 years

Jasper City School
90A Lawson Close, London E16 3LU
Tel: 07957 163043
Head Teacher: Ms Michelle Kintu
Age range: 3–16 years

Kaye Rowe Nursery School
Osborne Road, London E7 0PH
Tel: 020 8534 4403

Kids Inc Day Nursery – Chingford
3 Friday Hill West, Chingford Hatch, London E4 6UP
Tel: 020 8524 6745

Kids Inc Day Nursery – South Woodford
71 Cleveland Road, South Woodford, London E18 2AE
Tel: 020 8518 8855

Lantern of Knowledge Secondary School
30-36 Lindley Road, Leyton, London E10 6QT
Tel: 020 8539 5183
Head of School: Mr Shakil Ahmed
Age range: B11–16 years

Lanterns Nursery and Pre-school
Unit D, Great Eastern Enterprise Centre, 3 Millharbour, London E14 9XP
Tel: 020 7363 0951

Learningsure College
90a Lawson Close, Custom House, London E16 3LU
Tel: 020 7511 3444
Head of School: Mr John Ajiferuke
Age range: 11–16 years

Little Green Man Nursery
15 Lemna Road, Waltham Forest, London E11 1HX
Tel: 020 8539 7228
Age range: 0–5
No. of pupils: 46

London East Academy
46 Whitechapel Road, London E1 1JX
Tel: 020 7650 3070
Headteacher: Askor Ali
Age range: B11–16 years
A

London Islamic School
18-22 Damien Street, London E1 2HX
Tel: 020 7265 9667
Principal: Hafiz Mawlana Shamsul Haque
Age range: B11–16 years

London School of Commerce & IT
128 Commercial Road, London E1 1NL
Tel: 020 7702 2509
Head: Dr Abul Kalam
16

Low Hall Nursery
Low Hall Lane, London E17 8BE
Tel: 020 8520 1689

Lubavitch House School (Junior Boys)
135 Clapton Common, London E5 9AE
Tel: 020 8800 1044
Head: Mr R Leach
Age range: B5–11 years
No. of pupils: 101

Madani Girls School
Myrdle Street, London E1 1HL
Tel: 020 7377 1992
Principal: Muhammad S. Rahman
Age range: G11–18 years

Magic Roundabout Nursery – Docklands
Jack Dash House, 2 Lawn House Close, Marsh Wall, London E14 9YQ
Tel: 020 7364 6028

Magic Roundabout Nursery – Walthamstow
161 Wadham Road, Centre Way, Walthamstow, London E17 4HU
Tel: 020 8523 5551

Market Nursery
Wilde Close, Off Pownall Road, Hackney, London E8 4JS
Tel: 020 7241 0978
Head: Ms Hazel Babb
No. of pupils: 24

Mazahirul Uloom London
241 Mile End Road, Stepney Green, London E1 4AA
Tel: 020 7702 8533
Principal: Moulana Imdadur Rahman Al-Madani
Age range: 11–16 years

Noah's Ark Nursery
within Mildmay Hospital, Hackney Road, London E2 7NA
Tel: 020 7613 6346

Noor ul Islam Primary School
135 Dawlish Road, Leyton, London E10 6QW
Tel: 020 8558 0786
Interim Head Teacher: Aslam Hansa
Age range: 4–11 years

Normanhurst School
68-74 Station Road, Chingford, London E4 7BA
Tel: 020 8529 4307
Headmistress: Mrs Jacqueline Job
Age range: 2.5–16 years

Ohr Emes
148 Upper Clapton Road, London E5 9JZ
Tel: 020 8800 8932
Age range: B3–7 years

Oliver Thomas Nursery School
Mathews Avenue, East Ham, London E6 6BU
Tel: 020 8552 1177
Head Teacher: Dianne Walls
Age range: 3–5

Pillar Box Montessori Nursery & Pre-Prep School
107 Bow Road, London E3 2AN
Tel: 020 8980 0700
Director: Lorraine Redknapp
Age range: 0–5 years
Fees: Day £12,000

Quwwat-ul-Islam Girls' School
16 Chaucer Road, Forest
Gate, London E7 9NB
Tel: 020 8548 4736
Headteacher: Ms Shazia Member
Age range: G4–16 years

River House Montessori School
Great Eastern Enterprise, 3
Millharbour, London E14 9XP
Tel: 020 7538 9886
Principal: Ms Sarah Greenwood
Age range: 3–16 years

Snaresbrook Preparatory School
75 Woodford Road, South
Woodford, London E18 2EA
Tel: 020 8989 2394
Headteacher: Mr Ralph Dalton
Age range: 3.5–11 years

Talmud Torah Machzikei Hadass School
1 Belz Terrace, Clapton,
London E5 9SN
Tel: 020 8800 6599
Age range: B3–16 years

The Grove Montessori Nursery
Grosvenor Road, Wanstead,
London E11 2EW
Tel: 0203 404 4380
Age range: 3 months–5 years

The Happy Nest Nursery Ltd
Fellows Court Family
Centre, Weymouth Terrace,
Hackney, London E2 8LR
Tel: 020 7739 3193

The Music School
59a High Street, Wanstead,
London E11 2AE
Tel: 020 8502 0932

Tom Thumb Nursery
1-7 Beulah Road, London E17 9LG
Tel: 020 8520 1329
Age range: 2–5
No. of pupils: 32

Treehouse Nursery Schools – Cambridge Park
25 Cambridge Park,
Wanstead, London E11 2PU
Tel: 020 853 22535
Age range: 3 months–5 years

Treehouse Nursery Schools – Woodbine Place
35 Woodbine Place,
London E11 2RH
Tel: 020 8532 2535
Age range: 3 months–5 years

UK Community College (UKCC)
566 Romford Road, London E12 5AF
Tel: 07979 547727
Age range: 7–18 years

Walthamstow Montessori School
Penrhyn Hall, Penrhyn Avenue,
Walthamstow, London E17 5DA
Tel: 020 8523 2968
Principal: Ms Lorna Mahoney
Age range: 2–6 years

Whitechapel College
67 Maryland Square,
Stratford, London E15 1HF
Tel: 020 8555 3355
Principal:
Luke Julias Maughan-Pawsey

Winston House Preparatory School
140 High Road, London E18 2QS
Tel: 020 8505 6565
Head Teacher: Mrs Marian Kemp
Age range: 3–11 years

North London

5 E College of London
Selby Centre, Selby Road,
London N17 8JL
Tel: 020 8885 3456/5454
Head: Mr Raj Doshi

Annemount School
18 Holne Chase, Hampstead
Garden Suburb, London N2 0QN
Tel: 020 8455 2132
Principal: Mrs G Maidment
BA(Hons), MontDip
Age range: 2–7 years

Asquith Nursery – Crouch Hill
33 Crouch Hill, London N4 4AP
Tel: 020 7561 1533

Avenue Pre-Prep & Nursery School
2 Highgate Avenue,
Highgate, London N6 5RX
Tel: 020 8348 6815
Head of School: Ms Sarah Tapp
Age range: 2–7 years

Beis Chinuch Lebonos Girls School
Woodberry Down Centre,
Woodberry Down, London N4 2SH
Tel: 020 88097 737
Head of School: Mrs Leah Klein
Age range: G2–16 years

Beis Malka Girls School
93 Alkham Road, London N16 6XD
Tel: 020 8806 2070
Head of School: Mrs G Wind
Age range: G2–16 years

Beis Rochel D'Satmar Girls School
51-57 Amhurst Park, London N16 5DL
Tel: 020 8800 9060
Head of School: Mrs Elka Katz
Age range: G2–18 years

Bnois Jerusalem School
79-81 Amhurst Park,
London N16 5DL
Tel: 020 8211 7136
Head of School: Mrs M Landau
Age range: G2–16 years

Bobov Primary School
87-90 Egerton Road,
London N16 6UE
Tel: 020 8809 1025
Head of School: Mr Yossi Elzas
Age range: B2–13 years

Busy Bees at Enfield Highlands Village
2 Florey Square, Highlands
Village, London N21 1UJ
Tel: 020 8360 6610
Nursery Manager: Simone Prince
Age range: 3 months–5 years

Busy Bees Nursery
c/o David Lloyd Leisure Club,
Leisure Way, High Road,
Finchley, London N12 0QZ
Tel: 020 8343 8500
Manager: Toni Difonzo
Age range: 3months–5
No. of pupils: 18

Channing School
The Bank, Highgate, London N6 5HF
Tel: 020 8340 2328
Headmistress: Mrs Lindsey Hughes
Age range: G4–18 years

City of London Business College
Ebenezer House, 726-728 Seven
Sisters Road, London N15 5NH
Tel: 020 8800 6621
Head: Mr Kwateng

Coconut Nursery
133 Stoke Newington Church
Street, London N16 0UH
Tel: 020 7923 0720

Court Theatre Training Co
55 East Road, London N1 6AH
Tel: 020 7739 6868
Artistic Director: June Abbott

Dania Scandinavian School
Curran House, 3 Highbury
Crescent, London N5 1RN
Tel: 07933 619674
Headteacher: Ms Katie Howard
Age range: 2–11 years

Dwight School London
6 Friern Barnet Lane,
London N11 3LX
Tel: 020 8920 0600
Head: Chris Beddows
Age range: 2–18 years

Finchley & Acton Yochien School
6 Hendon Avenue, Finchley,
London N3 1UE
Tel: 020 8343 2191
Head of School: Ms Junko Tanabe
Age range: 2–6 years

Finsbury Park Day Nursery & Preschool
Dulas Street, Finsbury Park,
Islington, London N4 3AF
Tel: 0330 127 2279

Floral Place Day Nursery
2 Floral Place, Northampton
Grove, London N1 2PL
Tel: 020 7354 9945

Grange Park Preparatory School
13 The Chine, Grange Park,
Winchmore Hill, London N21 2EA
Tel: 020 8360 1469
Headteacher: Ms Flavia Rizzo
Age range: 3–11 years

Greek Secondary School of London
22 Trinity Road, London N22 8LB
Tel: +44 (0)20 8881 9320
Headteacher:
Ms Sandra Doropoulou
Age range: 12–18 years

Hackney Care For Kids
61 Evering Road, Hackney,
London N16 7PR
Tel: 020 7923 3471

Highgate
North Road, Highgate,
London N6 4AY
Tel: 020 8340 1524
Head Master: Mr Adam Pettitt MA
Age range: 4–18 years
No. of pupils: 1935

Highgate Junior School
Cholmeley House, 3 Bishopswood
Road, London N6 4PL
Tel: 020 8340 9193
Principal: Ms Philippa Studd
Age range: 7–11 years

Highgate Pre-Preparatory School
7 Bishopswood Road,
London N6 4PH
Tel: 020 8340 9196
Principal: Ms Sally Hancock
Age range: 4–7 years

Hyland House School
Holcombe Road, Tottenham,
London N17 9AB
Tel: 0208 520 4186
Headteacher: Mr Errol Gayle
Age range: 2–11 years

Impact Factory
Suite 121, Business Design Centre,
52 Upper Street, London N1 0QH
Tel: 020 7226 1877
Founding Partners:
Robin Chandler & Jo Ellen Grzyb

Keble Prep
Wades Hill, Winchmore
Hill, London N21 1BG
Tel: 020 8360 3359
Headmaster: Mr Perran Gill BA (Hons)
Age range: 3–13 years

Kerem House
18 Kingsley Way, London N2 0ER
Tel: 020 8455 7524
Headmistress: Mrs D Rose
Age range: 2–5
No. of pupils: 96
Fees: Day £2,025–£5,160

Kerem School
Norrice Lea, Hampstead Garden
Suburb, London N2 0RE
Tel: 020 8455 0909
Head Teacher: Ms Naomi Simon
Age range: 3–11 years

Laurel Way Playgroup
Nansen Village, 21 Woodside
Avenue, London N12 8AQ
Tel: 020 8445 7514
Head: Mrs Susan Farber
Age range: 3–5

London Studio Centre
42-50 York Way, Kings
Cross, London N1 9AB
Tel: 020 7837 7741
Director & CEO: Mr Nic Espinosa
Age range: 18+

**Lubavitch House
School (Senior Girls)**
107-115 Stamford Hill,
Hackney, London N16 5RP
Tel: 020 8800 0022
Headmaster:
Rabbi Shmuel Lew FRSA
Age range: G11–18 years
No. of pupils: 102
Fees: Day £3,900

**Lubavitch Orthodox Jewish
Nursery – North London**
107-115 Stamford Hill,
Hackney, London N16 5RP
Tel: 020 8800 0022
Head: Mrs F Sudak

**MARS Montessori
Islington Green Nursery**
4 Collins Yard, Islington
Green, London N1 2XU
Tel: 020 7704 2805
Head: Angela Euesden
Age range: 2–5
No. of pupils: 24

**New Park Montessori
School**
67 Highbury New Park,
Islington, London N5 2EU
Tel: 020 7226 1109

**New Southgate Day
and Nursery School**
60 Beaconsfield Road, New
Southgate, London N11 3AE
Tel: 0333 920 4841
Nursery Manager:
Ms Katerina Barotsaki
Age range: 3 months–5 years

Norfolk House School
10 Muswell Avenue, Muswell
Hill, London N10 2EG
Tel: +44 (0)2088 834584
Headteacher: Mr Tej Lander
Age range: 2–11 years

**NORTH BRIDGE HOUSE
SENIOR CANONBURY**
For further details see p. 61
6-9 Canonbury Place,
Islington, London N1 2NQ
Tel: 020 7428 1520
Head of School:
Mr Brendan Pavey
Age range: 11–18 years
No. of pupils: 220
Fees: Day £19,230–£21,735

**North London
Grammar School**
110 Colindeep Lane, Hendon,
London NW9 6HB
Tel: 0208 205 0052
Headteacher: Mr Fatih Adak
Age range: 7–18 years

**North London Rudolf
Steiner School**
1-3 The Campsbourne,
London N8 7PN
Tel: 020 8341 3770
Age range: 0–6 years

One-Tech (UK) Ltd
1st Floor, 12 Cheapside, High
Road, London N22 6HH
Tel: 020 8889 0707
Head: Mr Len Sutherland

Palmers Green High School
104 Hoppers Road, London N21 3LJ
Tel: 020 8886 1135
Head: Ms Sarah Proudlove
Age range: G3–17 years

**Pardes House
Grammar School**
Hendon Lane, Finchley,
London N3 1SA
Tel: 020 8349 4222
Head of School: Rabbi Yitzchok Lev
Age range: B10–16 years

Pentland Day Nursery
224 Squires Lane, Finchley,
London N3 2QL
Tel: 020 8970 2441
Principal: Rachele Parker

Phoenix Academy
85 Bounces Road, Edmonton,
London N9 8LD
Tel: 020 8887 6888
Head Teacher: Mr Paul Kelly
Age range: 5–18 years

**Phoenix Montessori
Nursery**
27 Stamford Hill, London N16 5TN
Tel: 020 8880 2550
Manageress: Kelly Murphy
Age range: 0–5 years

Rainbow Nursery
Yorkshire Grove Estate, 22-26
Nevill Road, London N16 8SP
Tel: 020 7254 7930
Age range: 3 months–5 years

**Rosemary Works
Independent School**
1 Branch Place, London N1 5PH
Tel: 02077 393950
Headteacher: Ms Amanda Parker
NPQH, MPhil
Age range: 3–11 years

**Salcombe Day
Nursery & Preschool**
33 The Green, Southgate,
London N14 6EN
Tel: 0371 705 3478

**Salcombe Preparatory
School**
Green Road, London N14 4AD
Tel: 020 8441 5356
Headmistress: Miss Nicola Sands
Age range: 3–11 years

Salcombe Pre-School
Green Road, Southgate,
London N14 4AD
Tel: 020 8441 5356
Headmistress: Mrs Sarah-Jane
Davies BA(Hons) QTS MEd

**Shakhsiyah School,
London**
1st Floor, 277 St Ann's Road,
London N15 5RG
Tel: 020 8802 8651
Executive Headteacher:
Mr Ziaur Rahman
Age range: 3–14 years

St Andrew's Montessori
St Andrew's Church, Thornhill
Square, London N1 1BG
Tel: 020 7700 2961
Principal:
Samantha Rawson MontDip
Age range: 2–6
No. of pupils: 40
Fees: Day £4,200–£6,525

St Paul's Steiner School
1 St Paul's Road, Islington,
London N1 2QH
Tel: 020 7226 4454
Head Teacher: Ms Anna Retsler
Age range: 3–14 years

**Sunrise Nursery,
Stoke Newington**
1 Cazenove Road, Stoke
Newington, Hackney,
London N16 6PA
Tel: 020 8806 6279
Principal: Didi Ananda Manika
Age range: 15 months–5 years

Sunrise Primary School
55 Coniston Road, Tottenham,
London N17 0EX
Tel: 020 8806 6279 (Office); 020
8885 3354 (School)
Head: Mrs Mary-Anne Lovage
MontDipEd, BA
Age range: 2–11 years
No. of pupils: 30
Fees: Day £5,550

**Talmud Torah Chaim
Meirim School**
26 Lampard Grove, London N16 6XB
Tel: 020 8806 0898
Age range: B5–13 years

**Talmud Torah Yetev
Lev School**
111-115 Cazenove Road,
London N16 6AX
Tel: 020 8806 3834
Age range: B3–11 years

Tawhid Boys School
21 Cazenove Road, Stamford
Hill, London N16 6PA
Tel: 020 8806 2999
Headteacher: Mr Usman Mapara
Age range: B11–16 years

Tayyibah Girls School
88 Filey Avenue, Hackney,
London N16 6JJ
Tel: 020 8880 0085
Head Teacher: Mrs Sumeya Patel
Age range: G4–18 years

**The Children's House
Nursery School**
77 Elmore Street, London N1 3AQ
Tel: 020 7354 2113
Age range: 2.5–4 years

The Children's House Upper School
King Henry's Walk, London N1 4PB
Tel: 020 7249 6273
Headteacher: Ms Ellie Grunewald
Age range: 4–7 years

The City College
University House, 55 East Road, London N1 6AH
Tel: 020 7253 1133
Principal: A Andrews MCMI
Age range: 18–40
🔞

The Dance Studio
2 Farm Road,, Winchmore Hill, London N21 3JA
Tel: 020 8360 5700
🔞

The Gower School Nursery
18 North Road, Islington, London N7 9EY
Tel: 020 7700 2445
Principal: Miss Emma Gowers
Age range: 3 months–5 years
✏️

The Gower School Primary
10 Cynthia Street, Barnsbury, London N1 9JF
Tel: 020 7278 2020
Principal: Miss Emma Gowers
Age range: 4–11 years
✏️

The Grove Nursery
Shepperton House, 83-93 Shepperton Road, Islington, London N1 3DF
Tel: 020 7226 4037
Owners: Ms Rebecca Browne & Ms Elaine Catchpole
Age range: 0–5

The Highgate Activity Nurseries
1 Church Road, Highgate, London N6 4QH
Tel: 020 8348 9248
Head: Helena Prior
Age range: 2–5
Fees: Day £5,460–£9,620
✏️

The Sam Morris Nursery
Sam Morris Centre, Parkside Crescent, London N7 7JG
Tel: 020 7609 1735

TTTYY School
14 Heathland Road, London N16 5NH
Tel: 020 8802 1348
Head of School: Rabbi Y.Y. Friesel
Age range: B2–13 years
🧍

Twinkle Stars Day Nursery
416 Seven Sisters Road, Hackney, London N4 2LX
Tel: 020 8802 0550
Admin Officer: Noori Mohamed
Age range: 1–5

Vita et Pax School
6a Priory Close, Green Road, Southgate, London N14 4AT
Tel: 020 8449 8336
Headteacher: Ms Allana Gay
Age range: 3–11 years

Woodberry Day Nursery
63 Church Hill, Winchmore Hill, London N21 1LE
Tel: 020 8882 6917
Manager: Michelle Miller
Age range: 6 weeks–5
No. of pupils: 62

Yesodey Hatorah Senior Girls' School
Egerton Road, London N16 6UB
Tel: 020 8826 5500
Acting Head Teacher: Mrs C Neuberger
Age range: 3–16 years
No. of pupils: 920

North-West London

Abbey Nursery School
Cricklewood Baptist Church, Sneyd Road, Cricklewood, London NW2 6AN
Tel: 020 8208 2202
Head: Mrs Ruby Azam

Al-Sadiq & Al-Zahra Schools
134 Salusbury Road, London NW6 6PF
Tel: 020 7372 7706
Heads: Mr Seyed Alireza Khoei & Mrs Zamina Rizvi
Age range: 3–16 years

Arnold House School
1 Loudoun Road, St John's Wood, London NW8 0LH
Tel: 020 7266 4840
Headmaster: Mr Giles F Tollit
Age range: B3–13 years
🧍

Barnet Hill Academy
10A Montagu Road, Hendon, London NW4 3ES
Tel: 020 3411 2660
Principal: Mr Alim Shaikh MA, PGCE, MPhil, NPQH
Age range: 3–11 years

Beehive On Queens Park Montessori School
147 Chevening Rd, London NW6 6DZ
Tel: 020 8969 2235
Headmistress: Ms Lucilla Baj
Age range: 2–5
Fees: Day £2,550

Beis Soroh Schneirer
Arbiter House, Wilberforce Road, London NW9 6AX
Tel: 020 8201 7771
Head of School: Mrs Sonia Mossberg
Age range: G2–11 years
🧍

Belmont, Mill Hill Preparatory School
The Ridgeway, London NW7 4ED
Tel: 020 8906 7270
Headmaster: Mr Leon Roberts MA
Age range: 7–13 years
No. of pupils: 550
Fees: Day £19,560
£ ✏️

Beth Jacob Grammar School for Girls
Stratford Road, Hendon, London NW4 2AT
Tel: 020 8203 4322
Age range: G11–17 years
🧍

Bluebells Nursery
Our Lady Help of Christians Church Hall, Lady Margaret Road, London NW5 2NE
Tel: 020 7284 3952
Principal: Ms Anita Pearson
Age range: 2–5
No. of pupils: 20

Brampton College
Lodge House, Lodge Road, Hendon, London NW4 4DQ
Tel: 020 8203 5025
Principal: Mr Bernard Canetti
Age range: 15–19 years
🔞 Ⓐ

Bright Horizons Bush Hill Park
2 Queen Anne's Place, Bush Hill Park, Enfield, London EN1 2PX
Tel: 0333 242 6851

British American Drama Academy
14 Gloucester Gate, London NW1 4HG
Tel: 020 7487 0730
Head: Paul Costello
🔞

Broadhurst School
19 Greencroft Gardens, London NW6 3LP
Tel: 020 7328 4280
Headmistress: Mrs Zoe Sylvester
Age range: 2–5 years
✏️

Brondesbury College
8 Brondesbury Park, London NW6 7BT
Tel: 020 8830 4522
Headteacher: Mr Amzad Ali
Age range: B11–16 years
🧍

Busy Bees at Mill Hill
30 Mill Way, Mill Hill, London NW7 3RB
Tel: 0208 906 9123
Nursery Manager: Danielle Baker
Age range: 0–5

Camden Community Nurseries
16 Acol Road, London NW6 3AG
Tel: 020 7624 2937

Chaston Nursery & Pre-preparatory School
Chaston Place, Off Grafton Terrace, London NW5 4JH
Tel: 020 7482 0701
Head: Mrs Sandra Witten DipEd, DMS
Age range: 0–5
No. of pupils: 69
Fees: Day £7,020–£12,732
£ ✏️

City Mission Nursery
2 Scrub Lane, London NW10 6RB
Tel: 020 8960 0838
Age range: 6 months–5 years

Collège Français Bilingue de Londres
87 Holmes Road, Kentish Town, London NW5 3AX
Tel: 020 7993 7400
Head of School: Mr David Gassian
Age range: 3–15 years
No. of pupils: 700
🌐

Devonshire House Preparatory School
2 Arkwright Road, Hampstead, London NW3 6AE
Tel: 020 7435 1916
Headmistress: Mrs S. Piper BA(Hons)
Age range: B2.5–13 years G2.5–11 years
No. of pupils: 543
Fees: Day £9,870–£20,475
£

Francis Holland School, Regent's Park, NW1
Clarence Gate, Ivor Place, Regent's Park, London NW1 6XR
Tel: 020 7723 0176
Head of School: Mrs Katharine Woodcock
Age range: G11–18 years
No. of pupils: 556 VIth120
Fees: Day £22,890
🧍 Ⓐ £ 🔞

Golders Green Day Nursery & Preschool
212 Golders Green Road, Golders Green, London NW11 9AT
Tel: 0371 454 3885

Goodwyn School
Hammers Lane, Mill Hill, London NW7 4DB
Tel: 020 8959 3756
Principal: Mr Struan Robertson
Age range: 3–11 years

Grimsdell, Mill Hill Pre-Preparatory School
Winterstoke House, Wills Grove, Mill Hill, London NW7 1QR
Tel: 020 8959 6884
Head: Mrs Kate Simon BA, PGCE
Age range: 3–7 years
No. of pupils: 188
Fees: Day £15,095
✏️

Hampstead Fine Arts College
Centre Studios, 41-43 England's Lane, London NW3 4YD
Tel: +44 (0)207 586 0312
Principal: Ms Candida Cave
Age range: 13–19 years
16:

Hampstead Hill School
St Stephen's Hall, Pond Street, Hampstead, London NW3 2PP
Tel: 020 7435 6262
Headteacher: Mr Ross Montague
Age range: 2–7+ years

Happy Child Day Nursery
St Anne's & St Andrew's Church Hall, 125 Salisbury Road, Queens Park, London NW6 6RG
Tel: 020 7625 1966
Age range: 2–5

Heathside School Hampstead
84a Heath Street, Hampstead, London NW3 1DN
Tel: +44 (0)20 3058 4011
Headteacher: Katherine Vintiner
Age range: 2–13 years
No. of pupils: 230
Fees: Day £17,642–£19,974

Hendon Day Nursery & Preschool
46 Allington Road, Hendon, London NW4 3DE
Tel: 0330 127 7304

HENDON PREP SCHOOL
For further details see p. 48
20 Tenterden Grove, Hendon, London NW4 1TD
Tel: 020 8203 7727
Email: admissions@hendonprep.co.uk
Website: www.hendonprep.co.uk
Headteacher: Mrs Tushi Gorasia
Age range: 3–11 years
No. of pupils: 170
£

Hereward House School
14 Strathray Gardens, Hampstead, London NW3 4NY
Tel: 020 7794 4820
Headmaster: Mr Pascal Evans
Age range: B4–13 years
No. of pupils: 173
Fees: Day £19,350–£19,890

Highgate Day Nursery and Preschool
Highgate Studios, 53-79 Highgate Road, London NW5 1TL
Tel: 020 7485 5252
Principal: Lorraine Thompson

IRIS School
100 Carlton Vale, London NW6 5HE
Tel: 020 7372 8051
Headteacher: Mr Seyed Abbas Hosseini
Age range: 6–16 years

Islamia Girls School
129 Salusbury Road, London NW6 6PE
Tel: 020 7372 3472
Headteacher: Mr Amzad Ali
Age range: G11–16 years

Joel Nursery
214 Colindeep Lane, Colindale, London NW9 6DF
Tel: 020 820 00189
Age range: 3 months–5 years

Kentish Town Day Nursery
37 Ryland Road, London NW5 3EH
Tel: 020 7284 3600
Manager: Carol Kewley
Age range: 3 months–5 years
No. of pupils: 55

Lakefield Catering & Educational Centre
Maresfield Gardens, Hampstead, London NW3 5RY
Tel: 020 7794 5669
Course Director: Mrs Maria Brown
Age range: G16–24
No. of pupils: 16
Fees: FB £1,160

London Academy of Dressmaking and Design
18 Dobree Avenue, Willesden, London NW10 2AE
Tel: 020 8451 7174
Principal: Mrs P A Parkinson MA
Age range: 13+
Fees: Day £2,650

Lyndhurst House Prep School
24 Lyndhurst Gardens, Hampstead, London NW3 5NW
Tel: 020 7435 4936
Head of School: Mr Andrew Reid MA (Oxon)
Age range: B4–13 years
No. of pupils: 125
Fees: Day £18,360–£20,790

MAPLE WALK PREP SCHOOL
For further details see p. 57
62A Crownhill Road, London NW10 4EB
Tel: 020 8963 3890
Email: admin@maplewalkschool.co.uk
Website: www.maplewalkschool.co.uk
Head Teacher: Claire Murdoch
Age range: 4–11 years
No. of pupils: 170
Fees: Day £4,194
£

Maria Montessori Children's House – Abbey Road
St Mary's Church, Abbey Road, West Hampstead, London NW6 4SN
Tel: 020 7435 3646
Age range: 2.5–6 years

Maria Montessori Institute
26 Lyndhurst Gardens, Hampstead, London NW3 5NW
Tel: 020 7435 3646
Director of Training & School: Mrs Lynne Lawrence BA, Mont Int Dip(AMI)
Age range: 2–12 years
No. of pupils: 50
Fees: Day £5,580–£13,560
16:

Maria Montessori School – Hampstead
26 Lyndhurst Gardens, Hampstead, London NW3 5NW
Tel: 020 7435 3646
Age range: 2.5–12 years

Mill Hill School
The Ridgeway, Mill Hill Village, London NW7 1QS
Tel: 020 8959 1176
Head: Mrs Jane Sanchez BSc (Hons) PGCE
Age range: 13–18 years (boarding from 13)
No. of pupils: 876 VIth312
Fees: Day £21,987 WB £31,140 FB £36,900

Naima Jewish Preparatory School
21 Andover Place, London NW6 5ED
Tel: 020 7328 2802
Headmaster: Mr Bill Pratt
Age range: 2–11 years

Nancy Reuben Primary School
48 Finchley Lane, Hendon, London NW4 1DJ
Tel: 020 8202 5646
Head Teacher: Mr Anthony Wolfson
Age range: 2–11 years

Nicoll Road Nursery School
40 Nicoll Road, Harlesden, London NW10 9AB
Tel: 020 8961 6648
Age range: 2–5

NORTH BRIDGE HOUSE NURSERY AND PRE-PREP HAMPSTEAD
For further details see p. 61
8 Netherhall Gardens, London NW3 5RR
Tel: 020 7428 1520
Head of School: Mrs Christine McLelland
Age range: 2–7 years
No. of pupils: 190

NORTH BRIDGE HOUSE NURSERY AND PRE-PREP WEST HAMPSTEAD
For further details see p. 61
85-87 Fordwych Rd, London NW2 3TL
Tel: 020 7428 1520
Head of School: Mrs Christine McLelland
Age range: 2–7 years

NORTH BRIDGE HOUSE PREP SCHOOL REGENT'S PARK
For further details see p. 61
1 Gloucester Avenue, London NW1 7AB
Tel: 020 7428 1520
Head of School: Mr Tom Le Tissier
Age range: 7–13 years
No. of pupils: 385
Fees: Day £20,193–£21,855

NORTH BRIDGE HOUSE SENIOR HAMPSTEAD
For further details see p. 61
65 Rosslyn Hill, London NW3 5UD
Tel: 020 7428 1520
Email: admissionsenquiries@northbridgehouse.com
Website: www.northbridgehouse.com
Executive Headteacher: Brendan Pavey
Age range: 2–18 years
No. of pupils: 1430

NW5 Theatre School
14 Fortess Road, London NW5 2EU
Tel: 020 8340 1498
Age range: 16–30
16: 16:

Octagon Nursery School
St Saviour's Church Hall, Eton Road, London NW3 4SU
Tel: 020 7586 3206

Rainbow Montessori School
13 Woodchurch Road, Hampstead, London NW6 3PL
Tel: 020 7328 8986
Head Mistress: Maggy Miller MontDip
Age range: 2–5 years

Ready Steady Go – Camden
123 St Pancras Way, London NW1 0SY
Tel: 020 7586 5862
Age range: 2–4

**Ready Steady Go
– Fitzroy Road**
Primrose Hill Community Centre,
29 Hopkinson's Place, Fitzroy
Road, London NW1 8TN
Tel: 020 7586 5862
Age range: 2–3

**Ready Steady Go
– Primrose Hill**
12a King Henry's Road,
London NW3 3RP
Tel: 020 7586 5862
Age range: 3–5

**Ready Steady Go –
St John's Wood**
21 Alexandra Road,
London NW8 0DP
Tel: 020 7586 5862
Age range: 2–5

Saint Christina's School
25 St Edmund's Terrace, St John's
Wood, London NW8 7PY
Tel: 020 7722 8784
Headteacher: Mr Alastair Gloag
Age range: 3–11 years

SARUM HALL SCHOOL
For further details see p. 63
15 Eton Avenue,
London NW3 3EL
Tel: 020 7794 2261
Email: admissions@
sarumhallschool.co.uk
Website:
www.sarumhallschool.co.uk
Headmistress: Miss Karen Coles
BEd (Hons), Exon
Age range: G3–11 years
No. of pupils: 185

**South Hampstead
High School GDST**
3 Maresfield Gardens,
London NW3 5SS
Tel: 020 7435 2899
Headmistress:
Mrs Victoria Bingham MA (Oxon)
Age range: G4–18 years

**Southbank International
School – Hampstead**
16 Netherhall Gardens,
London NW3 5TH
Tel: 020 7243 3803
Principal: Shirley Harwood
Age range: 3–11 years
No. of pupils: 210

St Christopher's School
32 Belsize Lane, Hampstead,
London NW3 5AE
Tel: 020 7435 1521
Head: Ms Sandrine Paillasse
Age range: G4–11 years

**ST JOHN'S WOOD PRE-
PREPARATORY SCHOOL**
For further details see p. 66
St Johns Hall, Lords Roundabout,
London NW8 7NE
Tel: 020 7722 7149
Email: info@sjwpre-prep.org.uk
Website:
www.sjwpre-prep.org.uk
Principal: Adrian Ellis
Age range: 3–7 years

St Margaret's School
18 Kidderpore Gardens,
Hampstead, London NW3 7SR
Tel: 020 7435 2439
Principal:
Mr Mark Webster BSc, PGCE
Age range: G4–16 years

**St Marks Square
Nursery School**
St Mark's Church, St Mark's
Square, Regents Park Road,
London NW1 7TN
Tel: +44 (0)20 7586 8383
Head: Dr Sheema Parsons B.Ed OBE
Age range: 2–6

St Martin's School
22 Goodwyn Avenue, Mill
Hill, London NW7 3RG
Tel: 020 8959 1965
Headteacher: Mrs Samantha Mbah
Age range: 3–11 years

**ST MARY'S SCHOOL
HAMPSTEAD**
For further details see p. 67
47 Fitzjohn's Avenue,
Hampstead, London NW3 6PG
Tel: 020 7435 1868
Email: office@stmh.co.uk
Website: www.stmh.co.uk
Headteacher:
Miss Charlotte Owen
Age range: G2 years 9
months–11 years
No. of pupils: 300
Fees: Day £9,330–£17,250

St Nicholas School
22 Salmon Street, London NW9 8PN
Tel: 020 8205 7153
Headmaster: Mr Matt Donaldson
BA (Hons), PGCE, PGDip (Surv)
Age range: 3 months–11 years

**St. Anthony's
School for Boys**
90 Fitzjohn's Avenue, Hampstead,
London NW3 6NP
Tel: 020 7431 1066
Head of School:
Mr Richard Berlie MA (Cantab)
Age range: B2.5–13
years G2.5–4 years
No. of pupils: 280

**St. Anthony's
School for Girls**
Ivy House, 94-96 North End
Road, London NW11 7SX
Tel: 020 3869 3070
Head of School: Mr Donal Brennan
Age range: G2.5–11 years
No. of pupils: 85
Fees: Day £18,000

The Academy School
3 Pilgrims Place, Hampstead, London NW3 1NG
Tel: 020 7435 6621
Headteacher:
Mr Garth Evans BA (Lond)
Age range: 6–13 years

**The American
School in London**
One Waverley Place,
London NW8 0NP
Tel: +44 (0)20 7449 1200
Head of School:
Ms Coreen R. Hester
Age range: 4–18 years

**The Beehive Montessori
on Queen's Park**
147 Chevening Road,
London NW6 6DZ
Tel: 020 8969 2235
Age range: 2–5

The Cavendish School
31 Inverness Street, Camden
Town, London NW1 7HB
Tel: 020 7485 1958
Head of School: Mrs Taryn Lombard
Age range: G3–11 years

The Hall School
23 Crossfield Road, Hampstead,
London NW3 4NU
Tel: 020 7722 1700
Headmaster: Mr Chris Godwin
Age range: B4–13 years

The Interior Design School
22 Lonsdale Road, Queens
Park, London NW6 6RD
Tel: 020 7372 2811
Principal: Ms Iris Dunbar

The Islamia Schools' Trust
129 Salusbury Road,
London NW6 6PE
Tel: 020 7372 3472

The King Alfred School
North End Road, London NW11 7HY
Tel: 020 8457 5200
Head: Robert Lobatto MA (Oxon)
Age range: 4–18 years
No. of pupils: 670

**The Mount, Mill Hill
International**
Milespit Hill, London NW7 2RX
Tel: +44 (0)20 3826 33
Head of School: Ms Sarah Bellotti
Age range: 13–17 years
No. of pupils: 80
Fees: Day £27,000 WB
£37,500 FB £44,250

The Mulberry House School
7 Minster Road, West
Hampstead, London NW2 3SD
Tel: 020 8452 7340
Headteacher:
Ms Victoria Playford BA Hons, QTS
Age range: 2–7+ years

The Oak Tree Nursery
2 Arkwright Road, Hampstead,
London NW3 6AD
Tel: 020 7435 1916
Head: Mrs S Alexander
Age range: 2 –3
Fees: Day £4,650

The Village Prep School
2 Parkhill Road, Belsize
Park, London NW3 2YN
Tel: 020 7485 4673
Head of School:
Ms Morven MacDonald
Age range: G2.5–11 years

Theatretrain
69 Great North Way,
London NW4 1HS
Tel: 020 8202 2006
Director: Kevin Dowsett CertEd,
AdvDip(Drama in Education)
Age range: 6–18

**Toddlers Inn
Nursery School**
Cicely Davies Hall, Cochrane
Street, London NW8 7NX
Tel: 020 7586 0520
Principal: Ms Laura McCole

Torah Vodaas
Brent Park Road, West Hendon
Broadway, London NW9 7AJ
Tel: 020 3670 4670
Head of School: Rabbi Y Feldman
Age range: B2–11 years

Trevor-Roberts School
55-57 Eton Avenue,
London NW3 3ET
Tel: 020 7586 1444
Co-Heads:
Simon & Amanda Trevor-Roberts
Age range: 5–13 years

**University College School
Hampstead (UCS) Junior**
11 Holly Hill, Hampstead,
London NW3 6QN
Tel: 020 7435 3068
Headmaster: Mr Lewis Hayward
Age range: B7–11 years

University College School Hampstead (UCS) Pre-Prep
36 College Crescent,
Hampstead, London NW3 5LF
Tel: 020 7722 4433
Headmistress: Ms Zoe Dunn
Age range: B4–7 years

University College School Hampstead (UCS) Senior
Frognal, Hampstead,
London NW3 6XH
Tel: 020 7435 2215
Headmaster: Mr Mark J Beard
Age range: B11–18 years
G16–18 years

Wentworth College
6-10 Brentmead Place,
London NW11 9LH
Tel: 020 8458 8524
Principal: Mr Manuel Guimaraes
Age range: 14–19 years

West Hampstead Day Nursery & Preschool
11 Woodchurch Road, West
Hampstead, London NW6 3PL
Tel: 0371 454 3596

York Rise Nursery
St Mary Brookfield Hall, York
Rise, London NW5 1SB
Tel: 020 7485 7962
Headmistress: Miss Becca Coles
Age range: 2–5

South-East London

Alleyn's School
Townley Road, Dulwich,
London SE22 8SU
Tel: 020 8557 1500
Head of School: Ms Jane Lunnon
Age range: 4–18 years

Anerley Montessori Nursery
45 Anerley Park, London SE20 8NQ
Tel: 020 8778 2810
Headmistress: Mrs P Bhatia
Age range: 3 months–5
Fees: Day £2,750–£4,600

Arco Academy
Camberwell Leisure Centre,
Artichoke Place, London SE5 8TS
Tel: 020 3189 1193
Principal: Ms Lisa Miller
Age range: 11–16 years

Bellenden Day Nursery
Faith Chapel, 198 Bellenden
Road, London SE15 4BW
Tel: 020 7639 4896
Manager: Jason Cranston

Blackheath Day Nursery
The Rectory Field, Charlton,
London SE3 8SR
Tel: 020 8305 2526
Headmistress: Mrs Shipley
Age range: 0–5
No. of pupils: 61

Blackheath High School GDST
Vanbrugh Park, Blackheath,
London SE3 7AG
Tel: 020 8853 2929
Acting Head: Ms Natalie Argile
Age range: G3–18 years

Blackheath Montessori Centre
Independents Road,
Blackheath, London SE3 9LF
Tel: 020 8852 6765
Headmistress:
Mrs Jane Skillen MontDip
Age range: 3–5
No. of pupils: 36

Blackheath Prep
4 St Germans Place,
Blackheath, London SE3 0NJ
Tel: 020 8858 0692
Head: Mr Alex Matthews
Age range: 3–11 years
No. of pupils: 385

Bright Horizons at Tabard Square
10-12 Empire Square, Tabard
Street, London SE1 4NA
Tel: 020 7407 2068

Broadfields Day Nursery
96 Broadfields Road, Catford,
London SE6 1NG
Tel: 020 8697 1488
Head: Elainne Dalton
Age range: 4 months–5

Clive Hall Day Nursery
rear of 54 Clive Road,
London SE21 8BY
Tel: 020 8761 9000

Colfe's Junior School
Upwood Road, London SE12 8AA
Tel: 020 8463 8266
Head of School:
Mrs M-C Gilfedder-Bonnar
Age range: 3–11 years

Colfe's School
Horn Park Lane, London SE12 8AW
Tel: 020 8852 2283
Head of School: Mr R Russell
Age range: 3–18 years

DLD College London
199 Westminster Bridge
Road, London SE1 7FX
Tel: +44 (0)20 7935 8411
Principal: Mr Irfan H Latif
Age range: 13–19 years

Dulwich College
Dulwich Common,
London SE21 7LD
Tel: 020 8693 3601
Master: Dr J A F Spence
Age range: B6 months–18
years G6 months–7 years
Fees: Day £21,672 WB
£42,408 FB £45,234

Dulwich College Kindergarten & Infants School
Eller Bank, 87 College
Road, London SE21 7HH
Tel: 020 8693 1538
Head: Mrs Miranda Norris
Age range: 3 months–7 years
No. of pupils: 251

Dulwich Nursery
adj Sainsbury's Dulwich Store, 80
Dog Kennel Hill, London SE22 8DB
Tel: 020 7738 4007
Principal: Amanda Shead

Dulwich Prep London
42 Alleyn Park, Dulwich,
London SE21 7AA
Tel: 020 8766 5500
Head Master: Miss Louise Davidson
Age range: B3–13 years
(boarding from 8) G3–5 years

East Greenwich Day Nursery and Preschool
Chavening Road, Greenwich,
London SE10 0LB
Tel: 0203 7803053
Nursery Manager:
Ms Loraine Thorpe
Age range: 3 months–5 years

Eltham College
Grove Park Road, Mottingham,
London SE9 4QF
Tel: 0208 857 1455
Headmaster: Mr Guy R Sanderson
Age range: 7–18 years

Eltham Elizabeth Terrace Day Nursery & Preschool
18-22 Elizabeth Terrace,
Eltham, London SE9 5DR
Tel: 0370 218 4543

Eltham Green Day Nursery
5 Lionel Road, Eltham,
London SE9 6DQ
Tel: 0800 085 4074
Age range: 3months–5
No. of pupils: 30

First Steps Montessori Day Nursery & Pre School
254 Upland Road, East
Dulwich, London SE22 0DN
Tel: 020 8299 6897
Principal: Karime Dinkha
Age range: 2–5
No. of pupils: 43

Five Steps Community Nursery
31-32 Alpine Road, London SE16 2RE
Tel: 020 7237 2376

Greenwich Steiner School
90 Mycenae Road, London SE3 7SE
Tel: 020 8858 4404
Executive Principal:
Mr Allan Osborne
Age range: 3–18 years

GSM London
Meridian House, Royal Hill,
Greenwich, London SE10 8RD
Tel: 0203 544 3171
Head: Dr W G Hunt

Half Moon Montessori Nursery
Methodist Church Hall, 155 Half
Moon Lane, London SE24 9HU
Tel: 020 7326 5300
Age range: 2–5

Happy Faces Nursery
161 Sumner Road, Peckham,
London SE15 6JL
Tel: 020 7701 3320

Heath House Preparatory School
37 Wemyss Road, Blackheath,
London SE3 0TG
Tel: 020 8297 1900
Head Teacher:
Mrs Sophia Laslett CertEd PGDE
Age range: 3–11 years

Herne Hill School
The Old Vicarage, 127 Herne
Hill, London SE24 9LY
Tel: 020 7274 6336
Headteacher: Mrs Ngaire Telford
Age range: 2–7 years

Hillyfields Day Nursery
41 Harcourt Road, Brockley,
London SE4 2AJ
Tel: 020 8694 1069
Head: Ms Lisa Reeves

James Allen's Girls' School
144 East Dulwich Grove,
Dulwich, London SE22 8TE
Tel: 020 8693 1181
Head of School:
Mrs Alex Hutchinson
Age range: G4–18 years

Kings Kids Christian School
100 Woodpecker Road,
Newcross, London SE14 6EU
Tel: 020 8259 3659
Headteacher: Mrs M Okenwa
Age range: 3–11 years

Little Cherubs Day Nursery
2a Bell Green Lane,
London SE26 5TB
Tel: 020 8778 3232

Lollipops Child Care Ltd
88 Southwood Road,
London SE9 3QT
Tel: 020 8859 5832
Principal: Miss L Thompson

**London Bridge
Business Academy**
7-13 Melior Street, London SE1 3QP
Tel: 020 7378 1000
Head: Shmina Mandal
16+

London Christian School
40 Tabard Street, London SE1 4JU
Tel: 02031 306430
Head Teacher:
Miss Nicola Collett-White
Age range: 3–11 years

**London College
of Engineering &
Management**
18-36 Wellington Street,
London SE18 6PF
Tel: 020 8854 6158
Head: Mr Shakhar Sharman
16+

**Magic Roundabout
Nursery – Kennington**
35 Sutherland House, Sutherland
Square, London SE17 3EE
Tel: 020 7277 3643

Marathon Science School
1-9 Evelyn Street, Surrey
Quays, London SE8 5RQ
Tel: 020 7231 3232
Headteacher: Mr Mehmet Yilmaz
Age range: B11–18 years

McAlpine Dance Studio
Longfield Hall, 50 Knatchbull
Road, London SE5 9QY
Tel: 020 8673 4992
16+

Mother Goose Nursery
248 Upland Road, East
Dulwich, London SE22 0NU
Tel: 020 8693 9429
Age range: 1–5

Mother Goose Nursery
34 Waveney Avenue,
Nunhead, London SE15 3UE
Tel: 020 7277 5951
Age range: 1–5

Mother Goose Nursery
The Pavilion, 65 Greendale Fields,
off Wanley Road, London SE5 8JZ
Tel: 020 7738 7700
Age range: 0–5

**Mother Goose Nursery
(Head Office)**
133 Brookbank Road,
Lewisham, London SE13 7DA
Tel: 020 8694 8700
Age range: 1–5

Nell Gwynn Nursery
Meeting House Lane,
London SE15 2TT
Tel: 020 7252 8265
Executive Head Teacher:
Lynne Cooper

**New Eltham Day
Nursery & Preschool**
699 Sidcup Road, New
Eltham, London SE9 3AQ
Tel: 0370 218 4271

**Oakfield Preparatory
School**
125-128 Thurlow Park Road, West
Dulwich, London SE21 8HP
Tel: 020 8670 4206
Head of School:
Mrs Moyra Thompson
Age range: 2–11 years
No. of pupils: 310
Fees: Day £12,324

**Octavia House
School, Kennington**
214b Kennington Road,
London SE11 6AU
Tel: 020 3651 4396 (option 3)
Assistant Principal: Ms Knight
Age range: 14–16 years

**Octavia House
School, Vauxhall**
Vauxhall Street, London SE11 5LG
Tel: 020 3651 4396 (option 1)
Assistant Principal: Ms Ross
Age range: 5–11 years

**Octavia House
School, Walworth**
Larcom Street, London SE17 1RT
Tel: 020 3651 4396 (option 2)
Assistant Principal: Mr Dickens
Age range: 11–14 years

**Peckham Rye Day
Nursery & Preschool**
24 Waveney Avenue, Peckham
Rye, London SE15 3UE
Tel: 0372 291 2937

Riverston School
63/69 Eltham Road, Lee,
London SE12 8UF
Tel: 020 8318 4327
Headmaster:
Mr David A T Ward MA
Age range: 9 months–19 years

**Rose House
Montessori School**
Vancouver Road, Forest
Hill, London SE23 2AG
Tel: 020 8699 9260
Principal: Mrs Dawn Nasser
Age range: 2–11 years

**Rosemead Preparatory
School & Nursery, Dulwich**
70 Thurlow Park Road,
Dulwich, London SE21 8HZ
Tel: 020 8670 5865
Headmaster: Mr Phil Soutar
Age range: 2.5–11 years

**School of Technology
& Management**
Kingshead House, Kingshead
Yard, London SE1 1NA
Tel: 020 7378 0052
16+

Skallywags Nursery
St Crispin Hall, Southwark
Park Road, Rotherhithe,
London SE16 2HU
Tel: 020 7252 3225
Headmistress:
Miss Allison Armstrong NVQ
Age range: 3 months–5 years

St Dunstan's College
Stanstead Road, London SE6 4TY
Tel: 020 8516 7200
Head of School: Mr Nick Hewlett
Age range: 3–18 years

**St Olave's Preparatory
School**
106-110 Southwood Road, New
Eltham, London SE9 3QS
Tel: 020 8294 8930
Headteacher:
Miss Claire Holloway BEd, QTS
Age range: 3–11 years

**St. Patrick's Montessori
Day Nursery**
91 Cornwall Road, London SE1 8TH
Tel: 020 7928 5557

**Sydenham High
School GDST**
15 & 19 Westwood Hill,
London SE26 6BL
Tel: 020 8557 7004
Head of School:
Ms Antonia Geldeard
Age range: G4–18 years

**The British School
of Osteopathy**
275 Borough High Street,
London SE1 1JE
Tel: 020 7407 0222
Principal & Chief Executive: Martin
Collins BSc(Hons), PhD, MSc, Cbiol,
MIBiol, FRSH, DO, ILTM
16+

The Cedars School
147 Central Hill, Upper
Norwood, London SE19 1RS
Tel: 020 8185 7770
Headmaster: Mr Robert Teague
Age range: B11–18 years

The Laurels School
1 Our Lady's Close, Upper
Norwood, London SE19 3FA
Tel: 020 8674 7229
Headmistress: Mrs Linda Sanders
BA Hons (Bristol), MA (Madrid)
Age range: G11–18 years

The New School London
St. Mary's Lodge, 149 Central
Hill, London SE19 1RT
Tel: 020 4513 0505
Co-Headteachers: Dhama
Sangarabalan & Callie Sharma
Age range: 4–16 years

The Pavilion Nursery
Catford Cricket Club Pavilion,
Penerley Road, London SE6 2LQ
Tel: 020 8698 0878
Head: Mrs Karen Weller
Age range: 2–5

The Pointer School
19 Stratheden Road,
Blackheath, London SE3 7TH
Tel: 020 8293 1331
Head of School: Ms Charlotte
Crookes MA (Cantab), MA, PGCE
Age range: 3–11 years

The Villa School & Nursery
54 Lyndhurst Grove, Peckham,
London SE15 5AH
Tel: 020 7703 6216
Head Teacher: Ms Louise Maughan
Age range: 2–7 years

The Village Montessori
Kingswood Hall, Kingswood
Place, London SE13 5BU
Tel: 020 8318 6720

The Village Nursery
St Mary's Centre, 180 Ladywell
Road, Lewisham, London SE13 7HU
Tel: 020 8690 6766
Principal: Frances Rogers

**Toad Hall Montessori
Nursery School**
37 St Mary's Gardens,
Kennington, London SE11 4UF
Tel: 020 7735 5087
Principal: Mrs V K Rees NNEB,
MontDip
Age range: 2–5
No. of pupils: 40
Fees: Day £6,300

Trinity Child Care
Holy Trinity Church Hall, Bryan
Road, London SE16 5HF
Tel: 020 7231 5842
Manager: Sharron Williams
Age range: 2–5
No. of pupils: 60
Fees: Day £6,240

Waterloo Day Nursery
The Chandlery, 50 Westminster
Bridge Road, London SE1 7QY
Tel: 020 7721 7432
Principal: Julie Ellis

West Dulwich Day Nursery & Preschool
Old Church, 226c Gipsy Road,
West Dulwich, London SE27 9RB
Tel: 0330 127 2141

Willow Park Montessori Nursery
19 Glenlyon Road, Eltham,
London SE9 1AL
Tel: 020 8850 8753
Principal: Ms Maura McMahon
Age range: 2.5–5 years

South-West London

345 Nursery School
Fitzhugh Community Clubroom,
Fitzhugh Grove, Trinity Road,
London SW18 3SA
Tel: 020 8870 8441
Principal: Mrs Annabel Dixon
Age range: 3–5
No. of pupils: 42
Fees: Day £3,555

ABACUS Early Learning Nursery School – Balham Day Nursery
135 Laitwood Road, Balham,
London SW12 9QH
Tel: 020 8675 8093

ABACUS Early Learning Nursery School – Stretham Day Nursery
7 Drewstead Road, Streatham
Hill, London SW16 1LY
Tel: 020 8677 9117
Principals:
Mrs M Taylor BEd & Ms S Petgrave
Age range: 12 mths–5 years
No. of pupils: 40

Academy of Live & Recorded Arts
Studio1, Royal Victoria
Patriotic Building, John Archer
Way, London SW18 3SX
Tel: 020 8870 6475
Principal: Anthony Castro
Age range: 18+
No. of pupils: 108
Fees: Day £3,000–£9,888

Alphabet Nursery School
Chatham Hall, Northcote Road,
Battersea, London SW11 6DY
Tel: 020 8871 7473
Principal: Mrs A McKenzie-Lewis
No. of pupils: 40
Fees: Day £1,500–£1,800

Al-Risalah Secondary School
145 Upper Tooting Road,
London SW17 7TJ
Tel: 020 8767 6057
Executive Principal: Suhayl Lee
Age range: 11–16 years

Balham Day Nursery & Preschool
36 Radbourne Road, Balham,
London SW12 0EF
Tel: 0345 527 4956

Battersea Day Nursery & Preschool
18 Latchemere Road,
Battersea, London SW11 2DX
Tel: 0203 906 6546

Battersea Pre-School & Nursery
Riverlight, Nine Elms Lane, Kirtling
Street, Battersea, London SW8 5BP
Tel: 020 7720 9336

Beechwood Nursery School
55 Leigham Court Road,
Streatham, London SW16 2NJ
Tel: 020 8677 8778
Age range: 0–5 years

Beehive Nursery School
St Margarets Church Hall, Putney
Park Lane, London SW15 5HU
Tel: 020 8780 5333
Headmistress: Lindsay Deans
Age range: 2–5
No. of pupils: 16
Fees: Day £1,140

Bees Knees Nursery School
within Brookside Community Hall,
12 Priory Lane, London SW15 5JL
Tel: 020 8876 8252
Headmistress: Jo Wood
Age range: 2–5

Bertrum House Nursery
290 Balham High Road,
London SW17 7AL
Tel: 020 8767 4051
Age range: 2–5 years

Bobby's Playhouse
16 Lettice Street, London SW6 4EH
Tel: 020 7384 1190
Principal: Mrs Emma Hannay
Age range: 3 months–5 years
Fees: Day £11,000

BROOMWOOD PREP, BOYS
For further details see p. 40
26 Bolingbroke Grove,
London SW11 6EL
Tel: 020 8682 8888
Email:
admissions@broomwood.com
Website: www.broomwood.com
Head (and Group Principal): Mr
Kevin Doble
Age range: B7–13 years
No. of pupils: 200
Fees: Day £7,535

BROOMWOOD PREP, GIRLS
For further details see p. 41
68-74 Nightingale Lane,
London SW12 8NR
Tel: 020 8682 8810
Email:
admissions@broomwood.com
Website: www.broomwood.com
Head: Mrs Louisa McCafferty
Age range: G7–13 years
No. of pupils: 200
Fees: Day £7,535

BROOMWOOD PRE-PREP AND LITTLE BROOMWOOD
For further details see p. 42
192 Ramsden Road,
London SW12 8RQ
Tel: 020 8682 8840
Email:
admissions@broomwood.com
Website: www.broomwood.com
Head: Mrs Caron Mackay
Age range: 3–7 years
No. of pupils: 300

Busy Bee Nursery School
19 Lytton Grove, Putney,
London SW15 2EZ
Tel: 020 8789 0132
Headmistress: Dr Sally Corbett
Age range: 2–5

Cameron Vale School
4 The Vale, Chelsea,
London SW3 6AH
Tel: 020 7352 4040
Headteacher: Ms Alison Melrose
Age range: 2–11 years

Carmena Christian Day Nurseries
47 Thrale Road, Streatham,
London SW16 1NT
Tel: 020 8677 8231
Head: Mrs S Allen

Centre Academy London
92 St John's Hill, Battersea,
London SW11 1SH
Tel: 020 7738 2344
Head of School:
Mrs. Kas Lee-Douglas
Age range: 9–19 years

Chelsea Kindergarten
St Andrews Church, Park Walk,
Chelsea, London SW10 0AU
Tel: 020 7352 4856
Headmistress:
Miss Lulu Tindall MontDip
Age range: 2–5
Fees: Day £3,900–£6,120

Clapham Day Nursery
3 Peardon Street, London SW8 3BW
Tel: 020 7498 3165
Manager:
Nicolette Warnes NNEB, NVQ4
Age range: 3 months–5
No. of pupils: 72

Clapham Montessori
St Paul's Community Centre,
St Paul's Church, Rectory
Grove, London SW4 0DX
Tel: 020 7498 8324
Head: Mrs R Bowles BSc, IntMontDip
Age range: 2–5

Clapham Park Montessori
St James' Church House, 10 West
Road, Clapham, London SW4 7DN
Tel: 020 7627 0352
Head: Mrs R Bowles BSc, IntMontDip
Age range: 2–5

Collingham College
23 Collingham Gardens,
London SW5 0HL
Tel: 020 7244 7414
Principal: Ms Sally Powell
Age range: 13–19 years

Crown Kindergartens
Coronation House, Ashcombe
Road, Wimbledon,
London SW19 8JP
Tel: 020 8540 8820
Principal: Mrs Acres
Age range: 1–5
No. of pupils: 28

Dawmouse Montessori Nursery School
34 Haldane Road, Fulham,
London SW6 7EU
Tel: 020 7381 9385
Principal: Mrs Emma V Woodcock
NNEB, MontDip
Age range: 2–5
No. of pupils: 72

DOLPHIN SCHOOL
For further details see p. 43
106 Northcote Road,
London SW11 6QW
Tel: 020 7924 3472
Email:
admissions@dolphinschool.org.uk
Website:
www.dolphinschool.org.uk
Head Teacher: Mr S Gosden
Age range: 2–11 years
No. of pupils: 162
Fees: Day £13,395–£14,670

Donhead Preparatory School
33 Edge Hill, Wimbledon,
London SW19 4NP
Tel: 020 8946 7000
Headteacher: Mr P J J Barr
Age range: B4–11 years

Eaton House Belgravia
3-5 Eaton Gate, London SW1W 9BA
Tel: 0203 917 5050
Headteacher: Mr Huw May
Age range: B2–11 years G2–4 years
No. of pupils: 220

Eaton House The Manor Boys' School
58 Clapham Common North Side, London SW4 9RU
Tel: 0203 917 5050
Head of Prep: Mrs Sarah Segrave
Age range: B2–13 years G2–4 years
No. of pupils: 510

Eaton House The Manor Girls' School
58 Clapham Common North Side, London SW4 9RU
Tel: 0203 917 5050
Headteacher: Mrs Claire Fildes
Age range: B2–4 years G2–11 years
No. of pupils: 260

Eaton Square Nursery School, Belgravia
28 & 30 Eccleston Street, London SW1W 9PY
Tel: +44 (0)20 7823 6217
Age range: 2–4 years

Eaton Square Nursery School, Pimlico
32A Lupus Street, London SW1V 3DZ
Tel: +44 (0)20 7976 6511
Age range: 2–4 years

Eaton Square Prep School
55-57 Eccleston Square, London SW1V 1PP
Tel: +44 (0)20 7931 9469
Head of School: Ms Trish Watt
Age range: 4–11 years

École Primaire Marie D'Orliac
60 Clancarty Road, London SW6 3AA
Tel: +44 (0)20 7736 5863
Director: Mr Blaise Fenart
Age range: 4–11 years

Elm Park Nursery School
90 Clarence Avenue, Clapham, London SW4 8JR
Tel: 020 8678 1990
Head: Ms Jacqueline Brooks
No. of pupils: 113

Emanuel School
Battersea Rise, London SW11 1HS
Tel: 020 8870 4171
Headmaster: Mr Robert Milne
Age range: 10–18 years

Eveline Day School
Swan House, 207 Balham High Road, London SW17 7BQ
Tel: 020 8673 3188
Head Teacher: Ms Eveline Drut
Age range: 2–11 years

Evergreen Primary School
9 Swan Mews, Fulham, London SW6 4QT
Tel: 07429 112217
Headteacher: Ms Rena Begum
Age range: 3–11 years

Falcons School for Girls
11 Woodborough Road, Putney, London SW15 6PY
Tel: 020 8992 5189
Headmistress: Ms Sara Williams-Ryan
Age range: G4–11 years

Falkner House
19 Brechin Place, South Kensington, London SW7 4QB
Tel: 02073 734501
Headteachers: Mrs Flavia Rogers & Mrs Eleanor Dixon
Age range: 2–11 years

Finton House School
171 Trinity Road, London SW17 7HL
Tel: 020 8682 0921
Head of School: Mr Ben Freeman
Age range: 4–11 years

First Steps School of Dance & Drama
234 Lillie Road, London SW6 7QA
Tel: 020 7381 5224
Age range: 3–17
Fees: Day £2,700

Francis Holland School, Sloane Square, SW1
39 Graham Terrace, London SW1W 8JF
Tel: 020 7730 2971
Head: Mrs Lucy Elphinstone MA(Cantab)
Age range: G4–18 years

Garden House School
Turks Row, Chelsea, London SW3 4TW
Tel: 020 7730 1652/6652
Principals: Mr Christian Warland & Mrs Sophie Strafford
Age range: 3–11 years

Gateway House Nursery School
St Judes Church Hall, Heslop Road, London SW12 8EG
Tel: 020 8675 8258
Principal: Miss Elizabeth Marshall
Age range: 2–4
No. of pupils: 30
Fees: Day £1,010–£1,060

Glendower Preparatory School
86/87 Queen's Gate, London SW7 5JX
Tel: 020 7370 1927
Headmistress: Mrs Nina Kingsmill Moore
Age range: G3–11 years

Hall School Wimbledon
17, The Downs, Wimbledon, London SW20 8HF
Tel: 020 8879 9200
Headmaster: Mr. A Hammond
Age range: 5–18 years
No. of pupils: 160
Fees: Day £4,570–£6,140

Happy Nursery Days
Valens House, 132a Uppertulse Hill, London SW2 2RX
Tel: 020 8674 7804
Age range: 3 months–5

Harrodian
Lonsdale Road, London SW13 9QN
Tel: 020 8748 6117
Headmaster: Mr James R Hooke
Age range: 4–18 years

Hill House
17 Hans Place, Chelsea, London SW1X 0EP
Tel: 020 7584 1331
Headmaster: Mr Richard Townend
Age range: 4–13 years

Hornsby House School
Hearnville Road, Balham, London SW12 8RS
Tel: 020 8673 7573
Headmaster: Mr Edward Rees
Age range: 4–11 years

Hurlingham Nursery
The Old Methodist Hall, Gwendolen Avenue, London SW15 6EH
Tel: 02081 030768
Head of Nursery: Mr Richard McLelland
Age range: 2–4 years

Hurlingham School
122 Putney Bridge Road, Putney, London SW15 2NQ
Tel: 020 8103 0823
Headmaster: Mr Simon Gould
Age range: 4–11 years

Ibstock Place School
Clarence Lane, Roehampton, London SW15 5PY
Tel: 020 8876 9991
Head of School: Mr Christopher J Wolsey
Age range: 4–18 years

Inchbald School of Design
Interior Design Faculty, 7 Eaton Gate, London SW1W 9BA
Tel: 020 7730 5508
Principal: Mrs Jacqueline Duncan FIIDA, FIDDA
Age range: 18–50
No. of pupils: 120

JJAADA Interior Design Academy
28 Abbeville Mews, 88 Clapham Park Road, London SW4 7BX
Tel: 020 7494 3363

Judith Blacklock Flower School
4/5 Kinnerton Place South, London SW1X 8EH
Tel: 020 7235 6235
Head: Judith Blacklock

Kensington Park School
40-44 Bark Place, Bayswater, London W2 4AT
Tel: +44 (0)20 7616 4400
Headmaster: Mr Stephen Mellor
Age range: 11–18 years

Kensington Prep School
596 Fulham Road, London SW6 5PA
Tel: 0207 731 9300
Head of School: Mrs Caroline Hulme-McKibbin
Age range: G4–11 years
Fees: Day £19,497

Kids Inc Day Nursery – East Sheen
459b Upper Richmond Road West, East Sheen, London SW14 7PR
Tel: 020 8876 8144

King's College School
Southside, Wimbledon Common, London SW19 4TT
Tel: 020 8255 5300
Head: Dr Anne Cotton
Age range: B7–18 years G16–18 years
No. of pupils: 1478

Ladybird Nursery School
9 Knowle Close, London SW9 0TQ
Tel: 020 7924 9505

L'ECOLE DE BATTERSEA
For further details see p. 52
Trott Street, Battersea,
London SW11 3DS
Tel: 020 7371 8350
Email:
admin@lecoledespetits.co.uk
Website:
www.lecoledebattersea.co.uk
Principal: Mrs F Brisset
Age range: 3–11 years
No. of pupils: 250
Fees: Day £5,075

L'ECOLE DES PETITS
For further details see p. 53
2 Hazlebury Road, Fulham,
London SW6 2NB
Tel: 020 7371 8350
Email:
admin@lecoledespetits.co.uk
Website:
www.lecoledespetits.co.uk
Principal: Mrs F Brisset
Age range: 3–6 years
No. of pupils: 120
Fees: Day £4,935

L'Ecole du Parc
12 Rodenhurst Road,
London SW4 8AR
Tel: 020 8671 5287
Headteacher: Mrs E Sicking-Bressler
Age range: 1–5
No. of pupils: 55
Fees: Day £4,000–£7,500

Little People of Fulham
250a Lillie Road, Fulham,
London SW6 7PX
Tel: 020 7386 0006
Owner: Miss Jane Gleasure
Age range: 4 months–5

Little Red Hen Nursery School
Christchurch Hall, Cabul
Road, London SW11 2PN
Tel: 020 7738 0321
Age range: 2–5
Fees: Day £1,470–£1,740

London Film Academy
The Old Church, 52a Walham
Grove, London SW6 1QR
Tel: 020 7386 7711
Founders & Joint Principals:
Daisy Gili & Anna Macdonald

LONDON PARK SCHOOL, CLAPHAM
For further details see p. 54
7-11 Nightingale Lane, Clapham
South, London SW4 9AH
Tel: 020 8161 0301
Email: admissions@
londonparkschools.com
Website:
www.londonparkschools.com
Head: Mr Paul Vanni
Age range: 11–16 (plus 16-18
in standalone Sixth Form)
No. of pupils: 250
Fees: Day £7,535

London Steiner School
9 Weir Road, Balham,
London SW12 0LT
Tel: 020 3417 3190
Age range: 3–14 years

LYCÉE FRANÇAIS CHARLES DE GAULLE DE LONDRES
For further details see p. 55
35 Cromwell Road,
London SW7 2DG
Tel: 020 7584 6322
Email:
inscription@lyceefrancais.org.uk
Website:
www.lyceefrancais.org.uk
Head of School: TBC
Age range: 3–18 years
No. of pupils: 3450
Fees: Day £7,631–£15,965

Magic Roundabout Nursery – Stockwell
Surrey Hall, Binfield Road,
Stockwell, London SW4 6TB
Tel: 020 7498 1194

MANDER PORTMAN WOODWARD – MPW LONDON
For further details see p. 58
90-92 Queen's Gate,
London SW7 5AB
Tel: 020 7835 1355
Email: london@mpw.ac.uk
Website: www.mpw.ac.uk
Principal: Mr Steve Boyes BA,
MSc, PGCE
Age range: 14–19 years
No. of pupils: 600
Fees: Day £10,765

Maria Montessori Children's House – Hornsey Rise
St Mary's Church Hall, Ashley Road,
Hornsey Rise, London N19 3AD
Tel: 020 7435 3646
Age range: 2.5–6 years

Melrose House Nursery School – SW18
39 Melrose Road, Southfields,
London SW18 1LX
Tel: 020 8874 7769
Head of School: Ruth Oates
Age range: 2–5

Melrose House Nursery School – SW6
55 Finlay Street, Fulham,
London SW6 6HF
Tel: 020 7736 9296
Head of School:
Caroline O'Gorman
Age range: 2–5

Miss Daisy's Nursery School
Fountain Court Club Room, Ebury
Square, London SW1W 9SU
Tel: 020 7730 5797
Head: Daisy Harrison
Age range: 2–5
No. of pupils: 30
Fees: Day £1,050–£5,550

Montessori School
St Paul's Community Centre,
Rectory Grove, Clapham,
London SW4 0DX
Tel: 020 7498 8324
Age range: 6 months–6

MORE HOUSE SCHOOL
For further details see p. 60
22-24 Pont Street, Knightsbridge,
London SW1X 0AA
Tel: 020 7235 2855
Email:
registrar@morehousemail.org.uk
Website:
www.morehouse.org.uk
Head: Ms Faith Hagerty
Age range: G11–18 years
No. of pupils: 145
Fees: Day £7,750

Newton Prep
149 Battersea Park Road,
London SW8 4BX
Tel: 020 7720 4091
Headmistress: Mrs Alison Fleming
BA, MA Ed, PGCE
Age range: 3–13 years
No. of pupils: 646
Fees: Day £10,575–£22,395

Nightingale Montessori Nursery
St Lukes Community Hall, 194
Ramsden Road, London SW12 8RQ
Tel: 020 8675 8070
Principal: Mrs Tejas Earp
Age range: 2–5

Noah's Ark Nursery Schools (Dolphin School Trust)
St Michael's Church Hall, Cobham
Close, London SW11 6SP
Tel: 020 7924 3472 opt 2
Head: Miss Annette Miller
Age range: 2–5
No. of pupils: 40
Fees: Day £4,725

Noah's Ark Nursery Schools (Dolphin School Trust)
Endlesham Church Hall, 48
Endlesham Road, London SW12 8JL
Tel: 020 924 3472 opt 2
Head: Miss Annette Miller
Age range: 2–5
No. of pupils: 32
Fees: Day £4,725

Noddy's Nursery School
Trinity Church Hall, Beaumont Road,
Wimbledon, London SW19 6SP
Tel: 020 8785 9191
Principal: Mrs Sarah Edwards NNEB,
Mont Dip
Age range: 2–5

Oliver House Preparatory School
7 Nightingale Lane,
London SW4 9AH
Tel: 020 8772 1911
Headteacher: Mr Rob Farrell
Age range: 3–11 years
No. of pupils: 144
Fees: Day £6,600–£15,090

Paint Pots Montessori School – The Boltons
St Mary The Boltons Church Hall,
The Boltons, London SW10 9TB
Tel: 07794 678 537
Head Teacher: Georgie Scully
Age range: 2 years 6
months–5 years

Parkgate House School
80 Clapham Common North
Side, London SW4 9SD
Tel: +44 (0)20 7350 2461
Principal: Miss Catherine Shanley
Age range: 2.5–11 years

Parsons Green Prep School
1 Fulham Park Road,
Fulham, London SW6 4LJ
Tel: 020 7371 9009
Head: Dr Pamela Edmonds
Age range: 4–11 years

Peques Anglo-Spanish School
St John's Church, North End
Road, Fulham, London SW6 1PB
Tel: 020 7385 0055
Managing Director: Margarita
Morro Beltran
Age range: 3 months–5

Playdays Nursery School Wimbledon
58 Queens Road, Wimbledon,
London SW19 8LR
Tel: 020 8946 8139
Nursery Manager: Charline Baker

Pooh Corner Kindergarten
St Stephen's Church Hall, 48
Emperor Gate, London SW7 4HJ
Tel: 020 7373 6111
Headmistress: Sarah Crowther

Prince's Gardens Preparatory School
10–13 Prince's Gardens,
London SW7 1ND
Tel: 0207 591 4622
Headmistress: Mrs Alison Melrose
Age range: 3–11 years

Prospect House School
75 Putney Hill, London SW15 3NT
Tel: 020 8246 4897
Headmaster: Mr Michael Hodge
BPED(Rhodes) QTS
Age range: 3–11 years
No. of pupils: 310
Fees: Day £9,954–£20,742
£ 🖊

Putney Day Nursery & Preschool
107-109 Norroy Road, Putney,
London SW15 1PH
Tel: 0330 134 7587

Putney High School GDST
35 Putney Hill, London SW15 6BH
Tel: 020 8788 4886
Headmistress: Mrs Suzie Longstaff
BA, MA, PGCE
Age range: G4–18 years
🧍 Ⓐ £ 🖊 16

Queen's Gate School
133 Queen's Gate, London SW7 5LE
Tel: 020 7589 3587
Principal: Miss Amy Wallace MA
MPhil (Cantab), PGCE (Oxon)
Age range: G4–18 years
No. of pupils: 500 VIth81
🧍 Ⓐ £ 🖊 16

Raynes Park Bushey Road Day Nursery & Preschool
c/o David Lloyd Leisure
Club, Bushey Road, Raynes
Park, London SW20 8DE
Tel: 0371 454 3482

Raynes Park Nursery and PreSchool
3 Spencer Road, Raynes Park,
Wimbledon, London SW20 0QN
Tel: 0333 920 1909
Nursery Manager: Ms Leanne
Eustace
Age range: 3 months–5 years

Redcliffe Gardens School
47 Redcliffe Gardens,
Chelsea, London SW10 9JH
Tel: 020 7352 9247
Head: Mrs Sarah Glencross
Age range: 2.5–11 years

Ringrose Kindergarten Chelsea
St Lukes Church Hall, St Lukes
Street, London SW3 3RP
Tel: 020 7352 8784
Age range: 2–5 years

Royal Academy of Dance
36 Battersea Square,
London SW11 3RA
Tel: 020 7326 8000
Chief Executive: Luke Rittner
16

Royal College of Art
Kensington Gore, London SW7 2EU
Tel: 020 7590 4444
Rector & Vice-Provost:
Professor Christopher Frayling
16

Sinclair House Preparatory School
59 Fulham High Street,
Fulham, London SW6 3JJ
Tel: 0207 736 9182
Principal:
Mrs Carlotta T M O'Sullivan
Age range: 2–11 years
No. of pupils: 120
Fees: Day £5,280–£17,025

Southfields Day Nursery and Pre-School
Duntshill Mill, 21 Riverdale
Drive, London SW18 4UR
Tel: 0330 057 6434
Nursery Manager:
Ms Lydia Howards
Age range: 3 months–5 years

Square One Nursery School
Lady North Hall, 12 Ravenna
Road, Putney, London SW15 6AW
Tel: 020 8788 1546
Principal: Mrs King

St Mary Magdalen Montessori Nursery School
61 North Worple Way,
London SW14 8PR
Tel: 020 8878 0756
Head:
Liz Maitland NNEB, RSH, MontDip
Age range: 2–5
£

St Mary's Summerstown Montessori
46 Wimbledon Road, Tooting,
London SW17 0UQ
Tel: 020 8947 7359
Head:
Liz Maitland NNEB, RSH, MontDip
Age range: 18 months–5 years
No. of pupils: 30
Fees: Day £1,300

St Michael's Montessori Nursery School
St Michael's Church, Elm Bank
Gardens, Barnes, London SW13 0NX
Tel: 020 8878 0116
Head Teacher: Debbie Goldberg
Age range: 2 1/2–5

St Paul's School
Lonsdale Road, Barnes,
London SW13 9JT
Tel: 020 8748 9162
High Master: Ms Sally-Anne Huang
Age range: B7–18 years
🧍 🧍 Ⓐ 🏛 £ 🖊 16

St Philip's School
6 Wetherby Place, London SW7 4NE
Tel: 020 7373 3944
Head Master: Mr A Thomas
Age range: B7–13 years
🧍 🖊

Streatham & Clapham High School GDST
42 Abbotswood Road,
London SW16 1AW
Tel: 020 8677 8400
Executive Head: Mrs Isabel Tobias
MA (Cantab), PGCE
Age range: G3–18 years
🧍 Ⓐ £ 🖊 16

Streatham Day Nursery and Preschool
113 Blegborough Road,
Streatham, London SW16 6DL
Tel: 0330 057 6267
Nursery Manager: Ms Nadia Kiani
Age range: 3 months–5 years

Streatham Montessori Nursery & Day Care
66 Blairderry Road, Streatham
Hill, London SW2 4SB
Tel: 020 8674 2208
Nursery Manager: Mrs Fehmida
Gangji
Age range: 1–5

Sussex House School
68 Cadogan Square,
London SW1X 0EA
Tel: 020 7584 1741
Headmaster: Mr N P Kaye
MA(Cantab), ACP, FRSA, FRGS
Age range: B8–13 years
🧍

Swedish School in London
82 Lonsdale Road, Barnes,
London SW13 9JS
Tel: 020 8741 1751
Head of School:
Ms. Jenny Abrahamsson
Age range: 3–18 years
16

Thames Christian School
12 Grant Road, London SW11 2FR
Tel: 020 7228 3933
Head of School: Mr Stephen
Holsgrove PhD
Age range: 11–16 years

The Boltons Nursery School
262b Fulham Road, Chelsea,
London SW10 9EL
Tel: 020 7351 6993
Age range: 2–5
No. of pupils: 60
Fees: Day £2,370–£4,200

The Bumble Bee Nursery School
Church of Ascension, Pountney
Road, London SW11 5TU
Headmistress: Deepti Bansal

The Castle Kindergarten
20 Henfield Road,
London SW19 3HU
Tel: 020 8544 0089
Principal: Ms Beverley Davis DipEd
Age range: 2–5

The Crescent I Kindergarten
Flat 1, No 10 Trinity Crescent,
London SW17 7AE
Tel: 020 8767 5882
Principal: Philip Evelegh

The Crescent II Kindergarten
Holy Trinity Church Hall, Trinity
Road, London SW17 7SQ
Tel: 020 8682 3020

The Eveline Day Nursery Schools, Furzedown
Seeley Hall, Chillerton Road,
Furzedown, London SW17 9BE
Tel: 020 8672 0501

The Eveline Day Nursery Schools, Tooting
30 Ritherdon Road, Upper
Tooting, London SW17 8QD
Tel: 020 8672 7549
Principal: Mrs T Larche

The Eveline Day Nursery Schools, Wandsworth
East Hill United Reformed
Church Hall, Geraldine Road,
Wandsworth, London SW18 2NR
Tel: 020 8870 0966

The Eveline Day Nursery Schools, Wimbledon
89a Quicks Road, Wimbledon,
London SW19 1EX
Tel: 020 8545 0699

The Hampshire School, Chelsea
15 Manresa Road, Chelsea,
London SW3 6NB
Tel: +44 (0)2073 527077
Headteacher: Mr Richard Lock
Age range: 3–11 years
🖊

The Knightsbridge Kindergarten
St. Peter's Church, 119 Eaton
Square, London SW1W 9AL
Tel: 020 7371 2306
Age range: 2–5

The Marmalade Bear Nursery School
St. Magdalene Church Hall, Trinity
Road, Tooting, London SW17 7HP
Tel: 0208 265 5224
Principal: Ms Rozzy Hyslop
Age range: 2–5
Fees: Day £3,270–£3,450
🖊

The Merlin School
4 Carlton Drive, London SW15 2BZ
Tel: 020 8788 2769
Headteacher: Miss Violet
McConville
Age range: 4–8 years
No. of pupils: 130
Fees: Day £5,510

The Montessori Childrens House Ltd
St John's Church, 1 Spencer Hill, London SW19 4NZ
Tel: 020 8971 9135
Age range: 2–5

The Montessori Pavilion – The Kindergarten School
Vine Road, Barnes, London SW13 0NE
Tel: 07554 277 746
Headmistress: Ms Georgina Dashwood
Age range: 3–8 years
No. of pupils: 50

The Mouse House Nursery School
27 Mallinson Road, London SW11 1BW
Tel: 020 7924 1893
Headmistress: Amanda White-Spunner
Age range: 2–5
Fees: Day £1,650–£4,125

The Norwegian School in London
28 Arterberry Road, Wimbledon, London SW20 8AH
Tel: 020 8947 6617
Headteacher: Ms Lise Meling Karlsen
Age range: 6–16 years

The Oval Montessori Nursery School
within Vauxhall Park, Fentiman Road, London SW8 1LA
Tel: 020 7735 4816
Head: Ms Louise Norwood
Age range: 2–5
Fees: Day £3,000

The Park Kindergarten
St Saviours Church Hall, 351 Battersea Park Road, London SW11 4LH
Tel: 020 7627 5125
Principal: Miss Lisa Neilsen MontDip
Age range: 2–5
Fees: Day £2,370

The Rainbow Playgroup
St Luke's Church Hall, St Luke's Street, London SW3 3RR
Tel: 020 7352 8156
Age range: 2–5

THE ROCHE SCHOOL
For further details see p. 69
11 Frogmore, London SW18 1HW
Tel: 020 8877 0823
Email: office@therocheschool.com
Website: www.therocheschool.com
Headmistress: Mrs Vania Adams BA(Hons), PGCE, MA
Age range: 2–11 years
No. of pupils: 270
Fees: Day £16,470–£17,190
£

The Rowans School
19 Drax Avenue, Wimbledon, London SW20 0EG
Tel: 020 8946 8220
Head of School: Miss Elizabeth Spratt BMus PGCE Primary QTS
Age range: 3–7 years

The Study Preparatory School
Wilberforce House, Camp Road, Wimbledon Common, London SW19 4UN
Tel: 020 8947 6969
Interim Head: Ms Helen Lowe
Age range: G4–11 years

The White House Preparatory School & Woodentops Kindergarten
24 Thornton Road, Clapham, London SW12 0LF
Tel: 020 8674 9514
Headmaster: Mr. Tony Lewis
Age range: 3–11 years
£

The Willow Nursery School
55 Grafton Square, Clapham Old Town, London SW4 0DE
Tel: 020 7498 0319
Head: Mrs Harriet Baring MontDip
Age range: 2–5
Fees: Day £3,000–£3,100

The Zebedee Nursery School
4 Parsons Green, London SW6 4TN
Tel: 020 7371 9224
Headmistress: Miss Su Gahan NNEB, RSH
Age range: 2–5
No. of pupils: 32
Fees: Day £3,900

Thomas's Academy
New King's Road, London SW6 4LY
Tel: 020 7736 2318
Head of School: Ms Suzanne Kelly
Age range: 4–11 years

Thomas's Battersea
28-40 Battersea High Street, London SW11 3JB
Tel: 020 7978 0900
Head of School: Mr Ben Thomas
Age range: 4–13 years

Thomas's Clapham
Broomwood Road, London SW11 6JZ
Tel: 020 7326 9300
Head of School: Mr Nathan Boller
Age range: 4–13 years

Thomas's Fulham
Hugon Road, London SW6 3ES
Tel: 020 7751 8200
Head of School: Ms Annette Dobson
Age range: 4–11 years

Thomas's Kindergarten
St Mary's Church, Battersea Church Road, London SW11 3NA
Tel: 020 7738 0400
Heads of School: Lucy Lee & Selbi Fryer
Age range: 2.5–4 years

Thomas's Outdoors
Stroud Crescent, London SW15 3EQ
Tel: 020 7751 8200
Head of School: Mr Paul Wild
Age range: 4–18 years

Thomas's Putney Vale
Stroud Crescent, London SW15 3EH
Tel: 020 3653 1640
Heads of School: Therese Andrews & Emma Oliver
Age range: 13–16 years

Tiggers Nursery School
87 Putney Bridge Road, London SW15 2PA
Tel: 020 8874 4668
Headmistress: Natasha Green MontDip
Age range: 2–5
Fees: Day £1,425–£1,725

Toots Day Nursery
214 Totterdown Street, Tooting, London SW17 8TD
Tel: 020 8767 7017
Principal: Angela Duffell
Age range: 1–5

Tower House School
188 Sheen Lane, East Sheen, London SW14 8LF
Tel: 020 8876 3323
Head: Mr Gregory Evans
Age range: B4–13 years

Twice Times Nursery School
The Cricket Pavilion in South Park, Clancarty Road, London SW6 3AF
Tel: 020 7731 4929
Heads: Mrs A Welch MontDip & Mrs S Henderson MontDip
Age range: 2–5
No. of pupils: 50

Ursuline Preparatory School
18 The Downs, Wimbledon, London SW20 8HR
Tel: 020 8947 0859
Head Teacher: Mrs Caroline Molina BA (Hons)
Age range: B3–4 years G3–11 years
No. of pupils: 145

Wandsworth Nursery & Pre-School Academy
Dolphin House, Riverside West, Smugglers Way, Wandsworth, London SW18 1DE
Tel: 020 8877 1135
Nursery Manager: Evelyn Herrera
Age range: 0–5

Wandsworth Preparatory School
The Old Library, 2 Allfarthing Lane, London SW18 2PQ
Tel: +44 (0)2088 704133
Headteacher: Ms Laura Nike
Age range: 4–11 years

Westminster Abbey Choir School
Dean's Yard, Westminster, London SW1P 3NY
Tel: 020 7654 4918
Acting Headmaster: Mr Mark Mitchell
Age range: B8–13 years

Westminster Cathedral Choir School
Ambrosden Avenue, London SW1P 1QH
Tel: 020 7798 9081
Headmaster: Mr Neil McLaughlan
Age range: B4–13 years

Westminster School
17A Dean's Yard, Westminster, London SW1P 3PB
Tel: 020 7963 1000
Head Master: Dr Gary Savage
Age range: B13–18 years
G16–18 years

Westminster Tutors
86 Old Brompton Road, South Kensington, London SW7 3LQ
Tel: 020 7584 1288
Principal: Joe Mattei
Age range: 14+ years
No. of pupils: VIth40
Fees: Day £4,000–£25,000

Westminster Under School
27 Vincent Square, London SW1P 2NN
Tel: 020 7821 5788
Master: Mrs C J Jefferson
Age range: B7–13 years

Wetherby Kensington
4 Wetherby Gardens, London SW5 0JN
Tel: 020 3910 9760
Executive Head: Mr Mark Snell
Age range: B4–8 years

Willington Independent Preparatory School
Worcester Road, Wimbledon,
London SW19 7QQ
Tel: 020 8944 7020
Headmaster: Mr Keith Brown
Age range: 3–11 years
(£)

Wimbledon Common Preparatory School
113 Ridgway, Wimbledon,
London SW19 4TA
Tel: 020 8946 1001
Head Teacher: Mr Andrew Forbes
Age range: B4–7 years
(†)

Wimbledon High School GDST
Mansel Road, Wimbledon,
London SW19 4AB
Tel: 020 8971 0900
Head of School:
Ms Fionnuala Kennedy
Age range: G4–18 years
(†)(A)(£)(✐)(16)

Wimbledon Park Montessori School
206 Heythorp Street, Southfields,
London SW18 5BU
Tel: 020 8944 8584
Head: Ms Clare Collins
Age range: 2–5
Fees: Day £830–£950
(✐)

Wimbledon School of Art
Merton Hall Road,
London SW19 3QA
Tel: 020 8408 5000
Principal: Professor Roderick Bugg
(16)

Young England Kindergarten
St Saviour's Hall, St George's
Square, London SW1V 3QW
Tel: 020 7834 3171
Principal: Mrs Kay C King MontDip
Age range: 2.5–5
Fees: Day £3,300–£4,950
(✐)

West London

Abercorn School
38 Portland Place, London W1B 1LS
Tel: 020 7100 4335
Headmaster:
Mr Christopher Hammond
Age range: 2–13 years

ABI College – London Campus
3 The Mount, Acton,
London W3 9NW
Tel: 020 8993 4500

Acorn Nursery School
2 Lansdowne Crescent,
London W11 2NH
Tel: 020 7727 2122
Principal:
Mrs Jane Cameron BEd(Hons)
Age range: 2–5
Fees: Day £2,400

Albemarle Independent College
18 Dunraven Street, Mayfair,
London W1K 7FE
Tel: 02074 097273
Co-Principals:
Beverley Mellon & James Eytle
Age range: 14–19 years
(16)(A)(16)

ArtsEd Day School & Sixth Form
14 Bath Road, Chiswick,
London W4 1LY
Tel: 020 8987 6666
Headteacher: Mr Matthew Bulmer
Age range: 11–18 years

Ashbourne College
17 Old Court Place,
Kensington, London W8 4PL
Tel: 020 7937 3858
Principal: Mr Michael Kirby MSc,
BApSc, MInstD
Age range: 13–21 years
(16)(A)(£)

Avenue House School
70 The Avenue, Ealing,
London W13 8LS
Tel: 020 8998 9981
Headteacher: Mr Conall Chivers
Age range: 4–11 years
(✐)

AZBUKA Russian-English Bilingual School
Studland Hall, Studland Street,
Hammersmith, London W6 0JS
Tel: 020 8392 2286
Head Teacher: Ms Maria Gavrilova
Age range: 2–11 years

Bales College
2 Kilburn Lane, London W10 4AA
Tel: 020 8960 5899
Principal: Mr William Moore
Age range: 11–18 years
(🌐)(16)(A)(🏛)(£)

Bassett House School
60 Bassett Road, Notting
Hill, London W10 6JP
Tel: 020 8969 0313
Headmistress: Mrs Kelly Gray
Age range: 3–11 years
No. of pupils: 120
Fees: Day £9,954–£20,742
(✐)

Blake College
162 New Cavendish Street,
London W1W 6YS
Tel: 020 7636 0658
Course Director:
D A J Cluckie BA, BSc
Fees: Day £4,720–£5,310
(16)(16)(🌐)

BPP University
Aldine Place, 142-144 Uxbridge
Road, London W12 8AA
Tel: (+44) 03331 226478
Head: Martin Taylor
(16)

Busy Bees at Hammersmith
30-40 Dalling Road,
Hammersmith, London W6 0JD
Tel: 020 8741 5382
Nursery Manager: Becky
Age range: 3 months–5 years

Bute House Preparatory School for Girls
Bute House, Luxemburg
Gardens, London W6 7EA
Tel: 020 7603 7381
Head of School: Ms Sian Bradshaw
Age range: G4–11 years
(†)(£)

Buttercups Day Nursery
38 Grange Road, Chiswick,
London W4 4DD
Tel: 020 8995 6750

Buttercups Day Nursery
9 Florence Road, Ealing,
London W5 3TU
Tel: 020 8840 4838

Buttercups Day Nursery
9 Florence Road, Ealing,
London W5 3TU
Tel: 020 8840 4838

Buttons Day Nursery School
99 Oaklands Road, London W7 2DT
Tel: 020 8840 3355
Head: Julie Parhar BSc, NVQ3
Age range: 3 months–5
No. of pupils: 62
(✐)

Campbell Harris Tutors
185 Kensington High Street,
London W8 6SH
Tel: 020 7937 0032
Principals: Mr Mark Harris &
Ms Claire Campbell
Age range: 13+
Fees: Day £4,000–£9,000
(16)(A)(£)(✐)

Caterpillar Montessori Nursery School
St Albans Church Hall, South
Parade, Chiswick, London W4 3HY
Tel: 020 8747 8531
Head: Mrs Alison Scott
Age range: 2–5
Fees: Day £2,700

Chepstow House School
108a Lancaster Road, Notting
Hill, London W11 1QS
Tel: 020 7243 0243
Headteacher: Ms Angela Barr
Age range: 2.5–11 years
(✐)

Chiswick & Bedford Park Prep School
Priory House, Priory Avenue,
London W4 1TX
Tel: 020 8994 1804
Head of School:
Ms Henrietta Adams
Age range: B3–7+ years
G3–11 years
(†)

Chiswick Nursery and Pre-School
4 Marlborough Road,
Chiswick, London W4 4ET
Tel: 020 8742 0011
Nursery Manager: Roxane Lovell
Age range: 0–5

Chiswick Park Nursery and Pre-School
Evershed Walk, London W4 5BW
Tel: 0333 920 0404
Nursery Manager:
Ms Rebecca Fergus
Age range: 3 months–5 years

Christie's Education
42 Portland Place, Marylebone,
London W1W 5BD
Tel: 0207 389 2004
Academic Director: Jon Waldon
(16)

Clifton Lodge School
8 Mattock Lane, Ealing,
London W5 5BG
Tel: 020 8579 3662
Head of School: Mr Michael Belsito
Age range: 3–11 years
No. of pupils: 130
Fees: Day £13,650–£16,305
(£)(✐)

College of Naturopathic & Complementary Medicine Ltd
41 Riding House Street,
London W1W 7BE
Tel: 01342 410 505
Head: Hermann Keppler
(16)

Connaught House School
47 Connaught Square,
Westminster, London W2 2HL
Tel: 020 7262 8830
Principal: Ms Victoria Hampton
Age range: 4–11 years
(£)

David Game College
31 Jewry Street, London EC3N 2ET
Tel: 02072 216665
Principal: D T P Game MA, MPhil
Age range: 13–22 years
(16)(A)(🏛)(16)

Devonshire Day Nursery
The Vicarage, Bennet Street,
Chiswick, London W4 2AH
Tel: 020 8995 9538
Manager: Dawn Freeman
Age range: 6 weeks–5
No. of pupils: 70

Durston House
12-14 Castlebar Road,
Ealing, London W5 2DR
Tel: 020 8991 6530
Headmaster: Mr Giles Entwisle
Age range: B4–13 years
No. of pupils: 326
Fees: Day £4,470–£5,720

Ealing Independent College
83 New Broadway, Ealing,
London W5 5AL
Tel: 020 8579 6668
Headteacher: Allan Cairns
Age range: 13–19 years
No. of pupils: 96

Eaton Square Senior School
106 Piccadilly, Mayfair,
London W1J 7NL
Tel: +44 (0)20 7491 7393
Headteacher: Dr Adrian Rainbow
Age range: 11–18 years

Ecole Française de Londres Jacques Prévert
59 Brook Green, Hammersmith,
London W6 7BE
Tel: 020 7602 6871
Director: Ms Sylvie Wanin
Age range: 4–11 years

Elmwood Montessori School
St Michaels Centre, Elmwood
Road, London W4 3DY
Tel: 020 8994 8177/995 2621
Headmistress: Mrs S Herbert BA
Age range: 2–5
Fees: Day £3,480–£4,440

Falcons Pre-Preparatory Chiswick
2 Burnaby Gardens,
Chiswick, London W4 3DT
Tel: 020 8747 8393
Head: Ms Liz McLaughlin
Age range: B2–7 years G2–4 years

FULHAM SCHOOL
For further details see p. 47
1-3 Chesilton Road,
London SW6 5AA
Tel: 020 8154 6751
Email:
senioradmin@fulham.school
Website: fulham.school
Executive Head of Fulham: Bex Tear
Age range: 3–18 years
No. of pupils: 650
Fees: Day £19,158–£22,431

Godolphin and Latymer School
Iffley Road, Hammersmith,
London W6 0PG
Tel: +44 (0)20 8741 1936
Head Mistress: Dr Frances Ramsey
Age range: G11–18 years
No. of pupils: 800
Fees: Day £25,185

Great Beginnings Montessori Nursery
39 Brendon Street, London W1H 5JE
Tel: 020 7258 1066
Head: Mrs Wendy Innes
Age range: 2–6 years

Greek Primary School of London
3 Pierrepoint Road, Acton,
London W3 9JR
Tel: 020 8896 2118
Primary School Head Teacher:
Ms Katerina Papagianni
Age range: 4–11 years

Halcyon London International School
33 Seymour Place, London W1H 5AU
Tel: +44 (0)20 7258 1169
Director: Mr Barry Mansfield
Age range: 11–18 years

Hammersmith Day Nursery & Pre-School
50 Richford Gate, 61-69 Richford
Street, London W6 7HZ
Tel: 0207 622 0484
Manager: Marion Bones NVQ
Age range: 3 months–5 years
No. of pupils: 70

Happy Child Day Nursery
283-287 Windmill Road,
Ealing, London W5 4DP
Tel: 020 8567 2244
Age range: 3 months–5

Happy Child Training Centre
109 Uxbridge Road, Ealing,
London W5 5TL
Tel: 020 8579 3955

Harvington School
20 Castlebar Road, Ealing,
London W5 2DS
Tel: 020 8997 1583
Headteacher: Mr Giles Entwisle
Age range: B3–7 years G3–11 years

Hawkesdown House School Kensington
27 Edge Street, Kensington,
London W8 7PN
Tel: 020 7727 9090
Headmistress:
Mrs S Gillam BEd (Cantab)
Age range: 2–8 years
No. of pupils: 100
Fees: Day £4,725–£21,120

Heathfield House School
Heathfield Gardens,
Chiswick, London W4 4JU
Tel: 020 8994 3385
Headteacher:
Ms Caroline Goodsman
Age range: 4–11 years

Holland Park Day Nursery and Pre-School
34 Ladbroke Grove, Notting
Hil, London W11 3BQ
Tel: 0333 363 4009
Age range: 3 months–5
Fees: Day £3,900

Holland Park Pre Prep School and Day Nursery
5, Holland Road, Kensington,
London W14 8HJ
Tel: 020 7602 9066/020
7602 9266
Head Mistress: Mrs Kitty Mason
Age range: 3 months–8 years
No. of pupils: 39
Fees: Day £9,180–£18,120

ICS London
7B Wyndham Place,
London W1H 1PN
Tel: +44 (0)20 729 88800
Head of School: Alec Jiggins
Age range: 3–18 years
No. of pupils: 175
Fees: Day £19,770–£28,920

Instituto Español Vicente Cañada Blanch
317 Portobello Road,
London W10 5SZ
Tel: +44 (0) 20 8969 2664
Head of School:
Mr Antonio Simón Saiz
Age range: 3–18 years

International School of London (ISL)
139 Gunnersbury Avenue,
London W3 8LG
Tel: +44 (0)20 8992 5823
Principal: Mr Richard Parker
Age range: 3–18 years
No. of pupils: 420
Fees: Day £20,850–£28,850

James Lee Nursery School
Gliddon Road, London W14 9BH
Tel: 020 8741 8877

KENSINGTON WADE SCHOOL
For further details see p. 49
Fulham Palace Road,
London W6 9ER
Tel: 020 3096 2888
Email:
office@kensingtonwade.com
Website:
www.kensingtonwade.com
Head: Mrs Suzanne Haigh
Age range: 3–11 years
No. of pupils: 108
Fees: Day £6,560

King Fahad Academy
Bromyard Avenue, Acton,
London W3 7HD
Tel: 020 8743 0131
Director General: Dr Tahani Aljafari
Age range: 3–18 years

La Petite Ecole Française
73 Saint Charles Square,
London W10 6EJ
Tel: +44 (0)20 8960 1278
Age range: 3–11 years

Ladbroke Square Montessori School
43 Ladbroke Square,
London W11 3ND
Tel: 020 7229 0125
Head Teacher: Lucy Morley
Age range: 3–5
Fees: Day £850–£1,350

Latymer Prep School
36 Upper Mall, Hammersmith,
London W6 9TA
Tel: 020 7993 0061
Principal: Ms Andrea Rutterford
Age range: 7–11 years

Latymer Upper School
King Street, Hammersmith,
London W6 9LR
Tel: 020 8629 2024
Head: Mr David Goodhew
Age range: 11–18 years

Le Herisson
River Court Methodist
Church, Rover Court Road,
Hammersmith, London W6 9JT
Tel: 020 8563 7664
Director: Maria Frost
Age range: 2–6 years
Fees: Day £8,730–£8,970

L'Ecole Bilingue
St David's Welsh Church, St
Mary's Terrace, London W2 1SJ
Tel: 020 7224 8427
Headteacher:
Ms Veronique Ferreira
Age range: 3–11 years

Leiths School of Food & Wine
16-20 Wendell Road, Shepherd's Bush, London W12 9RT
Tel: 020 8749 6400
Age range: 17+ years
16+

Little Cherubs Nursery School
The Carmelite Priory, Pitt Street, Kensington, London W8 4JH
Tel: 020 7376 4460/07810 712241
Principal: Mrs M Colvin MontDip
Age range: 2–5
No. of pupils: 42

Little People of Willow Vale
9 Willow Vale, London W12 0PA
Tel: 020 8749 2877
Head: Miss Jane Gleasure
Age range: 4 months–5

Little Sweethearts Montessori
St Saviours Church Hall, Warwick Avenue, London W9 2PT
Tel: 020 7266 1616

LLOYD WILLIAMSON SCHOOL FOUNDATION
For further details see p. 51
12 Telford Road, London W10 5SH
Tel: 020 8962 0345
Email: admin@lws.org.uk
Website: www.lloydwilliamson.co.uk
Co-Principals: Ms Lucy Meyer & Mr Aaron Williams
Age range: 4 months–16 years
Fees: Day £18,000

London Academy of Music & Dramatic Art
155 Talgarth Road, London W14 9DA
Tel: 020 8834 0500
Head of Examinations: Dawn Postans
Age range: 17+
16+ £

London College
1st Floor, 23-25 Eastcastle Street, London W1W 8DF
Tel: 020 7580 7552
Head: Mr David Kohn
16+

London Welsh School Ysgol Gymraeg Llundain
Hanwell Community Centre, Westcott Crescent, London W7 1PD
Tel: 020 8575 0237
Headteacher: Ms Tracey O'Brien
Age range: 3–11 years

MAIDA VALE SCHOOL
For further details see p. 56
18 Saltram Crescent, London W9 3HR
Tel: 020 4511 6000
Email: admissions@maidavaleschool.com
Website: www.maidavaleschool.com
Headmaster: Mr Magnus Bashaarat
Age range: 11–18 years
No. of pupils: 160
Fees: Day £8,073

Maria Montessori Children's House – Notting Hill
All Saints Church, Powis Gardens, Notting Hill, London W11 1JG
Tel: 020 7435 3646
Age range: 2.5–6 years

Maria Montessori Nursery School
Church of the Ascension Hall, Beaufort Road, Ealing, London W5 3EB
Tel: 07717 050761

Maria Montessori School – Bayswater
St Matthew's Church, St Petersburgh Place, Bayswater, London W2 4LA
Tel: 020 7435 3646
Age range: 2.5–12 years

Melrose Nursery School – Acton
St Gabriel's Church Hall, Noel Road, Acton, London W3 0JE
Tel: 020 8992 0855

Norland Place School
162-166 Holland Park Avenue, London W11 4UH
Tel: 020 7603 9103
Headmaster: Mr Patrick Mattar MA
Age range: 4–11 years

Notting Hill & Ealing High School GDST
2 Cleveland Road, West Ealing, London W13 8AX
Tel: (020) 8799 8400
Headmaster: Mr Matthew Shoults
Age range: G4–18 years

Notting Hill Preparatory School
95 Lancaster Road, London W11 1QQ
Tel: 020 7221 0727
Head of School: Mrs Sarah Knollys
Age range: 4–13 years
No. of pupils: 444
Fees: Day £7,689

One World Montessori Nursery
Church Court, London W6 0EU
Tel: 020 7603 6065
Age range: 1–4

Orchard House School
16 Newton Grove, Bedford Park, London W4 1LB
Tel: 020 8742 8544
Headmaster: Mr Kit Thompson
Age range: 3–11 years
No. of pupils: 273
Fees: Day £10,158–£21,159

Oxford House College – London
24 Great Chapel Street, London W1F 8FS
Tel: +44 (0) 20 7580 9785
Principal: Ms Muberra Orme
16+

Paint Pots Montessori School – Bayswater
St Stephens Church, Westbourne Park Road, London W2 5QT
Tel: 07527 100534
Head Teacher: Vinni Lewis
Age range: 2 years 6 months–5 years

Pembridge Hall School
18 Pembridge Square, London W2 4EH
Tel: 020 7229 0121
Head: Mrs Sophie Banks
Age range: G4–11 years

Playhouse Day Nursery
Leighton Hall, Elthorne Park Road, London W7 2JJ
Tel: 020 8840 2851
Head of School: Mrs Priti Patel

Portland Place School
56-58 Portland Place, London W1B 1NJ
Tel: 020 7307 8700
Headmaster: Mr David Bradbury
Age range: 10–16 years

Queen's College
43-49 Harley Street, London W1G 8BT
Tel: 020 7291 7000
Principal: Mr Richard Tillet
Age range: G11–18 years

Queen's College Preparatory School
61 Portland Place, London W1B 1QP
Tel: 020 7291 0660
Headmistress: Mrs Laura Hall
Age range: G4–11 years

RAVENSCOURT PARK PREPARATORY SCHOOL
For further details see p. 62
16 Ravenscourt Avenue, London W6 0SL
Tel: 020 8846 9153
Email: admissions@rpps.co.uk
Website: www.rpps.co.uk
Headmaster: Mr Carl Howes MA (Cantab), PGCE (Exeter)
Age range: 4–11 years
No. of pupils: 418
Fees: Day £6,632

Ray Cochrane Beauty School
118 Baker Street, London W1U 6TT
Tel: 02033 896888
Heads of Education: Xubin Yuan & Eleonora Androva
Age range: 16+ years
16+ 16+

Rolfe's Nursery School
34A Oxford Gardens, London W10 5UG
Tel: 020 7727 8300
Headteacher: Ms Annette Elstob
Age range: 2.5–5 years

Sassoon Academy
5 Ave Maria Lane, London EC4M 7AQ
Tel: 02080 163812
Academy Principal & Educator: Mr Joshua Gibson
Age range: 16+ years
16+ 16+

Southbank International School – Kensington
36-38 Kensington Park Road, London W11 3BU
Tel: +44 (0)20 7243 3803
Principal: Siobhan McGrath
Age range: 3–18 years
IB 16+

Southbank International School – Westminster
63-65 Portland Place, London W1B 1QR
Tel: 020 7243 3803
Principal: Dr Paul Wood
Age range: 11–19 years
IB 16+

St Augustine's Priory
Hillcrest Road, Ealing, London W5 2JL
Tel: 020 8997 2022
Headteacher: Mrs Sarah Raffray M.A., N.P.Q.H
Age range: B3–4 years G3–18 years
A 16+

ST BENEDICT'S SCHOOL
For further details see p. 64
54 Eaton Rise, Ealing,
London W5 2ES
Tel: 020 8862 2000
Email:
admissions@stbenedicts.org.uk
Website:
www.stbenedicts.org.uk
Headmaster: Mr A Johnson BA
Age range: 3–18 years
No. of pupils: 1083 VIth185
Fees: Day £14,940–£19,575
(A)(£)(🖋)(16)

St James Preparatory School
Earsby Street, London W14 8SH
Tel: 02073 481794
Headmistress: Mrs Hilary Wyatt
Age range: 3–11 years
(£)

St James Senior Girls' School
Earsby Street, London W14 8SH
Tel: 02073 481777
Headmistress: Mrs Sarah Labram BA
Age range: G11–18 years
(🏃)(A)(£)(🖋)(16)

St Matthews Montessori School
St Matthews Church Hall, North
Common Road, London W5 2QA
Tel: 07495 898 760
Head Teacher: Mrs Farah Virani
M.A., B.A., PGCE – Primary, Mont.
Dip.Adv.
Age range: 2–5

St Patrick's International College
London Sceptre Court Campus,
40 Tower Hill, London EC3N 4DX
Tel: 020 7287 6664
Principal: Mr Girish Chandra
(16)

St Paul's Girls' School
Brook Green, Hammersmith,
London W6 7BS
Tel: 020 7603 2288
High Mistress: Mrs Sarah Fletcher
Age range: G11–18 years
(🏃)(A)(£)(🖋)(16)

St Peter's Nursery
59a Portobello Road,
London W11 3DB
Tel: 020 7243 2617
Head of Nursery: Tracey Lloyd

Sylvia Young Theatre School
1 Nutford Place, London W1H 5YZ
Tel: 020 7258 2330
Principal: Sylvia Young OBE
Age range: 10–16 years
(£)(🖋)

Tabernacle School
32 St Anns Villas, Holland
Park, London W11 4RS
Tel: 020 7602 6232
Principal: Mrs P Wilson
Age range: 3–16 years

The Japanese School in London
87 Creffield Road, Acton,
London W3 9PU
Tel: 020 8993 7145
Age range: 6–16 years

The Jordans Montessori Nursery School
Holy Innocents Church,
Paddenswick Road,
London W6 0UB
Tel: 0208 741 3230
Principal: Ms Sara Green
Age range: 2–5
Fees: Day £1,356–£3,270
(🖋)

The Meadows Montessori School
Dukes Meadows Community
Centre, Alexandra Gardens,
London W4 2TD
Tel: 020 8742 1327/8995 2621
Headmistress: Mrs S Herbert BA
Age range: 2–5
Fees: Day £3,030–£3,870
(🖋)

The Minors Nursery School
10 Pembridge Square,
London W2 4ED
Tel: 020 7727 7253
Head: Ms Samantha Edwards
Age range: 2.5–5 years

The Square Montessori School
18 Holland Park Avenue,
London W11 3QU
Tel: 020 7221 6004
Principal: Mrs V Lawson-Tancred
No. of pupils: 20
Fees: Day £2,220

Thomas's Kensington
17-19 Cottesmore Gardens,
London W8 5PR
Tel: 020 7361 6500
Head of School: Ms Kelly Miller
Age range: 4–11 years

TLG West London
Tasso Baptist Church, 138
Greyhound Road, London W6 8NS
Tel: 07494486851
Head of Centre: Ms Tina Amadi
Age range: 11–16 years

Treetops Ealing Common
Woodgrange Avenue, Ealing
Common, London W5 3NY
Tel: 020 8992 0209
Age range: 3 months–5

Treetops West Ealing
Green Man Passage,
Ealing, London W13 0TG
Tel: 020 8566 5515
Age range: 3 months–5

West London College
Gliddon Road, Hammersmith,
London W14 9BL
Tel: 020 8741 1688
Principal: Paul S Smith BA(Hons), FRSA
(16)

Wetherby Preparatory School
Bryanston Square, London W1H 2EA
Tel: 020 7535 3520
Headmaster: Mr Mark White MA
(Hons), PGCE
Age range: B8–13 years
(🏃)

Wetherby Pre-Preparatory School
11 Pembridge Square,
London W2 4ED
Tel: 020 7727 9581
Headmaster: Mr Mark Snell
Age range: B2.5–8 years
(🏃)

Wetherby Senior School
100 Marylebone Lane,
London W1U 2QU
Tel: 020 7535 3530
Headmaster: Mr Joe Silvester
Age range: B11–18 years
(🏃)

Windmill Montessori Nursery School
62 Shirland Road, London W9 2EH
Tel: 020 7289 3410
Principal: Miss M H Leoni &
Miss J Davidson
No. of pupils: 48
Fees: Day £3,600
(🖋)

World of Children
Log Cabin Childrens Centre, 259
Northfield Avenue, London W5 4UA
Tel: 020 8840 3400

Young Dancers Academy
25 Bulwer Street, London W12 8AR
Tel: 020 8743 3856
Head: Mrs K Williams
Age range: 11–16 years
Fees: Day £12,237–£12,690

Schools in Greater London

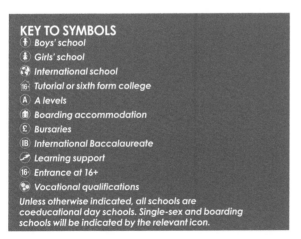

KEY TO SYMBOLS
- 🕉 *Boys' school*
- 🕉 *Girls' school*
- 🌐 *International school*
- 16 *Tutorial or sixth form college*
- Ⓐ *A levels*
- 🏛 *Boarding accommodation*
- £ *Bursaries*
- IB *International Baccalaureate*
- ✏ *Learning support*
- 16 *Entrance at 16+*
- 🎓 *Vocational qualifications*

Unless otherwise indicated, all schools are coeducational day schools. Single-sex and boarding schools will be indicated by the relevant icon.

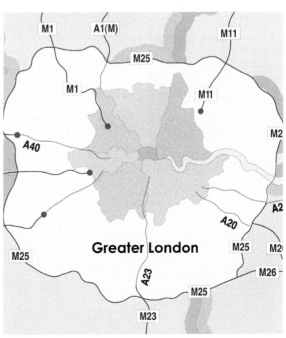

Greater London

Essex

Al-Noor Primary School
619-629 Green Lane, Goodmayes, Ilford, Essex IG3 9RP
Tel: 020 8597 7576
Headteacher: Mrs Someera Butt
Age range: 4–11 years

Avon House Preparatory School
490 High Road, Woodford Green, Essex IG8 0PN
Tel: 020 8504 1749
Headteacher:
Mrs Amanda Campbell
Age range: 3–11 years
No. of pupils: 268
Fees: Day £3,530–£3,950

Bancroft's School
High Road, Woodford Green, Essex IG8 0RF
Tel: 020 8505 4821
Head: Mr Simon Marshall MA, PGCE (Cantab), MA, MPhil (Oxon)
Age range: 7–18 years
(A)(£)(16)

Beehive Preparatory School
233 Beehive Lane, Redbridge, Ilford, Essex IG4 5ED
Tel: 020 8550 3224
Head Teacher: Mr Jamie Gurr
Age range: 2.5–11 years

Braeside School
130 High Road, Buckhurst Hill, Essex IG9 5SD
Tel: 020 8504 1133
Headmistress: Ms Chloe Moon
Age range: 2.5–16 years

CHIGWELL SCHOOL
For further details see p. 74
High Road, Chigwell, Essex IG7 6QF
Tel: 020 8501 5700
Email: admissions@chigwell-school.org
Website: www.chigwell-school.org
Head Teacher: Mr Damian King
Age range: 4–18 years
No. of pupils: 1057
(A)(£)(16)

Daiglen School
68 Palmerston Road, Buckhurst Hill, Essex IG9 5LG
Tel: 020 8504 7108
Headteacher: Mrs P Dear
Age range: 3–11 years

Eastcourt Independent School
1-5 Eastwood Road, Goodmayes, Ilford, Essex IG3 8UW
Tel: 020 8590 5472
Headmistress: Mrs Christine Redgrave BSc(Hons), DipEd, MEd
Age range: 3–11 years
No. of pupils: 220
Fees: Day £2,600

Gidea Park Preparatory School & Nursery
2 Balgores Lane, Gidea Park, Romford, Essex RM2 5JR
Tel: 01708 740381
Head of School: Mr Callum Douglas
Age range: 2–11 years
No. of pupils: 100
Fees: Day £10,775

Guru Gobind Singh Khalsa College
Roding Lane, Chigwell, Essex IG7 6BQ
Tel: 020 8559 9160
Principal: Mr Amarjit Singh Toor BSc(Hons), BSc, BT
Age range: 3–19 years

Immanuel School
Havering Grange, Havering Road, Romford, Essex RM1 4HR
Tel: 01708 764449
Principal: Ms Sarah Williams
Age range: 3–16 years

Kids Inc Day Nursery – Beehive Lane, Ilford
229-231 Beehive Lane, Ilford, Essex IG4 5EB
Tel: 020 8550 7400

Kids Inc Day Nursery – Clarence Avenue, Ilford
41 Clarence Avenue, Gants Hill, Ilford, Essex IG2 6JH
Tel: 020 8518 4486

Kids Inc Day Nursery – Loughton
29 Old Station Road, Loughton, Essex IG10 4PE
Tel: 020 8502 4488

Kids Inc Day Nursery – York Road, Ilford
81-85 York Road, Ilford, Essex IG1 3AF
Tel: 020 8478 6510

Loyola Preparatory School
103 Palmerston Road, Buckhurst Hill, Essex IG9 5NH
Tel: 020 8504 7372
Headmistress: Mrs K R Anthony
Age range: B3–11 years
No. of pupils: 200
Fees: Day £11,610
(♀)(£)

Maytime Montessori Nursery – Cranbrook Road
341 Cranbrook Road, Ilford, Essex IG1 4UF
Tel: 020 8554 3079

Maytime Montessori Nursery – Eastwood Road
2 Eastwood Road, Goodmayes, Essex IG3 8XB
Tel: 020 8599 3744

Maytime Montessori Nursery – Wanstead Park Road
293 Wanstead Park Road, Ilford, Essex IG1 3TR
Tel: 020 8554 6344

Oakfields Preparatory School
Harwood Hall, Harwood Hall Lane, Upminster, Essex RM14 2YG
Tel: 01708 220117
Headmistress: Katrina Carroll
Age range: 2.5–11 years
No. of pupils: 202
Fees: Day £10,296–£11,121

Oaklands School
6-8 Albion Hill, Loughton, Essex IG10 4RA
Tel: 020 8508 3517
Headmistress: Ms Sue Belej
Age range: 2.5–11 years

Park School for Girls
20-22 Park Avenue, Ilford, Essex IG1 4RS
Tel: 020 8554 2466
Head Teacher:
Mrs Catherine Redfern
Age range: G4–16 years
(♀)(16)

St Aubyn's School
Bunces Lane, Woodford Green, Essex IG8 9DU
Tel: 020 8504 1577
Headmaster: Mr Leonard Blom BEd(Hons) BA NPQH
Age range: 3–13 years

St Mary's Hare Park School & Nursery
South Drive, Gidea Park, Romford, Essex RM2 6HH
Tel: 01708 761220
Headteacher: Mr Ludovic Bernard
Age range: 2.5–11 years

The Ursuline Preparatory School Ilford
2-4 Coventry Road, Ilford, Essex IG1 4QR
Tel: 020 8518 4050
Acting Headteacher:
Mrs Lorraine Pereira
Age range: 3–11 years

Woodford Green Preparatory School
Glengall Road, Woodford Green, Essex IG8 0BZ
Tel: 020 8504 5045
Headmaster: Mr J P Wadge
Age range: 3–11 years
No. of pupils: 385
Fees: Day £3,945
(£)

Hertfordshire

Lyonsdown School
3 Richmond Road, New Barnet,
Barnet, Hertfordshire EN5 1SA
Tel: 020 8449 0225
Head: Mrs Rittu Hall
Age range: G3–11 years
No. of pupils: 180
Fees: Day £11,199–£12,237

Mount House School
Camlet Way, Hadley Wood,
Barnet, Hertfordshire EN4 0NJ
Tel: 020 8449 6889
Head: Mrs Sarah Richardson
Age range: 11–18 years

**Susi Earnshaw
Theatre School**
The Bull Theatre, 68 High Street,
Barnet, Hertfordshire EN5 5SJ
Tel: 020 8441 5010
Headteacher: Ms Julia Hammond
Age range: 9–16 years

**The Royal Masonic
School for Girls**
Rickmansworth Park,
Rickmansworth,
Hertfordshire WD3 4HF
Tel: 01923 773168
Headmaster: Mr Kevin Carson
M.Phil (Cambridge)
Age range: B2–4 years G2–18 years

Kent

Ashgrove School
116 Widmore Road,
Bromley, Kent BR1 3BE
Tel: 020 8460 4143
Head of School: Dr Patricia Ash
Age range: 3–11 years

**BABINGTON HOUSE
SCHOOL**
For further details see p. 72
Grange Drive, Chislehurst,
Kent BR7 5ES
Tel: 020 8467 5537
Email:
sjames@babingtonhouse.com
Website:
www.babingtonhouse.com
Headmaster: Mr Tim Lello MA,
FRSA, NPQH
Age range: 3–18 years
No. of pupils: 466

**Benedict House
Preparatory School**
1-5 Victoria Road, Sidcup,
Kent DA15 7HD
Tel: 020 8300 7206
Headteacher: Mr Craig Wardle
Age range: 3–11 years

Bickley Park School
14 & 24 Page Heath Lane,
Bickley, Bromley, Kent BR1 2DS
Tel: 020 8467 2195
Head of School: Ms Tammy Howard
Age range: B2.5–13
years G2.5–4 years

Bishop Challoner School
228 Bromley Road, Shortlands,
Bromley, Kent BR2 0BS
Tel: 020 8460 3546
Headteacher: Mr Mark Wallace BA
(Hons), MBA
Age range: 3–18 years

**Breaside Preparatory
School**
41-43 Orchard Road,
Bromley, Kent BR1 2PR
Tel: 020 8460 0916
Executive Principal: Mrs Karen A
Nicholson B.Ed, NPQH, Dip EYs
Age range: 2.5–11 years
No. of pupils: 376
Fees: Day £11,580–£13,494

Bromley High School GDST
Blackbrook Lane, Bickley,
Bromley, Kent BR1 2TW
Tel: 020 8781 7000/1
Head: Mrs A M Drew BA(Hons), MBA
(Dunelm)
Age range: G4–18 years

Darul Uloom London
Foxbury Avenue, Perry Street,
Chislehurst, Kent BR7 6SD
Tel: 020 8295 0637
Principal:
Mufti Muhammed Kamil Sheikh
Age range: B11–19 years

Farringtons School
Perry Street, Chislehurst,
Kent BR7 6LR
Tel: 020 8467 0256
Head: Mr David Jackson
Age range: 3–18 years
No. of pupils: 700 VIth100
Fees: Day £16,260 WB
£27,120 FB £34,050

**Merton Court
Preparatory School**
38 Knoll Road, Sidcup,
Kent DA14 4QU
Tel: 020 8300 2112
Headmaster: Mr Dominic Price
BEd, MBA
Age range: 3–11 years
No. of pupils: 308
Fees: Day £3,250–£4,925

**St Christopher's
The Hall School**
49 Bromley Road,
Beckenham, Kent BR3 5PA
Tel: 020 8650 2200
Headteacher: Mr Tom Carter
Age range: 3–11 years

St David's Prep
Justin Hall, Beckenham Road,
West Wickham, Kent BR4 0QS
Tel: 020 8777 5852
Head Teacher: Ms Julia Foulger
Age range: 3–11 years

West Lodge School
36 Station Road, Sidcup,
Kent DA15 7DU
Tel: 020 8300 2489
Head Teacher: Mr Robert Francis
Age range: 3–11 years

Wickham Court School
Layhams Road, West
Wickham, Kent BR4 9HW
Tel: 020 8777 2942
Principal: Ms Lisa Harries
Age range: 3–11 years

Middlesex

ACS Hillingdon International School
108 Vine Lane, Hillingdon, Uxbridge, Middlesex UB10 0BE
Tel: +44 (0) 1895 259771
Head of School: Mr Martin Hall
Age range: 4–18 years

Alpha Preparatory School
21 Hindes Road, Harrow, Middlesex HA1 1SH
Tel: 020 8427 1471
Headmaster: Mr Pádraic Fahy
Age range: 3–11 years

Ashton House School
50-52 Eversley Crescent, Isleworth, Middlesex TW7 4LW
Tel: 020 8560 3902
Headteacher: Mrs Angela Stewart
Age range: 3–11 years

Buckingham Preparatory School
458 Rayners Lane, Pinner, Harrow, Middlesex HA5 5DT
Tel: 020 8866 2737
Head of School: Mrs Sarah Hollis
Age range: B3–11 years

Buxlow Preparatory School
5/6 Castleton Gardens, Wembley, Middlesex HA9 7QJ
Tel: 020 8904 3615
Headteacher: Mr D May
Age range: 2–11 years

Edgware Jewish Girls – Beis Chinuch
296 Hale Lane, Edgware, Middlesex HA8 8NP
Tel: 020 8905 4376
Headteacher: Mr M Cohen
Age range: G3–11 years

Halliford School
Russell Road, Shepperton, Middlesex TW17 9HX
Tel: 01932 223593
Headmaster: Mr James Davies BMus (Hons) LGSM FASC ACertCM PGCE
Age range: B11–18 years G16–18 years
No. of pupils: 450
Fees: Day £19,200

Hampton Prep and Pre-Prep School
Gloucester Road, Hampton, Middlesex TW12 2UQ
Tel: 020 8979 1844
Headmaster: Mr Tim Smith
Age range: B3–11 years G3–7 years

Hampton School
Hanworth Road, Hampton, Middlesex TW12 3HD
Tel: 020 8979 5526
Headmaster: Mr Kevin Knibbs MA (Oxon)
Age range: B11–18 years

Harrow School
5 High Street, Harrow on the Hill, Middlesex HA1 3HP
Tel: 020 8872 8000
Head Master: Mr Alastair Land
Age range: B13–18 years

Holland House School
1 Broadhurst Avenue, Edgware, Middlesex HA8 8TP
Tel: 020 8958 6979
Headteacher: Mrs Emily Brown
Age range: 4–11 years
No. of pupils: 147

Jack & Jill Family of Schools
20 First Cross Road, Twickenham, Middlesex TW2 5QA
Tel: 03333 444630
Age range: B2–4 years G2–11 years

John Lyon School
Middle Road, Harrow on the Hill, Middlesex HA2 0HN
Tel: 020 8515 9443
Head: Miss Katherine Haynes BA, MEd, NPQH
Age range: 11–18 years
No. of pupils: 600

KEW HOUSE SCHOOL
For further details see p. 77
Kew House, 6 Capital Interchange Way, London, Middlesex TW8 0EX
Tel: 0208 742 2038
Email: admissions@kewhouseschool.com
Website: www.kewhouseschool.com
Headmaster: Mr Will Williams
Age range: 11–18 years
No. of pupils: 595
Fees: Day £8,073

Kids Inc Day Nursery – Enfield
8 Glyn Road, Southbury, Enfield, Middlesex EN3 4JL
Tel: 020 8805 1144

Lady Eleanor Holles
Hanworth Road, Hampton, Middlesex TW12 3HF
Tel: 020 8979 1601
Head of School: Mrs Heather Hanbury
Age range: G7–18 years
No. of pupils: 970
Fees: Day £21,738

Lady Nafisa School
Inglenook, Sipson Road, Sipson, West Drayton, Middlesex UB7 0JG
Tel: 02087 070001
Headteacher: Ms Fouzia Butt
Age range: G11–16 years

Melrose Nursery School – Sudbury
St Andrew's Church Hall, Church Gardens, 956 Harrow Road, Sudbury, Wembley, Middlesex HA0 2QA
Tel: 020 8904 6092

Melrose Nursery School – Wembley
St Michael's Church Hall, St Michael's Avenue, Tokyngton, Wembley, Middlesex HA9 6SL
Tel: 020 8795 1144

Menorah Foundation School
Abbots Road, Edgware, Middlesex HA8 0QS
Tel: 020 8906 9992
Headteacher: Karen Kent
Age range: B11–21 years

Merchant Taylors' School
Sandy Lodge, Northwood, Middlesex HA6 2HT
Tel: 01923 820644
Head Master: Mr S J Everson MA (Cantab)
Age range: B11–18 years

Newland House School
Waldegrave Park, Twickenham, Middlesex TW1 4TQ
Tel: 020 8865 1234
Head of School: Mr Chris Skelton
Age range: 3–13 years
No. of pupils: 448

North London Collegiate School
Canons, Canons Drive, Edgware, Middlesex HA8 7RJ
Tel: +44 (0)20 8952 0912
Interim Headmistress: Dr Hazel Bagworth-Mann
Age range: G4–18 years
No. of pupils: 1080
Fees: Day £6,283–£7,436

Northwood College for Girls GDST
Maxwell Road, Northwood, Middlesex HA6 2YE
Tel: 01923 825446
Head of School: Mrs Rebecca Brown
Age range: G3–18 years
No. of pupils: 844

Oak Heights
2-3 Red Lion Court, Alexandra Road, Hounslow, Middlesex TW3 1JS
Tel: 020 8577 1827
Head: Mr S Dhillon
Age range: 11–16 years

Orley Farm School
South Hill Avenue, Harrow, Middlesex HA1 3NU
Tel: 020 8869 7600
Headmaster: Mr Tim Calvey
Age range: 4–13 years

Quainton Hall School & Nursery
91 Hindes Road, Harrow, Middlesex HA1 1RX
Tel: 020 8515 9500
Headmaster: S Ford BEd (Hons), UWE Bristol
Age range: 3–11 years
Fees: Day £11,850–£13,050

Radnor House
Pope's Villa, Cross Deep, Twickenham, Middlesex TW1 4QG
Tel: +44 (0)20 8891 6264
Head: Mr Darryl Wideman MA Oxon, PGCE
Age range: 9–18 years

Reddiford School
36-38 Cecil Park, Pinner, Middlesex HA5 5HH
Tel: 020 8866 0660
Headteacher: Mrs J Batt CertEd, NPQH
Age range: 3–11 years

Regent College London
Regent House, 167 Imperial Drive, Harrow, Middlesex HA2 7HD
Tel: +44 (0)20 3870 6666
Co-Principals: Dr Selva Pankaj & Mrs Tharshiny Pankaj
Age range: 14–24 years

Roxeth Mead School
Buckholt House, 25 Middle Road, Harrow, Middlesex HA2 0HW
Tel: 020 8422 2092
Co-Headteachers: Mrs Suzanne Goodwin & Mrs Sarah Mackintosh
Age range: 0–7 years

St Catherine's Prep
Cross Deep, Twickenham,
Middlesex TW1 4QJ
Tel: 020 8891 2898
Headmistress:
Mrs Johneen McPherson MA
Age range: G5–11 years
No. of pupils: 95
Fees: Day £13,395–£14,085

St Christopher's School
71 Wembley Park Drive,
Wembley, Middlesex HA9 8HE
Tel: 020 8902 5069
Head of School: Mr Jonathan Coke
Age range: 2–11 years

St Helen's College
Parkway, Hillingdon, Uxbridge,
Middlesex UB10 9JX
Tel: 01895 234371
Head: Ms Shirley Drummond BA,
PGCert, MLDP, FCCT
Age range: 2–11 years
No. of pupils: 380
Fees: Day £10,560–£13,020

St Helen's School
Eastbury Road, Northwood,
Middlesex HA6 3AS
Tel: +44 (0)1923 843210
Headmistress: Mrs Alice Lucas
Age range: G3–18 years
No. of pupils: 1150

St John's School
Potter Street Hill, Northwood,
Middlesex HA6 3QY
Tel: 020 8866 0067
Headmaster: Mr Sean Robinson
Age range: B3–13 years

St Martin's School
40 Moor Park Road, Northwood,
Middlesex HA6 2DJ
Tel: 01923 825740
Headmaster: Mr S Dunn BEd (Hons)
Age range: B3–13 years

St. Catherine's School
Cross Deep, Twickenham,
Middlesex TW1 4QJ
Tel: 020 8891 2898
Headmistress: Mrs Johneen
McPherson MA
Age range: G5–18 years
No. of pupils: 434
Fees: Day £13,395–£16,875

St. John's Senior School
North Lodge, The Ridgeway,
Enfield, Middlesex EN2 8BE
Tel: +44 (0)20 8366 0035
Head Teacher: Mr A Tardios
Age range: 11–18 years

Tashbar of Edgware
Mowbray Road, Edgware,
Middlesex HA8 8JL
Age range: B3–11 years

**The Hall Pre-Preparatory
School & Nursery**
The Grange Country House,
Rickmansworth Road,
Northwood, Middlesex HA6 2RB
Tel: 01923 822807
Headmistress: Mrs S M Goodwin
Age range: 0–7 years

The Mall School
185 Hampton Road, Twickenham,
Middlesex TW2 5NQ
Tel: 0208 977 2523
Headmaster: Mr D C Price BSc, MA
Age range: B4–11 years

**The St Michael
Steiner School**
Park Road, Hanworth Park,
London, Middlesex TW13 6PN
Tel: 0208 893 1299
Age range: 3–18 years

**Twickenham
Preparatory School**
Beveree, 43 High Street,
Hampton, Middlesex TW12 2SA
Tel: 020 8979 6216
Headmaster: Mr Oliver Barrett
Age range: B4–13 years G4–11 years

Surrey

Al-Khair School
109-117 Cherry Orchard Road,
Croydon, Surrey CR0 6BE
Tel: 020 8662 8664
Headteacher: Mrs Aisha Chaudhry
Age range: 2–16 years

Broomfield House School
Broomfield Road, Kew Gardens,
Richmond, Surrey TW9 3HS
Tel: 020 8940 3884
Head of School: Ms Susie Byers
Age range: 3–11 years

Cambridge Tutors College
Water Tower Hill, Croydon,
Surrey CR0 5SX
Tel: 020 8688 5284/7363
Principal: Dr Chris Drew
Age range: 14–23 years

Canbury School
Kingston Hill, Kingston upon
Thames, Surrey KT2 7LN
Tel: 020 8549 8622
Headmistress: Ms Carolyn Yates
Age range: 11–18 years

Collingwood School
3 Springfield Road, Wallington,
Surrey SM6 0BD
Tel: 020 8647 4607
Headmaster: Mr Leigh Hardie
Age range: 3–11 years

Croydon High School GDST
Old Farleigh Road, Selsdon,
South Croydon, Surrey CR2 8YB
Tel: 02082 607543
Head: Ms Annabel Davies
Age range: G3–18 years

**Cumnor House
Kindergarten &
PreSchool, Purley**
13 Woodcote Lane, Purley,
Surrey CR8 3HB
Tel: 020 8668 5886
Head of School: Mrs Eloise Upfold
Age range: 2–4 years

**Cumnor House
Kindergarten & PreSchool,
South Croydon**
91 Pampisford Road, South
Croydon, Surrey CR2 6DH
Tel: 020 8660 4480
Head of School: Mrs Eloise Upfold
Age range: 2–4 years

**Cumnor House
School for Boys**
168 Pampisford Road, South
Croydon, Surrey CR2 6DA
Tel: 020 8645 2614
Head of School:
Miss Emma Edwards
Age range: B4–13 years
No. of pupils: 423
Fees: Day £3,880–£4,655

**Cumnor House
School for Girls**
1 Woodcote Lane, Purley,
Surrey CR8 3HB
Tel: 020 8668 0050
Head of School:
Mrs Amanda McShane
Age range: G4–11 years

Educare Small School
12 Cowleaze Road, Kingston
upon Thames, Surrey KT2 6DZ
Tel: 020 8547 0144
Head Teacher: Mrs E Steinthal
Age range: 3–11 years

Elmhurst School
44-48 South Park Hill Road, South
Croydon, Surrey CR2 7DW
Tel: 020 8688 0661
Head of School: Mrs Sara Marriott
Age range: B3–11 years
No. of pupils: 140
Fees: Day £3,680–£4,290

Falcons Prep Richmond
41 Kew Foot Road, Richmond,
Surrey TW9 2SS
Tel: 020 8948 9490
Headmistress: Ms Olivia Buchanan
Age range: B3–13 years

**Holy Cross Preparatory
School**
George Road, Kingston upon
Thames, Surrey KT2 7NU
Tel: 020 8942 0729
Headteacher: Mrs S Hair BEd(Hons)
Age range: G3–11 years

**Homefield Preparatory
School**
Western Road, Sutton,
Surrey SM1 2TE
Tel: 02086 420965
Headmaster: Mr John Towers
Age range: B4–13 years

Kew College Prep
24-26 Cumberland Road,
Kew, Surrey TW9 3HQ
Tel: 020 8940 2039
Head: Mrs Jane Bond BSc, MA(Ed),
PGCE
Age range: 3–11 years
No. of pupils: 284
£ ✏

KEW GREEN PREPARATORY SCHOOL
For further details see p. 76
Layton House, Ferry Lane,
Kew Green, Richmond,
Surrey TW9 3AF
Tel: 020 8948 5999
Email: admissions@kgps.co.uk
Website: www.kgps.co.uk
Headteacher: Mrs Sasha Davies
Age range: 2–11 years
No. of pupils: 275
Fees: Day £6,632
✏

King's House School
68 King's Road, Richmond,
Surrey TW10 6ES
Tel: 020 8940 1878
Head: Mr Mark Turner BA, PGCE,
NPQH
Age range: 3–13 years
No. of pupils: 425
Fees: Day £2,720–£6,530
✏

Kingston Grammar School
London Road, Kingston upon
Thames, Surrey KT2 6PY
Tel: 02085 465875
Head Master: Mr Stephen Lehec
Age range: 11–18 years
Ⓐ £ 16⁺

Laleham Lea School
29 Peaks Hill, Purley, Surrey CR8 3JJ
Tel: 020 8660 3351
Headteacher: Ms K Barry
Age range: 3–11 years
No. of pupils: 131
Fees: Day £9,576
£ ✏

MARYMOUNT INTERNATIONAL SCHOOL LONDON
For further details see p. 78
George Road, Kingston upon
Thames, Surrey KT2 7PE
Tel: +44 (0)20 8949 0571
Email: admissions@
marymountlondon.com
Website:
www.marymountlondon.com
Headmistress:
Mrs Margaret Giblin
Age range: G11–18 years
No. of pupils: 248
Fees: Day £28,830 WB
£46,740 FB £48,810
♿ 🏫 ⚲ £ IB ✏ 16⁺

Oakwood School
Coombe Road, Lloyd Park,
Croydon, Surrey CR0 5RD
Tel: 02086 688080
Headmistress: Ms Debbie Morrison
Age range: 3–11 years

Old Palace of John Whitgift School
Old Palace Road, Croydon,
Surrey CR0 1AX
Tel: 02086 882027
Head of School: Mrs Jane Burton
Age range: G3–18 years
No. of pupils: 650
Fees: Day £3,300–£5,536
♿ £ 16⁺

Old Vicarage School
46-48 Richmond Hill,
Richmond, Surrey TW10 6QX
Tel: 020 8940 0922
Headmistress: Mrs G D Linthwaite
Age range: G3–11 years
No. of pupils: 200
Fees: Day £5,200
♿ ✏

Park Hill School
8 Queens Road, Kingston upon
Thames, Surrey KT2 7SH
Tel: 020 8546 5496
Headmaster: Mr Alistair Bond
Age range: 2–11 years
✏

Rokeby School
George Road, Kingston upon
Thames, Surrey KT2 7PB
Tel: 020 8942 2247
Head: Mr J R Peck
Age range: B4–13 years
♿ ✏

Royal Russell Junior School
Coombe Lane, Croydon,
Surrey CR9 5BX
Tel: +44 (0)20 8657 4433
Junior School Headmaster: Mr John
Evans
Age range: 3–11 years

Royal Russell School
Coombe Lane, Croydon,
Surrey CR9 5BX
Tel: +44 (0)20 8657 4433
Headmaster:
Mr Christopher Hutchinson
Age range: 11–18 years
♿ Ⓐ ⚲ £ ✏ 16⁺

Seaton House School
67 Banstead Road South,
Sutton, Surrey SM2 5LH
Tel: 020 8642 2332
Headteacher: Mr Carl Bates
Age range: B3–5 years G3–11 years
♿

Shrewsbury House School
107 Ditton Road, Surbiton,
Surrey KT6 6RL
Tel: 020 8399 3066
Executive Head: Ms Joanna
Hubbard MA BA(Hons) PGCE
PGDipSEN
Age range: B7–13 years
♿ ✏

St David's School
Woodcote Valley Road,
Purley, Surrey CR8 3AL
Tel: 020 8660 0723
Headmistress: Cressida Mardell
Age range: 3–11 years
✏

St James Senior Boys' School
Church Road, Ashford,
Surrey TW15 3DZ
Tel: 01784 266930
Headmaster: Mr David Brazier
Age range: B11–18 years
♿ 🏫 Ⓐ £ ✏ 16⁺

Staines Preparatory School
3 Gresham Road, Staines-upon-
Thames, Surrey TW18 2BT
Tel: 01784 450909
Head of School: Ms Samantha
Sawyer B.Ed (Hons), M.Ed, NPQH
Age range: 3–11 years
No. of pupils: 298
Fees: Day £11,250–£13,500
£ ✏

Surbiton High School
13-15 Surbiton Crescent, Kingston
upon Thames, Surrey KT1 2JT
Tel: 02085 465245
Principal: Mrs Rebecca Glover
Age range: B4–11 years G4–18 years
♿ Ⓐ £ ✏ 16⁺

Sutton High School GDST
55 Cheam Road, Sutton,
Surrey SM1 2AX
Tel: 020 8642 0594
Head of School: Ms Beth Dawson
Age range: G3–18 years
♿ Ⓐ £ ✏ 16⁺

The Royal Ballet School (White Lodge)
White Lodge, Richmond Park,
Richmond, Surrey TW10 5HR
Tel: 020 8392 8440
Head of School:
Mr David Gajadharsingh
Age range: 11–19 years
(boarding from 11)
♿

The Study School
57 Thetford Road, New
Malden, Surrey KT3 5DP
Tel: 020 8942 0754
Headmaster: Mr Alistair Bond
Age range: 2–11 years

Trinity School
Shirley Park, Croydon,
Surrey CR9 7AT
Tel: 020 8656 9541
Head: Mr Alasdair Kennedy
Age range: B10–18 years
G16–18 years
♿ Ⓐ £ ✏ 16⁺

Unicorn School
238 Kew Road, Richmond,
Surrey TW9 3JX
Tel: 020 8948 3926
Headteacher: Mrs Polly Fraley
Age range: 3–11 years
✏

Westbury House
80 Westbury Road, New
Malden, Surrey KT3 5AS
Tel: 020 8942 5885
Headteacher: Miss Clare King
Age range: 2–11 years

Whitgift School
Haling Park, South Croydon,
Surrey CR2 6YT
Tel: +44 20 8633 9935
Headmaster:
Mr Christopher Ramsey
Age range: B10–18 years
No. of pupils: 1550
Fees: Day £22,269 WB
£35,973 FB £43,629
♿ 🏫 Ⓐ ⚲ £ IB ✏ 16⁺

Schools in the South-East

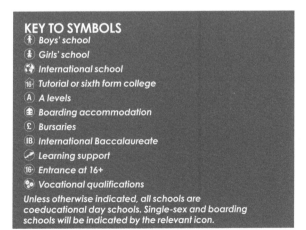

KEY TO SYMBOLS
- Boys' school
- Girls' school
- International school
- Tutorial or sixth form college
- A levels
- Boarding accommodation
- £ Bursaries
- IB International Baccalaureate
- Learning support
- 16 Entrance at 16+
- Vocational qualifications

Unless otherwise indicated, all schools are coeducational day schools. Single-sex and boarding schools will be indicated by the relevant icon.

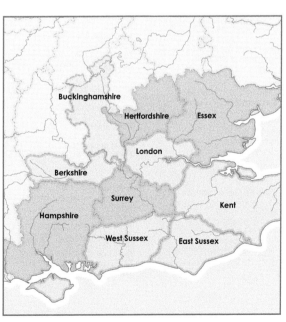

Berkshire

Alder Bridge Steiner-Waldorf School
Bridge House, Mill Lane, Padworth, Reading, Berkshire RG7 4JU
Tel: 0118 971 4471
Head of School: Lucia Dimarco
Age range: 3–14 years

Al-Madani Girls School
339-341 Bath Road, Slough, Berkshire SL1 5PR
Tel: 01628 298841
Head of School:
Tazmul Islam Rahman
Age range: G11–16 years

Al-Madani Independent Grammar School
1 Whittle Parkway, Slough, Berkshire SL1 6FE
Tel: 01753 202203
Age range: B11–16 years

Bradfield College
Bradfield, Berkshire RG7 6AU
Tel: 0118 964 4516
Headmaster: Dr Christopher Stevens
Age range: 13–18 years
No. of pupils: 820
Fees: Day £33,732 FB £42,165

Caversham Preparatory School
16 Peppard Road, Caversham, Reading, Berkshire RG4 8JZ
Tel: 01189 478 684
Head of School: Mrs Naomi Williams
Age range: 3–11 years

Claires Court Junior Boys
Ridgeway, The Thicket, Maidenhead, Berkshire SL6 3QE
Tel: 01628 327400
Head of Juniors: Ms Leanne Kirby
Age range: B4–11 years

Claires Court Nursery, Girls and Sixth Form
1 College Avenue, Maidenhead, Berkshire SL6 6AW
Tel: 01628 327500
Head of Juniors: Ms Leanne Kirby
Age range: B16–18 years G2–18 years

Claires Court Senior Boys
Ray Mill Road East, Maidenhead, Berkshire SL6 8TE
Tel: 01628 327600
Head of Senior Boys:
Mr James Wilding
Age range: B11–16 years

Crosfields School
Shinfield Road, Reading, Berkshire RG2 9BL
Tel: 0118 987 1810
Headmaster: Mr Craig Watson
Age range: 3–16 years

Darul Madinah Slough
50 Darvills Lane, Slough, Berkshire SL1 2PH
Tel: 01753 553841
Age range: 2–6 years

Dolphin School
Waltham Road, Hurst, Reading, Berkshire RG10 0FR
Tel: 0118 934 1277
Headmaster: Mr Adam Hurst
Age range: 3–13 years

Eagle House School
Sandhurst, Berkshire GU47 8PH
Tel: 01344 772134
Head: Mrs Jane Jones MA (Cantab)
Age range: 3–13 years
No. of pupils: 386
Fees: Day £13,035–£20,385 FB £27,390

Elstree School
Woolhampton Hill, Woolhampton, Reading, Berkshire RG7 5TD
Tel: 01189 713302
Headmaster: Mr Sid Inglis B.A. (Hons), P.G.C.E.
Age range: 3–13 years
No. of pupils: 270

Eton College
Windsor, Berkshire SL4 6DW
Tel: +44 (0)1753 370 611
Head Master: Mr Simon Henderson MA
Age range: B13–18 years
No. of pupils: 1342
Fees: FB £44,094

Eton End School
35 Eton Road, Datchet, Slough, Berkshire SL3 9AX
Tel: 01753 541075
Head of School: Mrs Rachael Cox
Age range: 3–11 years
No. of pupils: 210
Fees: Day £11,106–£14,193

Heathfield School
London Road, Ascot, Berkshire SL5 8BQ
Tel: 01344 898343
Head of School: Ms Sarah Wilson
Age range: G11–18 years (boarding from 11)
Fees: Day £7,840–£8,000 FB £12,650–£12,950

Hemdean House School
Hemdean Road, Caversham, Reading, Berkshire RG4 7SD
Tel: 0118 947 2590
Head Teacher: Mrs Helen Chalmers
Age range: 4–11 years
Fees: Day £3,250–£3,540

Herries Preparatory School
Dean Lane, Cookham Dean, Berkshire SL6 9BD
Tel: 01628 483350
Headteacher: Mr Robert Grosse
Age range: 3–11 years

Highfield Preparatory School
2 West Road, Maidenhead, Berkshire SL6 1PD
Tel: 01628 624918
Headteacher: Mrs Joanna Leach
Age range: B2–7 years G2–11 years

Holme Grange School
Heathlands Road, Wokingham, Berkshire RG40 3AL
Tel: 0118 978 1566
Headteacher: Mrs Claire Robinson BA (Open) PGCE NPQH
Age range: 3–16 years
No. of pupils: 660
Fees: Day £10,665–£16,140

Kids Inc Day Nursery – Crowthorne
59-61 Dukes Ride, Crowthorne, Berkshire RG45 6NS
Tel: 01344 780670

Lambrook School
Winkfield Row, Nr Ascot, Berkshire RG42 6LU
Tel: 01344 882717
Headmaster: Mr Jonathan Perry
Age range: 3–13 years
No. of pupils: 600

Langley Hall Arts Academy
Symphony House, 4 Waterside Court, Langley, Berkshire SL3 6EZ
Tel: 01753 900470
Principal: Mr Claudio Di Meo
Age range: 12–18 years

LEIGHTON PARK SCHOOL
For further details see p. 90
Shinfield Road, Reading, Berkshire RG2 7ED
Tel: 0118 987 9600
Email: admissions@leightonpark.com
Website: www.leightonpark.com
Head: Mr Matthew L S Judd BA, PGCE
Age range: 11–18 years
No. of pupils: 550

Long Close School
Upton Court Road, Upton, Slough, Berkshire SL3 7LU
Tel: 01753 520095
Headteacher: Miss K Nijjar BA (Hons), Med, MA
Age range: 2–16 years
No. of pupils: 329

Luckley House School
Luckley Road, Wokingham, Berkshire RG40 3EU
Tel: 0118 978 4175
Head: Mrs Areti Bizior
Age range: 11–18 years

Ludgrove
Wokingham, Berkshire RG40 3AB
Tel: 0118 978 9881
Head of School: Mr Simon Barber
Age range: B8–13 years

LVS ASCOT
For further details see p. 92
London Road, Ascot, Berkshire SL5 8DR
Tel: 01344 882770
Email: enquiries@lvs.ascot.sch.uk
Website: www.lvs.ascot.sch.uk
Principal: Mrs Christine Cunniffe BA (Hons), MMus, MBA
Age range: 4–18 years
No. of pupils: 833
Fees: Day £11,640–£20,985 FB £29,760–£36,660

Meadowbrook Montessori School
Malt Hill, Warfield, Berkshire RG42 6JQ
Tel: 01344 890869
Director of Education: Ms Serena Gunn
Age range: 4–11 years

Newbold School
Popeswood Road, Binfield, Bracknell, Berkshire RG42 4AH
Tel: 01344 421088
Headteacher: Mrs Jaki Crissey MA, BA, PGCE Primary
Age range: 3–11 years

OneSchool Global UK Reading Campus (Primary)
401 Old Whitley Wood Lane, Reading, Berkshire RG2 8QA
Tel: 0118 931 2938
Age range: 7–11 years

OneSchool Global UK Reading Campus (Senior)
The Quad, 14 Arkwright Road, Reading, Berkshire RG2 0LU
Tel: 03000 700421
Age range: 11–18 years

Our Lady's Preparatory School
19 The Avenue, Crowthorne, Wokingham, Berkshire RG45 6PB
Tel: 01344 773394
Headmaster: Mr Michael Stone
Age range: 4–11 years
No. of pupils: 130
Fees: Day £8,748

Padworth College
Sopers Lane, Reading, Berkshire RG7 4NR
Tel: 0118 983 2644
Principal: Lorraine Atkins
Age range: 14–19 years

Pangbourne College
Pangbourne, Reading, Berkshire RG8 8LA
Tel: 0118 984 2101
Headmaster: Thomas J C Garnier
Age range: 11–18 years
No. of pupils: 458
Fees: Day £6,300–£8,540 WB £8,210–£11,510 FB £9,050–£12,680

Papplewick School
Windsor Road, Ascot, Berkshire SL5 7LH
Tel: 01344 621488
Headmaster: Mr Tom Bunbury
Age range: B6–13 years

Queen Anne's School
6 Henley Road, Caversham, Reading, Berkshire RG4 6DX
Tel: 0118 918 7300
Head: Ms Elaine Purves
Age range: G11–18 years (boarding from 11)
No. of pupils: G450
Fees: Day £8,370 FB £13,590

Reading Blue Coat School
Holme Park, Sonning Lane, Sonning, Reading, Berkshire RG4 6SU
Tel: 0118 944 1005
Headmaster: Mr Peter Thomas
Age range: B11–18 years G16–18 years

Shakhsiyah School, Slough
Cippenham Lodge, Cippenham Lane, Slough, Berkshire SL1 5AN
Tel: 01753 518000
Acting-Head Teacher: Ms Sajeada Ahmed
Age range: 3–11 years

St Andrew's School
Buckhold, Pangbourne, Reading, Berkshire RG8 8QA
Tel: 0118 974 4276
Head Master: Ed Graham
Age range: 3–13 years (boarding from 7)
Fees: Day £3,890–£6,525

St Bernard's Preparatory School
Hawtrey Close, Slough, Berkshire SL1 1TB
Tel: 01753 521821
Headteacher: Mrs A Verma
Age range: 2.5–11 years

St Edward's Prep
64 Tilehurst Road, Reading, Berkshire RG30 2JH
Tel: 0118 957 4342
Headteacher: Mr Jonathan Parsons
Age range: 3–11 years

St George's Ascot
Wells Lane, Ascot, Berkshire SL5 7DZ
Tel: 01344 629900
Headmistress: Mrs Liz Hewer MA (Hons) (Cantab) PGCE
Age range: G11–18 years (boarding from 11)

St George's School Windsor Castle
Windsor Castle, Windsor, Berkshire SL4 1QF
Tel: 01753 865553
Head Master: Mr W Goldsmith BA (Hons), FRSA, FCCT
Age range: 3–13 years

St Joseph's College
Upper Redlands Road, Reading, Berkshire RG1 5JT
Tel: 0118 966 1000
Head of School: Mrs Laura Stotesbury
Age range: 3–18 years

St Mary's School Ascot
St Mary's Road, Ascot, Berkshire SL5 9JF
Tel: 01344 296614
Headmistress: Mrs Danuta Staunton
Age range: G11–18 years (boarding from 11)

St Piran's School
Gringer Hill, Maidenhead, Berkshire SL6 7LZ
Tel: 01628 594300
Headmaster: Mr Sebastian Sales
Age range: 2–11 years

Sunningdale School
Dry Arch Road, Sunningdale, Berkshire SL5 9PY
Tel: 01344 620159
Headmaster: Tom Dawson MA, PGCE
Age range: B7–13 years

The Abbey School
Kendrick Road, Reading, Berkshire RG1 5DZ
Tel: 0118 987 2256
Head: Mr Will le Fleming
Age range: G3–18 years
No. of pupils: 1000
Fees: Day £11,535–£19,830

The King's House School, Windsor
King's House, 77A Frances Road, Windsor, Berkshire SL4 3AQ
Tel: 01753 834850
Headteacher: Mrs Lyndsey Harding
Age range: 3–11 years

The Marist Preparatory School
King's Road, Sunninghill, Ascot, Berkshire SL5 7PS
Tel: 01344 624291
Vice Principal Prep Phase: Mrs Jane Gow
Age range: G2–11 years

The Marist School
King's Road, Sunninghill, Ascot, Berkshire SL5 7PS
Tel: 01344 624291
Principal: Ms Jo Smith
Age range: G2–18 years

The Oratory Prep School
Great Oaks, Goring Heath, Reading, Berkshire RG8 7SF
Tel: 0118 984 4511
Headteacher: Mr Andrew De Silva
Age range: 2–13 years (boarding from 7)
No. of pupils: 330
Fees: Day £3,600–£6,200 FB £7,790–£9,050

The Oratory School
Woodcote, Reading, Berkshire RG8 0PJ
Tel: 01491 683500
Head Master: Mr Joe Smith BA(Hons), MEd, PGCE
Age range: 11–18 years

The Vine Christian School
Three Mile Cross Church, Basingstoke Road, Three Mile Cross, Reading, Berkshire RG7 1HF
Tel: 0118 988 6464
Head of School: Mrs René Esterhuizen
Age range: 3–18 years

TLG Reading
Empress Road Centre, Empress Road Calcot, Reading, Berkshire RG31 4XR
Tel: 01189 432978
Head of Centre: Ms Rachel Owen
Age range: 11–16 years

Trinity Christian School
11 Glebe Road, Reading, Berkshire RG2 7AG
Tel: 0118 336 0477
Head of School: Ms Pearl Linkens
Age range: 4–11 years

Upton House School
115 St Leonard's Road, Windsor, Berkshire SL4 3DF
Tel: 01753 862610
Head: Mrs Rhian Thornton BA (Hons) NPQH LLE PGCE
Age range: 2–11 years
No. of pupils: 299
Fees: Day £3,383–£5,615

Waverley Preparatory School & Day Nursery
Waverley Way, Finchampstead, Wokingham, Berkshire RG40 4YD
Tel: 0118 973 1121
Principal: Mr Guy Shore
Age range: 3 months–11 years

Wellington College
Duke's Ride, Crowthorne, Berkshire RG45 7PU
Tel: +44 (0)1344 444000
Master: Mr James Dahl
Age range: 13–18 years
No. of pupils: 1100 VIth485
Fees: Day £32,940–£35,760 FB £45,090

Buckinghamshire

Akeley Wood School
Akeley Wood House, Buckingham,
Buckinghamshire MK18 5AE
Tel: 01280 814110
Headmaster: Mr Simon Antwis
Age range: 12 months–18 years
No. of pupils: 700 Vlth100
Fees: Day £10,665–£15,900
(A) (£) ⚲ (16)

Ashfold School
Dorton House, Dorton, Aylesbury,
Buckinghamshire HP18 9NG
Tel: 01844 238237
Headmaster: Mr Colin MacIntosh
Age range: 3–13 years
(🏕)

Baytul Ilm Secondary School
12a Clarke Road, Bletchley, Milton
Keynes, Buckinghamshire MK1 1LG
Tel: 01908 804163
Age range: B11–16 years
(🏃)

Broughton Manor Preparatory School
Newport Road, Broughton, Milton
Keynes, Buckinghamshire MK10 9AA
Tel: 01908 665234
Heads: Mr J Smith & Mrs R Smith
Age range: 2 months–11 years
(£)

Caldicott
Crown Lane, Farnham Royal,
Buckinghamshire SL2 3SL
Tel: 01753 649301
Headmaster: Mr Jeremy Banks BA
(Hons) QTS, MEd
Age range: B7–13 years
(flexi boarding from 7)
No. of pupils: 250
(🏃) (🏕) ⚲

Chesham Preparatory School
Two Dells Lane, Chesham,
Buckinghamshire HP5 3QF
Tel: 01494 782619
Headmaster: Mr Jonathan Beale
Age range: 3–13 years
⚲

Child First Aylesbury Pre-School
35 Rickfords Hill, Aylesbury,
Buckinghamshire HP20 2RT
Tel: 01296 433224
Age range: 3–5 years

Crown House Preparatory School
Bassetsbury Manor, Bassetsbury
Lane, High Wycombe,
Buckinghamshire HP11 1QX
Tel: 01494 529927
Headteacher: Mrs Sarah Hobby
Age range: 3–11 years
⚲

Dair House School
Bishops Blake, Beaconsfield
Road, Farnham Royal,
Buckinghamshire SL2 3BY
Tel: 01753 643964
Head of School: Mrs Janine Bull
Age range: 3–11 years
No. of pupils: 125
Fees: Day £1,020–£4,850
(£) ⚲

DAVENIES
For further details see p. 86
Station Road, Beaconsfield,
Buckinghamshire HP9 1AA
Tel: 01494 685400
Email: office@davenies.co.uk
Website: www.davenies.co.uk
Headmaster: Mr Carl Rycroft
BEd (Hons)
Age range: B4–13 years
No. of pupils: 334
Fees: Day £12,825–£19,350
(🏃) (£) ⚲

Gateway School
1 High Street, Great Missenden,
Buckinghamshire HP16 9AA
Tel: 01494 862407
Head of School:
Mrs Cath Bufton-Green
Age range: 2–11 years
⚲

Gayhurst School
Bull Lane, Gerrards Cross,
Buckinghamshire SL9 8RJ
Tel: 01753 969538
Headmaster: Gareth R A Davies
Age range: 3–11 years
⚲

Godstowe Preparatory School
Shrubbery Road, High Wycombe,
Buckinghamshire HP13 6PR
Tel: 01494 529273
Headmistress: Ms Kate Bailey
Age range: B3–7 years G3–13
years (boarding from 7)
(🏃) (🏕) (£) ⚲

Griffin House Preparatory School
Little Kimble, Aylesbury,
Buckinghamshire HP17 0XP
Tel: 01844 346154
Headmaster: Mr Tim Walford
Age range: 3–11 years
⚲

Heatherton School
10 Copperkins Lane, Amersham,
Buckinghamshire HP6 5QB
Tel: 01494 726433
Headteacher: Mrs Nicola Nicoll
Age range: B3–4 years G3–11 years
No. of pupils: 144
Fees: Day £3,240–£14,595
(🏃) (🏕) ⚲

High March
23 Ledborough Lane, Beaconsfield,
Buckinghamshire HP9 2PZ
Tel: 01494 675186
Head of School: Mrs Kate Gater
Age range: B3–4 years G3–11 years
No. of pupils: 282
Fees: Day £6,255–£17,325
(🏃) (£) ⚲

International School of Creative Arts (ISCA)
Framewood Road, Wexham,
Buckinghamshire SL2 4QS
Tel: +44 (0)1753 208820
Head of School: Mr Robert Hunter
Age range: 15–19 years
No. of pupils: 85
(🌐) (🏕)

Kids Inc Day Nursery – Aylesbury
The Pavilion, Watermead,
Aylesbury, Buckinghamshire
HP19 0FY
Tel: 01296 397407

Maltman's Green School
Maltmans Lane, Gerrards Cross,
Buckinghamshire SL9 8RR
Tel: 01753 883022
Headmistress: Mrs Jill Walker BSc
(Hons), MA Ed, PGCE
Age range: G2–11 years
No. of pupils: 315
Fees: Day £2,595–£5,700
(🏃) (£) ⚲

Milton Keynes Preparatory School
Tattenhoe Lane, Milton Keynes,
Buckinghamshire MK3 7EG
Tel: 01908 642111
Head of School: Mr Simon Driver
Age range: 2 months–11 years
(£)

Pipers Corner School
Pipers Lane, Great
Kingshill, High Wycombe,
Buckinghamshire HP15 6LP
Tel: 01494 718 255
Headmistress: Mrs H J Ness-Gifford
BA(Hons), PGCE
Age range: G4–18 years
(🏃) (A) (£) ⚲ (16) (🌐)

St Mary's School
94 Packhorse Road, Gerrards
Cross, Buckinghamshire SL9 8JQ
Tel: 01753 883370
Head of School: Mrs Patricia Adams
Age range: G3–18 years
(🏃) (A) (£) ⚲ (16)

Stowe School
Buckingham, Buckinghamshire
MK18 5EH
Tel: 01280 818000
Headmaster: Dr Anthony
Wallersteiner
Age range: 13–18 years
(🌐) (A) (🏕) (£) ⚲ (16)

Swanbourne House School
Swanbourne, Milton Keynes,
Buckinghamshire MK17 0HZ
Tel: 01296 720264
Head of School: Mrs Jane Thorpe
Age range: 4–13 years
(🏕) (£) ⚲

Teikyo School UK
Framewood Road, Wexham,
Buckinghamshire SL2 4QS
Tel: 01753 663711
Age range: 15–18 years
(🌐) (🏕) (IB)

The Beacon School
15 Amersham Road,
Chesham Bois, Amersham,
Buckinghamshire HP6 5PF
Tel: 01494 433654
Headmaster: Mr William Phelps
Age range: B3–13 years
(🏃) ⚲

The Grove Independent School
Redland Drive, Loughton, Milton
Keynes, Buckinghamshire MK5 8HD
Tel: 01908 690590
Principal: Mrs Deborah Berkin
Age range: 3 months–13 years

The Webber Independent School
Soskin Drive, Stantonbury
Fields, Milton Keynes,
Buckinghamshire MK14 6DP
Tel: 01908 574740
Principal: Mrs Hilary Marsden
Age range: 6 months–16 years
(A)

Thornton College
College Lane, Thornton, Milton
Keynes, Buckinghamshire MK17 0HJ
Tel: 01280 812610
Headteacher: Dr Louise Shaw
Age range: G3–18 years
(boarding from 8)
No. of pupils: 402
Fees: Day £11,190–£17,835 WB
£19,830–£25,095 FB £24,660–£30,585
(🏃) (🌐) (A) (🏕) ⚲

Thorpe House School
Oval Way, Gerrards Cross,
Buckinghamshire SL9 8QA
Tel: 01753 882474
Headmaster: Mr Nicholas Pietrek
Age range: B4–16 years
(🏃) ⚲

Wycombe Abbey
Frances Dove Way, High Wycombe,
Buckinghamshire HP11 1PE
Tel: +44 (0)1494 520381
Headmistress: Mrs Jo Duncan MA
(St Andrews), PGCE (Cantab)
Age range: G11–18 years
No. of pupils: 660
Fees: Day £33,150 FB £44,100
(🏃) (🌐) (A) (🏕) (£) ⚲ (16)

East Sussex

Annan The Froebel School
Lewes Road, Easons Green,
Uckfield, East Sussex TN22 5RE
Tel: 01825 841410
Principal: Ms Debby Hunter
Age range: 2–11 years

Bartholomews Tutorial College
22-23 Prince Albert Street,
Brighton, East Sussex BN1 1HF
Tel: 01273 205965/205141
Age range: 14+ years
No. of pupils: 40
Fees: Day £22,000
16 Ⓐ 🔗

Battle Abbey School
High Street, Battle, East
Sussex TN33 0AD
Tel: 01424 772385
Headmaster: Mr David Clark BA,
M Phil (Cantab)
Age range: 3 months–18
years (boarding from 11)
🌐 Ⓐ 🏫 £ 🔗 16

Bede's Prep School
Duke's Drive, Eastbourne,
East Sussex BN20 7XL
Tel: 01323 356939
Head: Mrs Leigh-Anne Morris
Age range: 3 months–13
years (boarding from 9)
No. of pupils: 336
Fees: Day £3,660–£6,390 FB £2,990
🏫 £ 🔗

BEDE'S SENIOR SCHOOL
For further details see p. 82
Upper Dicker, Hailsham,
East Sussex BN27 3QH
Tel: 01323 356609
Email: admissions@bedes.org
Website: www.bedes.org/senior
Head: Mr Peter Goodyer
Age range: 13–18 years
(boarding from 13)
No. of pupils: 832
Fees: Day £8,300 WB
£12,240 FB £12,990
🌐 Ⓐ 🏫 £ 🔗 16 🌐

Brighton & Hove Montessori School
67 Stanford Avenue, Brighton,
East Sussex BN1 6FB
Tel: 01273 702485
Headteacher: Mrs Daisy Cockburn
AMI, MontDip
Age range: 2–12 years
🔗

Brighton College
Eastern Road, Brighton,
East Sussex BN2 0AL
Tel: 01273 704200
Head Master: Richard Cairns
Age range: 3–18 years
🌐 Ⓐ 🏫 £ 🔗 16

Brighton Girls GDST
Montpelier Road, Brighton,
East Sussex BN1 3AT
Tel: 01273 280280
Head: Ms Rosie McColl
Age range: G4–18 years
🏃 Ⓐ £ 🔗 16

Brighton International School
5 Old Steine, Brighton,
East Sussex BN1 1EJ
Tel: 07796 997780
Head of School: Ms Juliet Cassells
Age range: 15–17 years
🌐

Buckswood School
Broomham Hall, Rye
Road, Guestling, Hastings,
East Sussex TN35 4LT
Tel: 01424 813 813
Co-Principals: Michael Shaw &
Kevin Samson
Age range: 10–19 years
🌐 Ⓐ 🏫 £ IB 🔗 16

Charters Ancaster Nursery
Woodsgate Place, Gunters Lane,
Bexhill-on-Sea, East Sussex TN39 4EB
Tel: 01424 216670
Nursery Manager: Gel Baker
Age range: 6 months–5 years

Claremont School
Bodiam, Nr Robertsbridge,
East Sussex TN32 5UJ
Tel: 01580 830396
Age range: 3 months–18
years (boarding from 10)
🏫

Darvell School
Darvell, Brightling Road,
Robertsbridge, East
Sussex TN32 5DR
Tel: 01580 883300
Age range: 6–14 years

Eastbourne College
Old Wish Road, Eastbourne,
East Sussex BN21 4JX
Tel: 01323 452323 (Admissions)
Headmaster: Mr Tom Lawson MA
(Oxon)
Age range: 13–18 years
🌐 Ⓐ 🏫 £ 🔗 16

Greenfields Independent Day & Boarding School
Priory Road, Forest Row,
East Sussex RH18 5JD
Tel: +44 (0)1342 822189
Executive Head: Mr. Jeff Smith
Age range: 2–18 years
(boarding from 10)
🌐 Ⓐ 🏫 🔗 16

JeMs Nursery
15 The Upper Drive, Hove,
East Sussex BN3 6GR
Tel: 07834 669181
Head: Ms. Penina Efune
Age range: 1–4 years
🔗

Lancing Prep Hove
The Droveway, Hove,
East Sussex BN3 6LU
Tel: 01273 503452
Headmistress: Mrs Kirsty Keep BEd
Age range: 3–13 years
🔗

Lewes Old Grammar School
140 High Street, Lewes,
East Sussex BN7 1XS
Tel: 01273 472634
Headmaster: Mr Robert Blewitt
Age range: 3–18 years
🔗 16

MAYFIELD SCHOOL
For further details see p. 93
The Old Palace, Mayfield,
East Sussex TN20 6PH
Tel: 01435 874642
Email:
registrar@mayfieldgirls.org
Website: www.mayfieldgirls.org
Head: Ms Antonia Beary MA,
MPhil (Cantab), PGCE
Age range: G11–18 years
(boarding from 11)
No. of pupils: 425
🏃 🌐 Ⓐ 🏫 £ 🔗 16

Michael Hall School
Kidbrooke Park, Priory Road,
Forest Row, East Sussex RH18 5JA
Tel: 01342 822275
Head of School: Emmeline Hawker
Age range: 0–19 years
🌐 🔗 16

ROEDEAN SCHOOL
For further details see p. 95
Roedean Way, Brighton,
East Sussex BN2 5RQ
Tel: 01273 667500
Email: info@roedean.co.uk
Website: www.roedean.co.uk
Head of School: Niamh Green
Age range: G11–18 years
(boarding from 11)
No. of pupils: 700
Fees: Day £6,290–£8,220
WB £11,120–£12,400 FB
£12,180–£14,745
🏃 🌐 Ⓐ 🏫 £ 🔗 16

Sacred Heart School
Mayfield Lane, Durgates,
Wadhurst, East Sussex TN5 6DQ
Tel: 01892 783414
Headteacher: Ms Johanna Collyer
Age range: 2–11 years
🔗

Skippers Hill Manor Preparatory School
Five Ashes, Mayfield,
East Sussex TN20 6HR
Tel: 01825 830234
Headmaster: Mr Phillip Makhouli
Age range: 2–13 years
Fees: Day £2,932–£5,062
£ 🔗

St Andrew's Prep
Meads Street, Eastbourne,
East Sussex BN20 7RP
Tel: 01323 733203
Headmaster: Tom Gregory
BA(Hons), PGCE
Age range: 9 months–13 years
No. of pupils: 374
🏫 £ 🔗

St Christopher's School
33 New Church Road, Hove,
East Sussex BN3 4AD
Tel: 01273 735404
Head of School: Ms Elizabeth Lyle
Age range: 4–13 years
🔗

The Brighton Waldorf School
Roedean Road, Brighton,
East Sussex BN2 5RA
Tel: 01273 386300
School Director:
Mr Damian Mooncie
Age range: 0–16 years
£ 🔗

The Drive Prep School
101 The Drive, Hove, East
Sussex BN3 6GE
Tel: 01273 738444
Head Teacher: Mrs S Parkinson
CertEd, CertPerfArts
Age range: 7–16 years

The Montessori Place
45 Cromwell Road, Hove,
East Sussex BN3 3ER
Tel: 01273 773 764
Head of School:
Mr Rob Gueterbock
Age range: 15 months–18 years

Vinehall
Robertsbridge, East Sussex TN32 5JL
Tel: 01580 880413
Headmaster: Joff Powis
Age range: 2–13 years
No. of pupils: 220
Fees: Day £10,350–£19,290 WB
£22,575–£23,100 FB £24,525–£25,125
🏫 £ 🔗

Windlesham School
190 Dyke Road, Brighton,
East Sussex BN1 5AA
Tel: 01273 553645
Headmaster: Mr John Ingrassia
Age range: 3–11 years
🔗

Essex

Alleyn Court School
Wakering Road, Southend-on-Sea, Essex SS3 0PW
Tel: 01702 582553
Headmaster: Mr Rupert W.J. Snow B.Ed, NPQH
Age range: 2.5–11 years

Apex Primary School
60-62 Argyle Road,
Ilford, Essex IG1 3BG
Tel: 020 8554 1208
Head Teacher: Ms Meherun Hamid
Age range: 3–11 years

Brentwood Preparatory School
Shenfield Road, Brentwood,
Essex CM15 8BD
Tel: +44 (0)1277 243300
Headmaster: Mr Jason Whiskerd
Age range: 3–11 years
No. of pupils: 584

Brentwood School
Middleton Hall Lane,
Brentwood, Essex CM15 8EE
Tel: 01277 243243
Headmaster: Mr Michael Bond
Age range: 3–18 years
No. of pupils: 1968
Fees: Day £21,783 FB £42,687

Colchester High School
Wellesley Road, Colchester,
Essex CO3 3HD
Tel: 01206 573389
Headteacher: Ms Karen Gracie-Langrick
Age range: 2.5–16 years
No. of pupils: 320
Fees: Day £9,465–£13,620

Coopersale Hall School
Flux's Lane, off Stewards Green Road, Epping, Essex CM16 7PE
Tel: 01992 577133
Headmistress: Ms Moreen Barnard
Age range: 2.5–11 years

Elm Green Preparatory School
Parsonage Lane, Little Baddow,
Chelmsford, Essex CM3 4SU
Tel: 01245 225230
Principal: Ms Ann Milner
Age range: 4–11 years

Felsted Preparatory School
Felsted, Great Dunmow,
Essex CM6 3JL
Tel: 01371 822610
Headmaster: Mr Simon James
Age range: 4–13 years

Felsted School
Felsted, Great Dunmow,
Essex CM6 3LL
Tel: +44 (0)1371 822600
Headmaster: Mr Chris Townsend
Age range: 4–18 years

Gosfield School
Cut Hedge Park, Halstead Road,
Gosfield, Halstead, Essex CO9 1PF
Tel: 01787 474040
Head of School: Mr Rod Jackson
Age range: 2–18 years
Fees: Day £7,680–£17,250

Heathcote School
Eves Corner, Danbury,
Chelmsford, Essex CM3 4QB
Tel: 01245 223131
Head of School: Mrs Samantha Scott
Age range: 2–11 years
No. of pupils: 105
Fees: Day £9,450

Holmwood House School
Chitts Hill, Lexden, Colchester,
Essex CO3 9ST
Tel: 01206 574305
Headmaster: Mr Edward Bond
Age range: 6 months–16 years

Littlegarth School
Horkesley Park, Nayland,
Colchester, Essex CO6 4JR
Tel: 01206 262332
Head of School: Ms Kathy Uttley
Age range: 2.5–11 years

Maldon Court Preparatory School
Silver Street, Maldon,
Essex CM9 4QE
Tel: 01621 853529
Headteacher: Elaine Mason
Age range: 1–11 years

New Hall School
The Avenue, Boreham,
Chelmsford, Essex CM3 3HS
Tel: 01245 467588
Principal: Mrs Katherine Jeffrey MA, BA, PGCE, MA(Ed Mg), NPQH
Age range: 1–18 years
No. of pupils: 1400
Fees: Day £9,621–£20,502 WB £18,234–£28,026 FB £21,177–£32,472

Octavia House School, Great Baddow
High Street, Great Baddow,
Essex CM2 7HH
Tel: 020 3651 4396 (option 4)
Assistant Principal: Ms Aboukhshem
Age range: 5–11 years

Oxford House School
2-4 Lexden Road, Colchester,
Essex CO3 3NE
Tel: 01206 576686
Head Teacher: Mrs Sarah Leyshon
Age range: 2.5–11 years

Saint Nicholas School
Hillingdon House, Hobbs Cross Road, Harlow, Essex CM17 0NJ
Tel: 01279 429910
Headmaster: Mr Terence Ayres
Age range: 2.5–16 years

Saint Pierre School
16 Leigh Road, Leigh-on-Sea,
Southend-on-Sea, Essex SS9 1LE
Tel: 01702 474164
Headmaster:
Mr Peter Spencer-Lane
Age range: 2.5–11 years

St Cedd's School
178a New London Road,
Chelmsford, Essex CM2 0AR
Tel: 01245 392810
Head: Mr Matthew Clarke
Age range: 3–11 years
No. of pupils: 400
Fees: Day £9,600–£12,300

St John's School
Stock Road, Billericay,
Essex CM12 0AR
Tel: 01277 623070
Headteacher: Mr A. Angeli BA (Hons)
Age range: 2–16 years

St Margaret's Preparatory School
Hall Drive, Gosfield,
Halstead, Essex CO9 1SE
Tel: 01787 472134
Headteacher: Mrs Carolyn Moss
Age range: 2–11 years
Fees: Day £3,240–£4,055

St Mary's School
91 Lexden Road, Colchester,
Essex CO3 3RB
Tel: 01206 572544
Principal: Mrs Nicola Griffiths
Age range: B3–4 years G3–16 years

St Michael's Church Of England Preparatory School
198 Hadleigh Road, Leigh-on-Sea,
Southend-on-Sea, Essex SS9 2LP
Tel: 01702 478719
Headmaster: Mr James Mobbs
Age range: 3–11 years

St Philomena's Catholic School
Hadleigh Road, Frinton-on-Sea, Essex CO13 9HQ
Tel: 01255 674492
Head of School: Mrs P Mathews ACIS, BA Hons, PGCE, MA, NPQH
Age range: 4–11 years

St. Anne's Preparatory School
154 New London Road,
Chelmsford, Essex CM2 0AW
Tel: 01245 353488
Head of School: Valerie Eveleigh
Age range: 3–11 years

Stephen Perse Junior School, Dame Bradbury's School
Ashdon Road, Saffron Walden, Essex CB10 2AL
Tel: 01223 454700 (Ext: 4000)
Age range: 1–11 years

Thorpe Hall School
Wakering Road, Southend-on-Sea, Essex SS1 3RD
Tel: 01702 582340
Headmaster: Mr Stephen Duckitt
Age range: 2–16 years

TLG Tendring
Frinton Free Church,
Connaught Avenue, Frinton-
on-Sea, Essex CO13 9PW
Tel: 01255 679585
Head of Centre: Mr Ben Pratt
Age range: 11–16 years

Ursuline Preparatory School
Old Great Ropers, Great
Ropers Lane, Warley,
Brentwood, Essex CM13 3HR
Tel: 01277 227152
Headmistress:
Mrs Pauline Wilson MSc
Age range: 3–11 years

Widford Lodge Preparatory School
Widford Road, Chelmsford,
Essex CM2 9AN
Tel: 01245 352581
Headteacher: Miss Michelle Cole
A.C.I.B. – P.G.C.E.
Age range: 2.5–11 years

Woodlands School, Great Warley
Warley Street, Great Warley,
Brentwood, Essex CM13 3LA
Tel: 01277 233288
Head: Mr David Bell
Age range: 2–11 years

Woodlands School, Hutton Manor
428 Rayleigh Road, Hutton,
Brentwood, Essex CM13 1SD
Tel: 01277 245585
Head: Ms Paula Hobbs
Age range: 3–11 years

Hampshire

Alton School
Anstey Lane, Alton,
Hampshire GU34 2NG
Tel: 01420 82070
Headmaster: Mr Karl Guest
Age range: 0–18 years
No. of pupils: 400

Ballard School
Fernhill Lane, New Milton,
Hampshire BH25 5SU
Tel: 01425 626900
Headmaster: Mr Andrew McCleave
Age range: 2–16 years
No. of pupils: 472
Fees: Day £3,105–£5,715

Bedales Prep, Dunhurst & Pre-Prep, Dunannie
Alton Road, Steep, Petersfield,
Hampshire GU32 2DR
Tel: 01730 300200 / 01730 300400
Head of Bedales Prep, Dunhurst:
Mr Colin Baty
Age range: 3–13 years

Bedales School
Church Road, Steep, Petersfield,
Hampshire GU32 2DG
Tel: 01730 300100
Head of School: Mr Will Goldsmith
Age range: 13–18 years

Boundary Oak School
Roche Court, Wickham Road,
Fareham, Hampshire PO17 5BL
Tel: 01329 280955
Executive Headmaster: Mr James
Polansky MA (Cantab) PGCE
Age range: 2–16 years
No. of pupils: 348
Fees: Day £9,195–£14,886 WB
£16,155–£21,078 FB £18,144–£23,067

Brockwood Park School
Brockwood Park, Bramdean,
Alresford, Hampshire SO24 0LQ
Tel: +44 (0)1962 771744
Principal: Mr Antonio Autor
Age range: 14–19 years

Charlton House Independent School
55-57 Midanbury Lane,
Southampton, Hampshire SO18 4DJ
Tel: 023 8067 1739
Head Teacher:
Mr Matthew Robinson
Age range: 9 months–11 years

Churcher's College
Petersfield, Hampshire GU31 4AS
Tel: 01730 263033
Headmaster: Mr Simon Williams ,
MA, BSc
Age range: 3–18 years
Fees: Day £11,535–£17,265

Daneshill School
Stratfield Turgis, Basingstoke,
Hampshire RG27 0AR
Tel: 01256 882707
Head of School: Jim Massey
Age range: 2–13 years
No. of pupils: 303
Fees: Day £11,550–£15,615

Ditcham Park School
Ditcham Park, Petersfield,
Hampshire GU31 5RN
Tel: 01730 825659
Headmaster:
Mr Graham Spawforth MA, MEd
Age range: 2.5–16 years

Durlston Court
Becton Lane, Barton-on-Sea, New
Milton, Hampshire BH25 7AQ
Tel: 01425 610010
Headmaster: Mr Richard May
Age range: 2–16 years
(Year 9 from 2023)
No. of pupils: 260

Embley
Embley Park, Romsey,
Hampshire SO51 6ZE
Tel: 01794 512206
Headteacher: Mr Cliff Canning
Age range: 2–18 years
No. of pupils: 600
Fees: Day £9,165–£17,004 WB
£29,310 FB £9,598–£33,636

Farleigh School
Red Rice, Andover,
Hampshire SP11 7PW
Tel: 01264 710766
Headmaster: Fr Simon Everson
Age range: 3–13 years
No. of pupils: 460

Farnborough Hill
Farnborough Road, Farnborough,
Hampshire GU14 8AT
Tel: 01252 545197
Head: Mrs A Neil BA, MEd, PGCE
Age range: G11–18 years

Fitrah SIPS
55 Northumberland Road,
Southampton, Hampshire SO14 0EJ
Tel: 02380 570 849
Age range: 4–16 years

Forres Sandle Manor
Fordingbridge, Hampshire SP6 1NS
Tel: 01425 653181
Head of School: Mr Robert Tasker
Age range: 2–16 years
No. of pupils: 145

Glenhurst School
16 Beechworth Road, Havant,
Hampshire PO9 1AX
Tel: 023 9248 4054
Age range: 3 months–5 years

Highfield and Brookham School
Highfield Lane, Liphook,
Hampshire GU30 7LQ
Tel: 01428 728000
Headteacher: Mrs Suzannah Cryer
BA (QTS)
Age range: 2–13 years
No. of pupils: 468

Hurst Lodge School
Yateley Hall, Firgrove Road,
Yateley, Hampshire GU46 6HJ
Tel: 01252 227002
Principal: Ms Victoria Smit
Age range: 4–19 years

Inwoods Small School
Brockwood Park, Bramdean,
Alresford, Hampshire SO24 0LQ
Tel: +44 (0)1962 771065
Age range: 5–11 years

King Edward VI School
Wilton Road, Southampton,
Hampshire SO15 5UQ
Tel: 023 8070 4561
Head Master: Mr N T Parker
Age range: 11–18 years
No. of pupils: 965
Fees: Day £18,645

Kingscourt School
182 Five Heads Road,
Catherington, Hampshire PO8 9NJ
Tel: 023 9259 3251
Head of School:
Amanda Bembridge
Age range: 3–11 years
No. of pupils: 158
Fees: Day £2,856

Lord Wandsworth College
Long Sutton, Hook,
Hampshire RG29 1TA
Tel: 01256 862201
Head of School: Mr Adam Williams
Age range: 11–18 years

Madani Academy
Merefield House, Nutfield Place,
Portsmouth, Hampshire PO1 4JZ
Tel: 02392 830764
Headteacher: Mr Luthfur Rahman
Age range: 4–16 years

Mayville High School
35-37 St Simon's Road, Southsea,
Portsmouth, Hampshire PO5 2PE
Tel: 023 9273 4847
Headteacher: Mrs Rebecca Parkyn
Age range: 2–16 years

Meoncross School
Burnt House Lane, Stubbington, Fareham, Hampshire PO14 2EF
Tel: 01329 662182
Headmaster: Mr Mark Cripps
Age range: 2.5–16 years
No. of pupils: 405
Fees: Day £8,736–£12,576

Moyles Court School
Moyles Court, Ringwood, Hampshire BH24 3NF
Tel: 01425 472856
Headmaster:
Mr Richard Milner-Smith
Age range: 2–16 years

Portsmouth High School GDST
Kent Road, Southsea, Portsmouth, Hampshire PO5 3EQ
Tel: 023 9282 6714
Headmistress:
Mrs Jane Prescott BSc NPQH
Age range: G3–18 years
No. of pupils: 500
Fees: Day £2,574–£4,800

Prince's Mead School
Worthy Park House, Kings Worthy, Winchester, Hampshire SO21 1AN
Tel: 01962 888000
Headmaster: Mr Peter Thacker
Age range: 3–11 years

Ringwood Waldorf School
Folly Farm Lane, Ashley, Ringwood, Hampshire BH24 2NN
Tel: 01425 472664
Age range: 3–18 years

Rookwood School
Weyhill Road, Andover, Hampshire SP10 3AL
Tel: 01264 325900
Headmaster: Mr A Kirk-Burgess BSc, PGCE, MSc (Oxon)
Age range: 2–18 years (boarding from 7)

Salesian College
119 Reading Road, Farnborough, Hampshire GU14 6PA
Tel: 01252 893000
Headmaster: Mr Gerard Owens
Age range: B11–18 years G16–18 years

Sherborne House School
39 Lakewood Road, Chandlers Ford, Eastleigh, Hampshire SO53 1EU
Tel: 02380 252440
Headmaster: Mr Mark Beach
Age range: 6 months–11 years

Sherfield School
South Drive, Sherfield-on-Loddon, Hook, Hampshire RG27 0HU
Tel: 01256 884800
Headmaster: Mr Nick Brain BA(Hons), PGCE, MA, NPQH
Age range: 3 months–18 years (boarding from 9)
No. of pupils: 625

St Neot's School
St Neot's Road, Eversley, Hampshire RG27 0PN
Tel: 0118 9739650
Headmaster: Mr Jonathan Slot
Age range: 2–13 years

St Nicholas' School
Redfields House, Redfields Lane, Church Crookham, Fleet, Hampshire GU52 0RF
Tel: 01252 850121
Headmistress: Dr O Wright PhD, MA, BA Hons, PGCE
Age range: B3–7 years G3–16 years

St Swithun's Prep
Alresford Road, Winchester, Hampshire SO21 1HA
Tel: 01962 835750
Head of School (retiring summer 2023): Mr Jonathan Brough
Age range: B3–4 years G3–11 years
No. of pupils: 209

ST SWITHUN'S SCHOOL
For further details see p. 97
Alresford Road, Winchester, Hampshire SO21 1HA
Tel: 01962 835700
Email: office@stswithuns.com
Website: www.stswithuns.com
Head of School:
Jane Gandee MA(Cantab)
Age range: G11–18 years
No. of pupils: 492 VIth137
Fees: Day £23,478 FB £39,492

Stockton House School
Stockton Avenue, Fleet, Hampshire GU51 4NS
Tel: 01252 616323
Early Years Manager: Mrs Jenny Bounds BA EYPS
Age range: 2–5 years

Stroud School, King Edward VI Preparatory
Highwood House, Highwood Lane, Romsey, Hampshire SO51 9ZH
Tel: 01794 513231
Headmistress: Mrs Rebecca Smith
Age range: 3–13 years
Fees: Day £4,060–£6,515

The Gregg Prep School
17-19 Winn Road, Southampton, Hampshire SO17 1EJ
Tel: 023 8055 7352
Headteacher: Mr M Pascoe
Age range: 4–11 years

The Gregg School
Townhill Park House, Cutbush Lane, Southampton, Hampshire SO18 3RR
Tel: 023 8047 2133
Headteacher: Mrs S Sellers
Age range: 11–16 years

The King's School
Lakesmere House, Allington Lane, Fair Oak, Eastleigh, Southampton, Hampshire SO50 7DB
Tel: 023 8060 0986
Headteacher: Mrs Heather Bowden
Age range: 4–16 years

The New Forest Small School
1 Southampton Road, Lyndhurst, Hampshire SO43 7BU
Tel: 02380 284415
Headteacher: Ms Maz Wilberforce
Age range: 3–16 years

The Pilgrims' School
3 The Close, Winchester, Hampshire SO23 9LT
Tel: 01962 854189
Interim Head of School: Mr Alistair Duncan
Age range: B4–13 years

The Portsmouth Grammar School
High Street, Portsmouth, Hampshire PO1 2LN
Tel: +44 (0)23 9236 0036
Age range: 2.5–18 years

Thorngrove School
The Mount, Highclere, Newbury, Hampshire RG20 9PS
Tel: 01635 253172
Headmaster: Mr Adam King
Age range: 2.5–13 years

Twyford School
Twyford, Winchester, Hampshire SO21 1NW
Tel: 01962 712269
Headmaster: Mr Andrew Harvey
Age range: 2–13 years

Walhampton
Walhampton, Lymington, Hampshire SO41 5ZG
Tel: 01590 613300
Head: Mr Jonny Timms
Age range: 2–13 years (boarding from 7)

West Hill Park School
St Margaret's Lane, Titchfield, Hampshire PO14 4BS
Tel: 01329 842356
Headmaster: Mr Chris Ward
Age range: 3–13 years

Winchester College
College Street, Winchester, Hampshire SO23 9NA
Tel: 01962 621100
Headmaster: Dr. T R Hands
Age range: B13–18 years (boarding from 13)

Yateley Manor School
51 Reading Road, Yateley, Hampshire GU46 7UQ
Tel: 01252 405500
Headmaster: Mr Robert Upton
Age range: 3–13 years

Hertfordshire

Abbot's Hill School
Bunkers Lane, Hemel Hempstead, Hertfordshire HP3 8RP
Tel: 01442 240333
Headmistress: Mrs K Gorman BA, MEd (Cantab)
Age range: G4–16 years
No. of pupils: 482

Aldenham School
Elstree, Hertfordshire WD6 3AJ
Tel: 01923 858122
Headmaster: Mr James Fowler
Age range: 3–18 years

Aldwickbury School
Wheathampstead Road, Harpenden, Hertfordshire AL5 1AD
Tel: 01582 713022
Headmaster: Mr Paul Symes
Age range: B4–13 years

Beechwood Park School
Beechwood Park, Pickford Lane, Markyate, Nr St Albans, Hertfordshire AL3 8AW
Tel: 01582 840333
Head of School (until July 2023): Mrs Maureen Cussans
Age range: 3 months–13 years
No. of pupils: 529
Fees: Day £13,170

BERKHAMSTED SCHOOL
For further details see p. 84
Overton House, 131 High Street, Berkhamsted, Hertfordshire HP4 2DJ
Tel: 01442 358001
Email: admissions@berkhamsted.com
Website: www.berkhamsted.com
Principal: Mr Richard Backhouse MA(Cantab)
Age range: 3–18 years
No. of pupils: 1883 VIth411
Fees: Day £10,110–£23,175 WB £31,500 FB £37,575

Bishop's Stortford College
School House, Maze Green Road, Bishop's Stortford, Hertfordshire CM23 2PQ
Tel: +44 (0)1279 838575
College Head: Ms Kathy Crewe-Read
Age range: 13–18 years

Bishop's Stortford College Prep School
School House, Maze Green Road, Bishop's Stortford, Hertfordshire CM23 2PQ
Tel: +44 (0)1279 838583
Head of the Prep School: Mr Bill Toleman
Age range: 4–13 years

Charlotte House Preparatory School
88 The Drive, Rickmansworth, Hertfordshire WD3 4DU
Tel: 01923 772101
Head: Miss P Woodcock
Age range: G3–11 years

Duncombe School
4 Warren Park Road, Bengeo, Hertford, Hertfordshire SG14 3JA
Tel: 01992 414100
Headmaster: Mr Jeremy Phelan M.A. (Ed)
Age range: 2–11 years
No. of pupils: 301
Fees: Day £10,380–£14,565

Edge Grove School
Aldenham Village, Watford, Hertfordshire WD25 8NL
Tel: 01923 855724
Head of School: Mr Ed Balfour
Age range: 3–13 years
No. of pupils: 500

Egerton Rothesay School
Durrants Lane, Berkhamsted, Hertfordshire HP4 3UJ
Tel: 01442 865275
Headteacher: Mr Colin Parker BSc(Hons), Dip.Ed (Oxon), PGCE, C.Math MIMA
Age range: 6–19 years

Gurukula – The Hare Krishna Primary School
Hartspring Cottage, Elton Way, Watford, Hertfordshire WD25 8HB
Tel: 01923 851 005
Head of School: Ms Gunacuda Dasi (Gwyneth Milan)
Age range: 4–12 years

Haberdashers' Boys' School
Butterfly Lane, Elstree, Borehamwood, Hertfordshire WD6 3AF
Tel: 020 8266 1700
Headmaster: Mr Gus Lock
Age range: B4–18 years
No. of pupils: 1500

Haberdashers' Girls' School
Aldenham Road, Elstree, Borehamwood, Hertfordshire WD6 3BT
Tel: 020 8266 2300
Headmistress: Mrs Rose Hardy
Age range: G4–18 years
No. of pupils: 1200

Haileybury
Haileybury, Hertford, Hertfordshire SG13 7NU
Tel: +44 (0)1992 706353
The Master: Mr Martin Collier MA BA PGCE
Age range: 11–18 years (boarding from 11)
No. of pupils: 902 VIth357
Fees: Day £6,595–£9,920 FB £8,615–£13,580

Heath Mount School
Woodhall Park, Watton-at-Stone, Hertford, Hertfordshire SG14 3NG
Tel: 01920 830230
Headmaster: Mr Chris Gillam BEd(Hons)
Age range: 3–13 years
No. of pupils: 492 B270 G222
Fees: Day £12,435–£19,185

Howe Green House School
Great Hallingbury, Bishop's Stortford, Hertfordshire CM22 7UF
Tel: 01279 657706
Headmistress: Ms Deborah Mills BA (Hons) Q.T.S
Age range: 2–11 years
No. of pupils: 177
Fees: Day £433–£4,313

Immanuel College
87/91 Elstree Road, Bushey, Hertfordshire WD23 4EB
Tel: 020 8950 0604
Head: Mr Mike Buchanan
Age range: 4–18 years

Kingshott
Stevenage Road, St Ippolyts, Hitchin, Hertfordshire SG4 7JX
Tel: 01462 432009
Headmaster: Mr David Weston
Age range: 3–13 years
No. of pupils: 400
Fees: Day £6,555–£14,115

Little Acorns Montessori School
Building 19 & 21, The Lincolnsfield Centre, Bushey Hall Drive, Bushey, Hertfordshire WD23 2ES
Tel: 01923 230705
Age range: 3 months–5 years

Lochinver House School
Heath Road, Little Heath, Potters Bar, Hertfordshire EN6 1LW
Tel: 01707 653064
Headmaster: Mr Ben Walker BA(Hons)
Age range: B4–13 years
No. of pupils: 345
Fees: Day £12,060–£15,840

Lockers Park
Lockers Park Lane, Hemel Hempstead, Hertfordshire HP1 1TL
Tel: 01442 251712
Headmaster: Mr Gavin Taylor
Age range: B4–13 years
No. of pupils: 171
Fees: Day £11,505–£18,225 WB £26,325

Longwood School
Bushey Hall Drive, Bushey, Hertfordshire WD23 2QG
Tel: 01923 253715
Headteacher: Ms Claire May
Age range: 3 months–11 years

Manor Lodge School
Rectory Lane, Ridge Hill, Shenley, Hertfordshire WD7 9BG
Tel: 01707 642424
Head Teacher: Mrs A Lobo BEd(Hons)
Age range: 3–11 years
No. of pupils: 456
Fees: Day £3,820–£4,500

Merchant Taylors' Prep
Moor Farm, Sandy Lodge Road, Rickmansworth, Hertfordshire WD3 1LW
Tel: 01923 825648
Head of School: Dr Karen McNerney
Age range: B3–13 years

Queenswood
Shepherd's Way, Brookmans Park, Hatfield, Hertfordshire AL9 6NS
Tel: 01707 602500
Principal: Mrs Jo Cameron
Age range: G11–18 years (boarding from 11)
No. of pupils: 418
Fees: Day £7,115–£8,440 WB 7,325–10,615 FB £8,395–£11,810

Radlett Preparatory School
Kendal Hall, Watling Street, Radlett, Hertfordshire WD7 7LY
Tel: 01923 856812
Principal: Mr M Pipe BA Hons, QTS
Age range: 4–11 years

Sherrardswood School
Lockleys, Welwyn,
Hertfordshire AL6 0BJ
Tel: 01438 714282
Headmistress: Mrs Anna Wright
Age range: 2–18 years

St Albans High School for Girls
Townsend Avenue, St Albans,
Hertfordshire AL1 3SJ
Tel: 01727 853800
Head: Ms Amber Waite
Age range: G4–18 years

St Albans Independent College
69 London Road, St Albans,
Hertfordshire AL1 1LN
Tel: 01727 842348
Principals:
Mr. A N Jemal & Mr Elvis Cotena
Age range: 14–19 years

St Albans School
Abbey Gateway, St Albans,
Hertfordshire AL3 4HB
Tel: 01727 855521
Headmaster: Mr JWJ Gillespie
MA(Cantab), FRSA
Age range: B11–18 years
G16–18 years

St Christopher School
Barrington Road, Letchworth
Garden City, Hertfordshire SG6 3JZ
Tel: 01462 650 850
Head of School:
Ms Emma-Kate Henry
Age range: 3–18 years

St Columba's College
King Harry Lane, St Albans,
Hertfordshire AL3 4AW
Tel: 01727 892040
Head: Mr David Shannon-Little
Age range: 4–18 years
No. of pupils: 805

St Edmund's College & Prep School
Old Hall Green, Nr Ware,
Hertfordshire SG11 1DS
Tel: 01920 824247
Headmaster: Mr Matthew Mostyn
BA (Hons) MA (Ed)
Age range: 3–18 years
(boarding from 11)

St Francis' College
Broadway, Letchworth Garden
City, Hertfordshire SG6 3PJ
Tel: 01462 670511
Headmistress: Mrs B Goulding
Age range: G3–18 years
(boarding from 10)

St Hilda's School
28 Douglas Road, Harpenden,
Hertfordshire AL5 2ES
Tel: 01582 712307
Headmaster: Mr Dan Sayers
Age range: B2.5–4 years
G2.5–11 years
No. of pupils: 150
Fees: Day £3,285–£4,260

St Hilda's School, Bushey
High Street, Bushey,
Hertfordshire WD23 3DA
Tel: 020 8950 1751
Headmistress:
Miss Sarah-Jane Styles MA
Age range: B2–4 years G2–11 years

St Joseph's In The Park
St Mary's Lane, Hertingfordbury,
Hertford, Hertfordshire SG14 2LX
Tel: 01992 513810
Head of School: Mr Douglas Brown
Age range: 2–11 years

St Margaret's School, Bushey
Merry Hill Road, Bushey,
Hertfordshire WD23 1DT
Tel: +44 (0)20 8416 4400
Headteacher: Lara Péchard
Age range: 2–18 years
No. of pupils: 650

St. John's Prep School
The Ridgeway, Potters Bar,
Hertfordshire EN6 5QT
Tel: +44 (0)1707 657294
Head Teacher: Mrs C Tardios
Age range: 3–11 years

Stanborough Primary School
Appletree Walk, Watford,
Hertfordshire WD25 0DQ
Tel: 01923 673291
Head of School: Mrs T Madden
Age range: 3–11 years

Stanborough Secondary School
Stanborough Park, Garston,
Watford, Hertfordshire WD25 9JT
Tel: 01923 673268
Interim Head: Mr K. James
Age range: 11–18 years

Stormont
The Causeway, Potters Bar,
Hertfordshire EN6 5HA
Tel: 01707 654037
Head Teacher: Miss Louise Martin
Age range: G4–11 years

The Christian School (Takeley)
Dunmow Road, Brewers End,
Takeley, Bishop's Stortford,
Hertfordshire CM22 6QH
Tel: 01279 871182
Headmaster: Mr M E Humphries
Age range: 3–16 years

The King's School
Elmfield, Ambrose Lane,
Harpenden, Hertfordshire AL5 4DU
Tel: 01582 767566
Headteacher: Mr Andy Reeves
Age range: 2–16 years

The Purcell School, London
Aldenham Road, Bushey,
Hertfordshire WD23 2TS
Tel: 01923 331100
Principal: Mr Paul Bambrough
Age range: 10–18 years

Tring Park School for the Performing Arts
Mansion Drive, Tring,
Hertfordshire HP23 5LX
Tel: 01442 824255
Principal: Mr Stefan Anderson MA,
ARCM, ARCT
Age range: 8–19 years
No. of pupils: 370 Vlth171
Fees: Day £15,405–£24,885
FB £26,190–£37,605

Westbrook Hay Prep School
London Road, Hemel Hempstead,
Hertfordshire HP1 2RF
Tel: 01442 256143
Headmaster: Mark Brain
Age range: 3–13 years
No. of pupils: 340
Fees: Day £10,905–£15,690

York House School
Sarratt Road, Croxley
Green, Rickmansworth,
Hertfordshire WD3 4LW
Tel: 01923 772395
Headmaster: Mr Jon Gray BA(Ed)
Age range: 3–13 years
No. of pupils: 395
Fees: Day £3,876–£5,164

Kent

Ashford School
East Hill, Ashford, Kent TN24 8PB
Tel: +44 (0)1233 625171
Head: Mr Michael Hall
Age range: 3 months–18 years (boarding from 11)
No. of pupils: 1034 VIth140
Fees: Day £9,030–£19,026 WB £27,846 FB £38,778
🧗 Ⓐ 🏫 £ 🖉 16⁺

Beech Grove School
Forest Drive, Nonington, Dover, Kent CT15 4FB
Tel: 01304 843 707
Headteacher: Timothy Maas
Age range: 6–18 years

Beechwood School
12 Pembury Road, Tunbridge Wells, Kent TN2 3QD
Tel: 01892 532747
Headmaster: Mr Justin Foster-Gandey
Age range: 3–18 years
🏫 🖉 16⁺

Benenden School
Cranbrook, Kent TN17 4AA
Tel: 01580 240592
Headmistress: Ms Samantha Price
Age range: G11–18 years (boarding from 11)
🧗 🌐 🏫 🖉 16⁺

Bethany School
Curtisden Green, Goudhurst, Cranbrook, Kent TN17 1LB
Tel: 01580 211273
Headmaster: Mr Francie Healy BSc, HDipEd, NPQH
Age range: 11–18 years
No. of pupils: 346 VIth77
Fees: Day £18,795–£20,760 WB £29,175–£32,205 FB £31,455–£35,400
🌐 Ⓐ 🏫 £ 🖉 16⁺

Bronte School
7 Pelham Road, Gravesend, Kent DA11 0HU
Tel: 01474 533805
Headmistress: Ms Emma Wood
Age range: 4–11 years
🖉

Bryony School
Marshall Road, Rainham, Gillingham, Kent ME8 0AJ
Tel: 01634 231511
Head of School: Mrs N Gee
Age range: 2–11 years
🖉

Chartfield School
45 Minster Road, Westgate on Sea, Kent CT8 8DA
Tel: 01843 831716
Head & Proprietor: Miss L P Shipley
Age range: 3–11 years
🖉

COBHAM HALL SCHOOL
For further details see p. 85
Brewers Road, Cobham, Kent DA12 3BL
Tel: 01474 823371
Email: admissions@cobhamhall.com
Website: www.cobhamhall.com
Headteacher: Mrs Wendy Barrett
Age range: B16–18 years G11–18 years (boarding from 11)
No. of pupils: 150
Fees: Day £7,100–£8,250 FB £11,500–£13,250
🧗 🌐 🏫 £ 🖉 16⁺

Dover College
Effingham Crescent, Dover, Kent CT17 9RH
Tel: 01304 205969
Head of School: Mr Simon Fisher
Age range: 3–18 years
🌐 🏫 🖉 16⁺

Dulwich Prep Cranbrook
Coursehorn, Cranbrook, Kent TN17 3NP
Tel: 01580 712179
Headmaster: Mr Paul David BEd(Hons)
Age range: 2–16 years
🏫 🖉

EARLSCLIFFE
For further details see p. 87
29 Shorncliffe Road, Folkestone, Kent CT20 2NB
Tel: 01303 253951
Email: admissions@earlscliffe.co.uk
Website: www.earlscliffe.co.uk
Headteacher: Mr Joss Williams
Age range: 15–19 years
No. of pupils: 130
Fees: Day £9,100 WB £11,745 FB £13,650
🌐 Ⓐ 🏫

Fosse Bank School
Mountains, Noble Tree Road, Hildenborough, Tonbridge, Kent TN11 8ND
Tel: 01732 834212
Acting Head: Mrs Shiralee Davies
Age range: 2–11 years
£

Gad's Hill School
Gravesend Road, Higham, Rochester, Kent ME3 7PA
Tel: 01474 822366
Headmaster: Mr Paul Savage
Age range: 3–16 years

Haddon Dene School
57 Gladstone Road, Broadstairs, Kent CT10 2HY
Tel: 01843 861176
Headmistress: Mrs Joanne Parpworth
Age range: 3–11 years
🖉

Hilden Grange School
62 Dry Hill Park Road, Tonbridge, Kent TN10 3BX
Tel: 01732 352706
Headmaster: Mr Malcolm Gough
Age range: 3–13 years
🖉

Hilden Oaks Preparatory School & Nursery
38 Dry Hill Park Road, Tonbridge, Kent TN10 3BU
Tel: 01732 353941
Head of School: Mrs. K Joiner
Age range: 3 months–11 years
£ 🖉

Holmewood House School
Barrow Lane, Langton Green, Tunbridge Wells, Kent TN3 0EB
Tel: 01892 860000
Head of School: Mrs Ruth O'Sullivan
Age range: 3–13 years
No. of pupils: 450
🏫 £ 🖉

Kent College Pembury
Old Church Road, Pembury, Tunbridge Wells, Kent TN2 4AX
Tel: +44 (0)1892 822006
Head of School: Miss Katrina Handford
Age range: G3–18 years (boarding from 8)
No. of pupils: 500
Fees: Day £22,575 WB £28,200 FB £35,700
🧗 🌐 Ⓐ 🏫 £ 🖉 16⁺

Kent College, Canterbury
Whitstable Road, Canterbury, Kent CT2 9DT
Tel: +44 (0)1227 763 231
Head of Kent College: Mr Mark Turnbull
Age range: 3 months–18 years (boarding from 8 years)
No. of pupils: 800
Fees: Day £6,029–£6,932 FB £9,326–£12,883
🌐 Ⓐ 🏫 £ IB 🖉 16⁺

Kids Inc Day Nursery – Bluewater
West Village, Bluewater, Greenhithe, Kent DA9 9SE
Tel: 01322 386624

King's School Rochester
Satis House, Boley Hill, Rochester, Kent ME1 1TE
Tel: 01634 888555
Principal: Mr B Charles
Age range: 3–18 years
No. of pupils: 638 VIth101
Fees: Day £3,770–£7,175 FB £8,175–£11,775
🌐 Ⓐ 🏫 £ 🖉 16⁺

Lorenden Preparatory School
Painter's Forstal, Faversham, Kent ME13 0EN
Tel: 01795 590030
Head of School: Mr Richard McIntosh
Age range: 3–11 years
No. of pupils: 122
£ 🖉

Marlborough House School
High Street, Hawkhurst, Kent TN18 4PY
Tel: 01580 753555
Head: Mr Eddy Newton
Age range: 2.5–13 years
No. of pupils: 250
Fees: Day £9,165–£18,690
🏫 £ 🖉

Northbourne Park School
Betteshanger, Deal, Kent CT14 0NW
Tel: 01304 611215
Headmaster: Mr Sebastian Rees BA(Hons), PGCE, NPQH
Age range: 2–13 years (boarding from 7)
No. of pupils: 188
Fees: Day £9,243–£17,607 WB £22,161 FB £25,659
🏫 £ 🖉

OneSchool Global UK Maidstone Campus
Heath Road, Maidstone, Kent ME17 4HT
Tel: 03000 700 507
Age range: 7–18 years

Radnor House, Sevenoaks
Combe Bank Drive, Sevenoaks, Kent TN14 6AE
Tel: 01959 563720
Head of School: Mr Fraser Halliwell
Age range: 2–18 years
🖉 16⁺

Rochester Independent College
254 St Margaret's Banks, Rochester, Kent ME1 1HY
Tel: +44 (0)163 482 8115
Head of School: Mr Alistair Brownlow
Age range: 11–18 years
🌐 16⁺ 🏫

Rose Hill School
Coniston Avenue, Tunbridge Wells, Kent TN4 9SY
Tel: 01892 525591
Head: Ms Emma Neville
Age range: 3–13 years
🖉

Russell House School
Station Road, Otford, Sevenoaks, Kent TN14 5QU
Tel: 01959 522352
Headmaster: Mr Craig McCarthy
Age range: 2–11 years

Sackville School
Tonbridge Road, Hildenborough,
Tonbridge, Kent TN11 9HN
Tel: 01732 838888
Headteacher: Ms Leoni Ellis
Age range: 11–18 years

Saint Ronan's School
Water Lane, Hawkhurst,
Kent TN18 5DJ
Tel: 01580 752271
Headmaster: Mr William Trelawny-
Vernon BSc(Hons)
Age range: 3–13 years

Sevenoaks Preparatory School
Godden Green, Sevenoaks,
Kent TN15 0JU
Tel: 01732 762336
Headmaster: Mr Luke Harrison
Age range: 2–13 years

Sevenoaks School
High Street, Sevenoaks,
Kent TN13 1HU
Tel: +44 (0)1732 455133
Head of School: Mr Jesse R Elzinga
AB MSt FCCT
Age range: 11–18 years
No. of pupils: 1189
Fees: Day £26,721–£30,348
FB £42,921–£46,566

Solefield School
Solefields Road, Sevenoaks,
Kent TN13 1PH
Tel: 01732 452142
Headmistress: Ms Helen McClure
Age range: B4–13 years

Somerhill
Tonbridge, Kent TN11 0NJ
Tel: 01732 352124
Principal: Mr Duncan Sinclair
Age range: 2–13 years

Spring Grove School
Harville Road, Wye, Kent TN25 5EZ
Tel: 01233 812337
Head of School:
Mrs Therésa Jaggard
Age range: 2–11 years
No. of pupils: 229
Fees: Day £9,780–£13,775

St Andrew's School
24-28 Watts Avenue, Rochester,
Medway, Kent ME1 1SA
Tel: 01634 843479
Principal: Mrs E Steinmann-Gilbert
Age range: 2.5–11 years

St Edmund's School
St Thomas Hill, Canterbury,
Kent CT2 8HU
Tel: 01227 475601
Head: Mr Edward O'Connor MA
(Cantab), MPhil (Oxon), MEd
(Cantab)
Age range: 2–18 years
(boarding from 11)
No. of pupils: 602

St Faith's Prep
5 The Street, Ash, Canterbury,
Kent CT3 2HH
Tel: 01304 813409
Headmaster: Mr Lawrence Groves
Age range: 2–11 years

St Lawrence College
College Road, Ramsgate,
Kent CT11 7AE
Tel: 01843 572931
Head of College: Mr Barney Durrant
Age range: 3–18 years
No. of pupils: 585
Fees: Day £8,394–£18,558
FB £29,454–£38,952

St Michael's Preparatory School
Otford Court, Row Dow, Otford,
Sevenoaks, Kent TN14 5RY
Tel: 01959 522137
Head: Mr Nik Pears
Age range: 2–13 years

Steephill School
Off Castle Hill, Fawkham,
Longfield, Kent DA3 7BG
Tel: 01474 702107
Head: Mr John Abbott
Age range: 3–11 years

Sutton Valence Preparatory School
Church Road, Chart Sutton,
Maidstone, Kent ME17 3RF
Tel: 01622 842117
Head: Miss C Corkran
Age range: 2–11 years

Sutton Valence School
North Street, Sutton
Valence, Kent ME17 3HL
Tel: 01622 845200
Headmaster: Mr James A Thomas
MA (Cantab) MA (London) NPQH
Age range: 11–18 years
(boarding from 11)
No. of pupils: 557

The Granville School
2 Bradbourne Park Road,
Sevenoaks, Kent TN13 3LJ
Tel: 01732 453039
Headmistress: Mrs Louise Lawrance
B. Prim. Ed. (Hons)
Age range: B3–4 years G3–11 years

The Junior King's School, Canterbury
Milner Court, Sturry,
Canterbury, Kent CT2 0AY
Tel: 01227 714000
Head of School: Ms Emma Károlyi
Age range: 3–13 years

The King's School, Canterbury
Lattergate Office, 25 The Precincts,
Canterbury, Kent CT1 2ES
Tel: 01227 595501
Head of School: Ms Jude Lowson
Age range: 13–18 years

The Mead School
16 Frant Road, Tunbridge
Wells, Kent TN2 5SN
Tel: 01892 525837
Headmistress:
Ms Catherine Openshaw
Age range: 3–11 years

The New Beacon School
Brittains Lane, Sevenoaks,
Kent TN13 2PB
Tel: 01732 452131
Headmaster: Mr Mike Piercy
Age range: B3–13 years G3–4 years
No. of pupils: 350

The Worthgate School
68 New Dover Road,
Canterbury, Kent CT1 3LQ
Tel: +44 (0)1227 866540
Acting Principal:
Dr Nicola Robinson
Age range: 13–21 years
No. of pupils: 450
Fees: Day £17,370–£27,990
FB £13,230–£19,140

TONBRIDGE SCHOOL
For further details see p. 100
High Street, Tonbridge,
Kent TN9 1JP
Tel: 01732 304297
Email:
admissions@tonbridge-school.org
Website:
www.tonbridge-school.co.uk
Headmaster: Mr James Priory
MA (Oxon)
Age range: B13–18 years
No. of pupils: 795
Fees: Day £35,067 FB £46,740

Walthamstow Hall School
Holly Bush Lane, Sevenoaks,
Kent TN13 3UL
Tel: 01732 451334
Headmistress: Miss Stephanie Ferro
Age range: G3–18 years

Wellesley House
114 Ramsgate Road,
Broadstairs, Kent CT10 2DG
Tel: 01843 862991
Headmaster: Mr G D Franklin
Age range: 2–13 years

Surrey

ABERDOUR SCHOOL
For further details see p. 80
Brighton Road, Burgh Heath,
Tadworth, Surrey KT20 6AJ
Tel: +44 (0)1737 354119
Email:
enquiries@aberdourschool.co.uk
Website:
www.aberdourschool.co.uk
Headmaster: Mr S. D. Collins
Age range: 2–11 years
No. of pupils: 335
Fees: Day £4,920–£17,070
£ 🖋

ACS Cobham International School
Heywood, Portsmouth Road,
Cobham, Surrey KT11 1BL
Tel: +44 (0) 1932 867251
Head of School:
Mr Barnaby Sandow
Age range: 2–18 years
🌐 🏛 IB 🖋 16+

ACS Egham International School
London Road, Egham,
Surrey TW20 0HS
Tel: +44 (0) 1784 430800
Head of School: Mr Jeremy Lewis
Age range: 4–18 years
🌐 IB 🖋 16+

Aldro School
Lombard Street, Shackleford,
Godalming, Surrey GU8 6AS
Tel: 01483 810266
Headmaster: Mr Chris Carlier
Age range: 7–13 years
🏛

Amesbury School
Hazel Grove, Hindhead,
Surrey GU26 6BL
Tel: 01428 604322
Head of School:
Mr Jonathan Whybrow
Age range: 2–13 years
🏛 £ 🖋

Banstead Preparatory School
Sutton Lane, Banstead,
Surrey SM7 3RA
Tel: 01737 363601
Head of School: Mr Jon Chesworth
Age range: 2–11 years

Barfield School
Guildford Road, Runfold,
Farnham, Surrey GU10 1PB
Tel: 01252 782271
Headmaster: Mr Andy Boyle
Age range: 2–11 years
🖋

Barrow Hills School
Roke Lane, Witley, Godalming,
Surrey GU8 5NY
Tel: +44 (0)1428 683639
Headmaster: Mr Philip Oldroyd
Age range: 2–13 years
No. of pupils: 216
Fees: Day £16,785
£ 🖋

BELMONT SCHOOL
For further details see p. 81
Pasturewood Road, Holmbury St
Mary, Dorking, Surrey RH5 6LQ
Tel: 01306 730852
Email:
admissions@belmont-school.org
Website:
www.belmont-school.org
Headteacher: Mrs Helen Skrine
BA, PGCE, NPQH, FRSA
Age range: 3–16 years
No. of pupils: 190

Bishopsgate School
Bishopsgate Road, Englefield
Green, Egham, Surrey TW20 0YJ
Tel: 01784 432109
Headmaster: Mr R Williams
Age range: 3–13 years
No. of pupils: 370
£ 🖋

Box Hill School
London Road, Mickleham,
Dorking, Surrey RH5 6EA
Tel: 01372 373382
Headmaster: Cory Lowde
Age range: 11–18 years
No. of pupils: 410
Fees: Day £21,585 WB £31,635
🌐 🏛 £ IB 🖋 16+

Caterham School
Harestone Valley Road,
Caterham, Surrey CR3 6YA
Tel: 01883 343028
Headmaster:
Mr C. W. Jones MA(Cantab)
Age range: 3–18 years
🌐 A 🏛 £ 🖋 16+

Charterhouse
Godalming, Surrey GU7 2DX
Tel: +44 (0)1483 291501
Head: Dr Alex Peterken
Age range: B13–18 years
(boarding from 13) G16–18 years
No. of pupils: 940
Fees: Day £12,180 FB £14,740
🎖 🌐 A 🏛 £ IB 🖋 16+

Chinthurst School
52 Tadworth Street, Tadworth,
Surrey KT20 5QZ
Tel: 01737 812011
Head: Miss Catherine Trundle
Age range: 3–11 years
🖋

City of London Freemen's School
Ashtead Park, Ashtead,
Surrey KT21 1ET
Tel: +44 (0)1372 822400
Headmaster: Mr Roland J. Martin
Age range: 7–18 years
🌐 A 🏛 £ 🖋 16+

Claremont Fan Court School
Claremont Drive, Esher,
Surrey KT10 9LY
Tel: 01372 473794
Head: Mr William Brierly
Age range: 2.5–18 years
No. of pupils: 1100
A £ 🖋 16+

Coworth Flexlands School
Chertsey Road, Chobham,
Surrey GU24 8TE
Tel: 01276 855707
Head of School: Miss Nicola Cowell
Age range: 2.5–11 years
No. of pupils: 120
🖋

Cranleigh School
Horseshoe Lane, Cranleigh,
Surrey GU6 8QQ
Tel: +44 (0) 1483 273666
Headmaster: Mr Martin Reader
MA, MPhil, MBA
Age range: 7–18 years
(including Prep School)
No. of pupils: 683 VIth256
Fees: Day £35,175 FB £42,720
🌐 A 🏛 £ 🖋 16+

Cranmore School
Epsom Road, West Horsley,
Surrey KT24 6AT
Tel: 01483 280340
Headmaster: Mr Barry Everitt
Age range: 2–18 years
A 🖋

Danes Hill School
Leatherhead Road, Oxshott,
Surrey KT22 0JG
Tel: 01372 842509
Head of School: Mrs Maxine Shaw
Age range: 3–13 years
No. of pupils: 706
Fees: Day £4,952–£6,984
£ 🖋

Danesfield Manor School
Rydens Avenue, Walton-on-
Thames, Surrey KT12 3JB
Tel: 01932 220930
Head Teacher: Mrs Jo Smith
Age range: 2–11 years
🖋

Downsend School
1 Leatherhead Road,
Leatherhead, Surrey KT22 8TJ
Tel: 01372 372197
Headmaster: Mr Ian Thorpe
Age range: 2–16 years
No. of pupils: 792
Fees: Day £11,970–£17,985
🖋

Drayton House Nursery School
35 Austen Road, Guildford,
Surrey GU1 3NP
Tel: 01483 504707
Headmistress:
Ms Jennifer Tyson-Jones
Age range: 6 months–5 years
🖋

Duke of Kent School
Peaslake Road, Ewhurst,
Surrey GU6 7NS
Tel: 01483 277313
Head: Mrs Sue Knox BA(Hons) MBA
MEd
Age range: 3–16 years
No. of pupils: 316
Fees: Day £2,740–£6,540
🌐 £ 🖋

Dunottar School
High Trees Road, Reigate,
Surrey RH2 7EL
Tel: 01737 761945
Headmaster: Mr Mark Tottman
Age range: 11–18 years
A £ 16+

Edgeborough
84 Frensham Road, Frensham,
Farnham, Surrey GU10 3AH
Tel: 01252 792495
Headmaster: Mr Daniel Cox
Age range: 2–13 years
(boarding from 7)
No. of pupils: 370
🏛 🖋

Epsom College
College Road, Epsom,
Surrey KT17 4JQ
Tel: 01372 821000
Acting Headmaster: Mr Paul
Williams
Age range: 11–18 years
(boarding from 13)
🌐 A 🏛 £ 🖋 16+

Essendene Lodge School
Essendene Road, Caterham,
Surrey CR3 5PB
Tel: 01883 348349
Headteacher: Mrs K Ali
Age range: 2–11 years
🖋

Ewell Castle School
Church Street, Ewell, Epsom,
Surrey KT17 2AW
Tel: 020 8393 1413
Principal: Mr Silas Edmonds
Age range: 3–18 years
No. of pupils: 670
Fees: Day £5,382–£18,141

(A) (£) (16)

Feltonfleet School
Byfleet Road, Cobham,
Surrey KT11 1DR
Tel: 01932 862264
Headmistress: Mrs Shelley Lance
Age range: 3–13 years
(boarding from 7)
No. of pupils: 492

Frensham Heights
Rowledge, Farnham,
Surrey GU10 4EA
Tel: 01252 792561
Head: Mr Rick Clarke
Age range: 3–18 years
(boarding from 11)

Glenesk School
Ockham Road North, East
Horsley, Surrey KT24 6NS
Tel: 01483 282329
Headmistress: Mrs Sarah Bradley
Age range: 2–7 years
No. of pupils: 120
Fees: Day £12,762–£14,424

Gordon's School
West End, Woking, Surrey GU24 9PT
Tel: 01276 858084
Head Teacher: Andrew Moss MEd
Age range: 11–18 years
No. of pupils: 938 VIth317
Fees: Day £9,081 WB
£18,222 FB £19,446

Greenfield School
Old Woking Road, Woking,
Surrey GU22 8HY
Tel: 01483 772525
Headmistress:
Mrs. Tania Botting MEd
Age range: 6 months–11 years
No. of pupils: 347

Guildford High School
London Road, Guildford,
Surrey GU1 1SJ
Tel: 01483 561440
Headmistress:
Mrs F J Boulton BSc, MA
Age range: G4–18 years

Hall Grove School
London Road, Bagshot,
Surrey GU19 5HZ
Tel: 01276 473059
Principal: Mr Alastair Graham
Age range: 3–13 years
(boarding from 8)

Halstead Preparatory School
Woodham Rise, Woking,
Surrey GU21 4EE
Tel: 01483 772682
Head: Mrs S Maher BSc
Age range: G2–11 years

Hazelwood School
Wolf's Hill, Limpsfield,
Oxted, Surrey RH8 0QU
Tel: 01883 712194
Head: Mrs Lindie Louw
Age range: 9 months–13 years
No. of pupils: 572
Fees: Day £3,800–£6,055

Hoe Bridge School
Hoe Place, Old Woking Road,
Woking, Surrey GU22 8JE
Tel: 01483 760018
Headmaster: Mr C Webster MA BSc
(Hons) PGCE
Age range: 2–16 years

Hurtwood House
Holmbury St. Mary, Dorking,
Surrey RH5 6NU
Tel: 01483 279000
Principal: Mr Cosmo Jackson
Age range: 16–18 years
No. of pupils: 360
Fees: Day £29,748 FB £44,622

Kids Inc Day Nursery – Guildford
Railton Road, Queen Elizabeth
Park, Guildford, Surrey GU2 9LX
Tel: 01483 237999

KING EDWARD'S WITLEY
For further details see p. 88
Petworth Road, Godalming,
Surrey GU8 5SG
Tel: 01428 686700
Email: admissions@kesw.org
Website: www.kesw.org
Head: Mrs Joanna Wright
Age range: 11–18 years
No. of pupils: 435
Fees: Day £5,960–£7,555
WB £11,195–£11,630 FB
£11,790–£12,250

Kingswood House School
56 West Hill, Epsom, Surrey KT19 8LG
Tel: 01372 723590
Headmaster: Mr Duncan Murphy
BA (Hons), MEd, FRSA
Age range: 4–16 years
No. of pupils: 250

Lingfield College
Racecourse Road, Lingfield,
Surrey RH7 6PH
Tel: 01342 832407
Headmaster:
Mr R Bool B.A. Hons, MBA
Age range: 2–18 years

Little Downsend Ashtead
Ashtead Lodge, 22 Oakfield
Road, Ashtead, Surrey KT21 2RE
Tel: 01372 385439
Head of School:
Ms Vanessa Conlan
Age range: 2–6 years

Little Downsend Epsom
Epsom Lodge, 6 Norman Avenue,
Epsom, Surrey KT17 3AB
Tel: 01372 385438
Head of School:
Ms Vanessa Conlan
Age range: 2–6 years

Little Downsend Leatherhead
13 Epsom Road, Leatherhead,
Surrey KT22 8ST
Tel: 01372 385437
Head of School:
Ms Vanessa Conlan
Age range: 2–6 years

Longacre School
Hullbrook Lane, Shamley Green,
Guildford, Surrey GU5 0NQ
Tel: 01483 893225
Head of School: Mr Matthew Bryan
MA(Cantab.), MA(Oxon.), MSc,
FRSA
Age range: 2–11 years

Lyndhurst School
36 The Avenue, Camberley,
Surrey GU15 3NE
Tel: 01276 22895
Head: Mr Andrew Rudkin
Age range: 3–11 years

Manor House School, Bookham
Manor House Lane, Little Bookham,
Leatherhead, Surrey KT23 4EN
Tel: 01372 457077
Headteacher: Ms Tracey Fantham
BA (Hons) MA NPQH
Age range: B2–6 years G2–16 years
No. of pupils: 300
Fees: Day £9,747–£18,315

Micklefield School
10 Somers Road, Reigate,
Surrey RH2 9DU
Tel: 01737 224212
Head: Mr R Ardé
Age range: 3–11 years
No. of pupils: 210
Fees: Day £10,965–£13,935

Milbourne Lodge School
Arbrook Lane, Esher,
Surrey KT10 9EG
Tel: 01372 462737
Head: Mrs Judy Waite
Age range: 4–13 years
No. of pupils: 278
Fees: Day £14,475–£18,195

Notre Dame School
Cobham, Surrey KT11 1HA
Tel: 01932 869990
Head of Seniors: Mrs Anna King
MEd, MA (Cantab), PGCE
Age range: B2–7 years G2–18 years

Oakhyrst Grange School
160 Stanstead Road,
Caterham, Surrey CR3 6AF
Tel: 01883 343344
Headmaster: Mr Alex Gear
Age range: 4–11 years

OneSchool Global UK Hindhead Campus
Tilford Road, Hindhead,
Surrey GU26 6SJ
Tel: 01428 601800
Age range: 7–18 years

OneSchool Global UK Kenley Campus
Victor Beamish Avenue,
Kenley, Surrey CR3 5FX
Tel: 01883 338634
Age range: 7–18 years

Parkside School
The Manor, Stoke d'Abernon,
Cobham, Surrey KT11 3PX
Tel: 01932 862749
Headteacher: Ms Nicole Janssen
Age range: B2–13 years G2–4 years
No. of pupils: 270

Prior's Field
Priorsfield Road, Godalming,
Surrey GU7 2RH
Tel: 01483 810551
Head of School: Mrs Tracey Kirnig
Age range: G11–18 years
(boarding from 11)

Reed's School
Sandy Lane, Cobham,
Surrey KT11 2ES
Tel: 01932 869001
Headmaster: Mr Mark Hoskins
Age range: B11–18 years
(boarding from 11) G16–18 years

Reigate Grammar School
Reigate Road, Reigate,
Surrey RH2 0QS
Tel: 01737 222231
Headmaster: Mr Shaun Fenton MA
(Oxon) MEd (Oxon)
Age range: 11–18 years

Reigate St Mary's Prep & Choir School
Chart Lane, Reigate,
Surrey RH2 7RN
Tel: 01737 244880
Headmaster:
Mr Marcus Culverwell MA
Age range: 2–11 years

RGS Guildford
High Street, Guildford,
Surrey GU1 3BB
Tel: 01483 880600
Headmaster: Dr J M Cox BSc, PhD
Age range: B11–18 years

RGS Guildford Prep
Maori Road, Guildford,
Surrey GU1 2EL
Tel: 01483 880650
Head of School:
Mr Toby Freeman-Day
Age range: B3–11 years

Ripley Court School
Rose Lane, Ripley, Surrey GU23 6NE
Tel: 01483 225217
Headmistress: Ms Aislinn Clarke
Age range: 3–11 years

Rowan Preparatory School
6 Fitzalan Road, Claygate,
Esher, Surrey KT10 0LX
Tel: 01372 462627
Headmistress: Mrs Susan Clarke
BEd, NPQH
Age range: G2–11 years

Rydes Hill Preparatory School
Rydes Hill House, Aldershot Road,
Guildford, Surrey GU2 8BP
Tel: 01483 563160
Headmistress: Mrs Sarah Norville
Age range: B3–7 years G3–11 years

Shrewsbury House Pre-Preparatory School
22 Milbourne Lane, Esher,
Surrey KT10 9EA
Tel: 01372 462781
Head: Mr Jon Akhurst BA (Hons)
PGCE
Age range: 3–7 years

Sir William Perkins's School
Guildford Road, Chertsey,
Surrey KT16 9BN
Tel: 01932 574900
Head: Mr C C Muller
Age range: G11–18 years
No. of pupils: 600
Fees: Day £6,246

St Catherine's, Bramley
Station Road, Bramley,
Guildford, Surrey GU5 0DF
Tel: 01483 899609
Headmistress: Ms Alice Phillips
Age range: G4–18 years
(boarding from 11)

St Christopher's School
6 Downs Road, Epsom,
Surrey KT18 5HE
Tel: 01372 721807
Headteacher: Bronia Grehan
Age range: 3–7 years

St George's College
Weybridge Road, Addlestone,
Weybridge, Surrey KT15 2QS
Tel: 01932 839300
Headmistress: Mrs Rachel Owens
Age range: 11–18 years

St George's Junior School
Thames Street, Weybridge,
Surrey KT13 8NL
Tel: 01932 839400
Headmaster: Mr Antony Hudson
Age range: 3–11 years

St Hilary's School
Holloway Hill, Godalming,
Surrey GU7 1RZ
Tel: 01483 416551
Headmistress: Mrs Jane
Whittingham BEdCert,
ProfPracSpLD
Age range: 2–11 years

St Ives School
Three Gates Lane, Haslemere,
Surrey GU27 2ES
Tel: 01428 643734
Head Teacher: Kay Goldsworthy
Age range: 2–11 years

St John's School
Epsom Road, Leatherhead,
Surrey KT22 8SP
Tel: 01372 373000
Acting Head: Mrs Rebecca Evans
Age range: 11–18 years
(boarding from 11)
Fees: Day £22,500–
£25,560 WB £32,441

St Teresa's Effingham (Preparatory School)
Effingham, Surrey RH5 6ST
Tel: 01372 453456
Headteacher: Ms Sarah Conrad
Age range: B2–4 years G2–11 years

St Teresa's Effingham (Senior School)
Effingham, Surrey RH5 6ST
Tel: +44 (0)1372 452037
Headmistress: Ms Claire McShane
Age range: G11–18 years
(boarding from 11)

St. Andrew's School
Church Hill House, Horsell,
Woking, Surrey GU21 4QW
Tel: 01483 760943
Headmaster: Mr D Fitzgerald
Age range: 3–13 years
No. of pupils: 310
Fees: Day £4,392–£17,280

St. Edmund's School
Portsmouth Road, Hindhead,
Surrey GU26 6BH
Tel: 01428 604808
Headmaster: Mr A J Walliker
MA(Cantab), MBA, PGCE
Age range: 2–16 years

TASIS THE AMERICAN SCHOOL IN ENGLAND
For further details see p. 98
Coldharbour Lane,
Thorpe, Surrey TW20 8TE
Tel: +44 (0)1932 582316
Email:
ukadmissions@tasisengland.org
Website: www.tasisengland.org
Head of School: Mr Bryan Nixon
Age range: 3–18 years
(boarding from 13)
No. of pupils: 650
Fees: Day £13,280–
£29,080 FB £54,510

The Hawthorns School
Pendell Court, Bletchingley,
Redhill, Surrey RH1 4QJ
Tel: 01883 743048
Headmaster: Mr Adrian Floyd
Age range: 2–13 years

The Royal School, Haslemere
Farnham Lane, Haslemere,
Surrey GU27 1HQ
Tel: 01428 605805
Head: Mrs Pippa Smithson BA
(Hons), PGCE, MEd
Age range: 6 weeks–18
years (boarding from 11)
No. of pupils: 315
Fees: Day £3,681–£6,414
WB £9,435 FB £10,731

Tormead School
Cranley Road, Guildford,
Surrey GU1 2JD
Tel: 01483 575101
Head of School: Mr David Boyd
Age range: G4–18 years

Warlingham Park School
Chelsham Common,
Warlingham, Surrey CR6 9PB
Tel: 01883 626844
Head of School: Ms Annie Ingrassia
Age range: 2–11 years

Weston Green School
Weston Green Road, Thames
Ditton, Surrey KT7 0JN
Tel: 020 8398 2778
Head Teacher: Mrs Sarah Evans BA
Hons, NPQH
Age range: 2–11 years
No. of pupils: 195

Woldingham School
Marden Park, Woldingham,
Surrey CR3 7YA
Tel: 01883 349431
Head of School:
Dr James Whitehead
Age range: G11–18 years
(boarding from 11)
No. of pupils: 626
Fees: Day £23,160–£25,365
FB £34,170–£42,330

Woodcote House School
Snows Ride, Windlesham,
Surrey GU20 6PF
Tel: 01276 472115
Headmaster: Mr D.M.K. Paterson
Age range: B7–13 years
(boarding from 7)

Yehudi Menuhin School
Stoke Road, Stoke d'Abernon,
Cobham, Surrey KT11 3QQ
Tel: 01932 864739
Headmaster: Mr Ben Gudgeon
Age range: 8–19 years

West Berkshire

Brockhurst & Marlston House Schools
Hermitage, Newbury, West Berkshire RG18 9UL
Tel: 01635 200293
Headmaster: Mr David Fleming MA (Oxon), MSc
Age range: 2–13 years
(boarding from 7)

Cheam School
Headley, Newbury, West Berkshire RG19 8LD
Tel: +44 (0)1635 268242
Headmaster: Mr William Phelps
Age range: 2–13 years
(boarding from 8)

Downe House School
Downe House, Cold Ash, Thatcham, West Berkshire RG18 9JJ
Tel: +44 (0)1635 200286
Headmistress: Mrs Emma McKendrick BA(Liverpool)
Age range: G11–18 years
(boarding from 11)
No. of pupils: 590
Fees: Day £10,960 FB £14,740

Horris Hill
Newtown, Newbury, West Berkshire RG20 9DJ
Tel: 01635 40594
Headmaster: Mr Rob Stewart
Age range: B2–13 years
(boarding from 8)

St Gabriel's
Sandleford Priory, Newbury, West Berkshire RG20 9BD
Tel: 01635 555680
Principal: Mr Ricki Smith
Age range: 6 months–18 years

St. Michael's School
Harts Lane, Burghclere, Newbury, West Berkshire RG20 9JW
Tel: 01635 278137
Headmaster: Rev. Fr. John Brucciani
Age range: B4–18 years
(boarding from 11) G4–11 years

West Sussex

Ardingly College
College Road, Ardingly, Haywards Heath, West Sussex RH17 6SQ
Tel: +44 (0)1444 893320
Headmaster: Mr Ben Figgis
Age range: 13–18 years

Ardingly College Preparatory School
College Road, Haywards Heath, West Sussex RH17 6SQ
Tel: +44 (0)1444 893320
Head of Prep School: Mr Harry Hastings
Age range: 2.5–13 years

Brambletye
Brambletye, East Grinstead, West Sussex RH19 3PD
Tel: 01342 321004
Headmaster: Mr Will Brooks
Age range: 2–13 years

Burgess Hill Girls
Keymer Road, Burgess Hill, West Sussex RH15 0EG
Tel: 01444 241050
Head of School: Lars Fox
Age range: B2.5–4 years G2.5–18 years
No. of pupils: 557 VIth70
Fees: Day £9,825–£22,410 FB £34,560–£39,900

Christ's Hospital
Horsham, West Sussex RH13 0LJ
Tel: 01403 211293
Head Teacher: Mr Simon Reid
Age range: 11–18 years

Conifers School
Egmont Road, Easebourne, Midhurst, West Sussex GU29 9BG
Tel: 01730 813243
Head of School: Miss Emma Fownes
Age range: 2–13 years

Copthorne Prep School
Effingham Lane, Copthorne, West Sussex RH10 3HR
Tel: 01342 712311
Headmaster: Mr Nathan Close
Age range: 2–13 years

Cottesmore School
Buchan Hill, Pease Pottage, West Sussex RH11 9AU
Tel: 01293 520648
Head of School: Mr Tom Rogerson
Age range: 4–13 years

Cumnor House Sussex
London Road, Danehill, Haywards Heath, West Sussex RH17 7HT
Tel: 01825 790347
Headmaster: Mr Fergus Llewellyn
Age range: 2–13 years
(boarding from 11)

Dorset House School
The Manor, Church Lane, Bury, Pulborough, West Sussex RH20 1PB
Tel: 01798 831456
Headmaster: Mr Matt Thomas Med BA Ed (Hons) (Exeter) FRGS
Age range: 4–13 years
(boarding from 9)
No. of pupils: 140
Fees: Day £9,315–£18,945 WB £1,258–£4,488

Farlington School
Strood Park, Horsham, West Sussex RH12 3PN
Tel: 01403 254967
Headmaster: Mr James Passam
Age range: 4–18 years
No. of pupils: 340
Fees: Day £2,050–£6,350 WB £10,500 FB £11,300

Great Ballard School
Eartham House, Eartham, Nr Chichester, West Sussex PO18 0LR
Tel: 01243 814236
Head of School: Mr Matt King
Age range: 2.5–16 years
No. of pupils: 136
Fees: Day £8,580–£16,200

Great Walstead School
East Mascalls Lane, Lindfield, Haywards Heath, West Sussex RH16 2QL
Tel: 01444 483528
Headmaster: Mr Chris Calvey
Age range: 2.5–13 years
No. of pupils: 345
Fees: Day £3,098–£5,938

Handcross Park School
London Road, Handcross, Haywards Heath, West Sussex RH17 6HF
Tel: 01444 400526
Headmaster: Mr Richard Brown
Age range: 2–13 years
(boarding from 8)

Hurst College
College Lane, Hurstpierpoint, West Sussex BN6 9JS
Tel: 01273 833636
Headmaster: Mr. Dominic Mott
Age range: 4–18 years
(boarding from 13)
No. of pupils: 1295

Lancing College
Lancing, West Sussex BN15 0RW
Tel: 01273 452213
Head Master: Mr Dominic T Oliver MPhil
Age range: 13–18 years

Lancing Prep Worthing
Broadwater Road, Worthing, West Sussex BN14 8HU
Tel: 01903 201123
Head: Mrs Heather Beeby
Age range: 2–13 years

Oakwood Preparatory School
Chichester, West Sussex PO18 9AN
Tel: 01243 575209
Headteacher: Mrs Clare Bradbury
Age range: 2.5–11 years
No. of pupils: 310
Fees: Day £3,450–£5,520

Our Lady of Sion School
Gratwicke Road, Worthing, West Sussex BN11 4BL
Tel: 01903 204063
Headmaster: Mr Steven Jeffery
Age range: 3–18 years

Pennthorpe School
Church Street, Horsham,
West Sussex RH12 3HJ
Tel: 01403 822391
Hea: Ms Lydia Waller
Age range: 2–13 years

Rikkyo School in England
Guildford Road, Rudgwick,
Horsham, West Sussex RH12 3BE
Tel: +44 (0)1403 822107
Principal: Mr Tohru Okano
Age range: 10–18 years

Seaford College
Lavington Park, Petworth,
West Sussex GU28 0NB
Tel: 01798 867392
Headmaster: J P Green MA BA
Age range: 5–18 years
No. of pupils: 943 VIth264
Fees: Day £3,960–£8,210 WB
£8,245–£11,115 FB £12,690

Shoreham College
St Julian's Lane, Shoreham-by-
Sea, West Sussex BN43 6YW
Tel: 01273 592681
Principal: Mrs Sarah Bakhtiari
Age range: 3–16 years

Slindon College
Slindon House, Top Road, Slindon,
Arundel, West Sussex BN18 0RH
Tel: 01243 814320
Headteacher:
Mrs Sotiria Vlahodimou
Age range: B8–18 years
(boarding from 11)

Sompting Abbotts Preparatory School
Church Lane, Sompting,
West Sussex BN15 0AZ
Tel: 01903 235960
Headmaster: Mr Stuart Douch
Age range: 2–13 years

The Prebendal School
52-55 West Street, Chichester,
West Sussex PO19 1RT
Tel: 01243 772220
Head: Ms Alison Napier
Age range: 3–13 years
(boarding from 7)

Westbourne House School
Shopwyke, West Sussex PO20 2BH
Tel: 01243 782739
Headmaster: Mr Martin Barker
Age range: 2.5–13 years
(boarding from 7)

Windlesham House School
London Road, Washington,
Pulborough, West Sussex RH20 4AY
Tel: 01903 874700
Headmaster: Mr Ben Evans
Age range: 4–13 years
(boarding from 7)

Worth School
Paddockhurst Road, Turners Hill,
Crawley, West Sussex RH10 4SD
Tel: +44 (0)1342 710200
Head Master: Mr Stuart McPherson
Age range: 11–18 years
(boarding from 13)

International Schools in London and the South-East

London

Central London

Accent London
12 Bedford Square,
London WC1B 3JA
Tel: 020 7813 7723
Head: Natasa Blecic
🌐 16+

École Jeannine Manuel – London
43-45 Bedford Square,
London WC1B 3DN
Tel: 020 3829 5970
Head of School: Pauline Prévot
Age range: 3–18 years
No. of pupils: 585
Fees: Day £20,760
🌐 £ IB

Guildhouse School
43-45 Bloomsbury Square,
London WC1A 2RA
Tel: +44 (0)1223 341300
Headmaster: Mr James Slocombe
Age range: 15–24 years
🌐 🏫 £ 16+

North London

Dwight School London
6 Friern Barnet Lane,
London N11 3LX
Tel: 020 8920 0600
Head: Chris Beddows
Age range: 2–18 years
🌐 £ IB 16+

North-West London

Collège Français Bilingue de Londres
87 Holmes Road, Kentish
Town, London NW5 3AX
Tel: 020 7993 7400
Head of School: Mr David Gassian
Age range: 3–15 years
No. of pupils: 700
🌐

Mill Hill School
The Ridgeway, Mill Hill
Village, London NW7 1QS
Tel: 020 8959 1176
Head:
Mrs Jane Sanchez BSc (Hons) PGCE
Age range: 13–18 years
(boarding from 13)
No. of pupils: 876 VIth312
Fees: Day £21,987 WB £31,140
FB £36,900
🌐 A 🏫 £ 16+

Southbank International School – Hampstead
16 Netherhall Gardens,
London NW3 5TH
Tel: 020 7243 3803
Principal: Shirley Harwood
Age range: 3–11 years
No. of pupils: 210
🌐 IB

The American School in London
One Waverley Place,
London NW8 0NP
Tel: +44 (0)20 7449 1200
Head of School:
Ms Coreen R. Hester
Age range: 4–18 years
🌐 16+

The Mount, Mill Hill International
Milespit Hill, London NW7 2RX
Tel: +44 (0)20 3826 33
Head of School: Ms Sarah Bellotti
Age range: 13–17 years
No. of pupils: 80
Fees: Day £27,000 WB £37,500
FB £44,250
🌐 🏫

South-East London

DLD College London
199 Westminster Bridge
Road, London SE1 7FX
Tel: +44 (0)20 7935 8411
Principal: Mr Irfan H Latif
Age range: 13–19 years
🌐 16+ A 🏫 £

Dulwich College
Dulwich Common,
London SE21 7LD
Tel: 020 8693 3601
Master: Dr J A F Spence
Age range: B6 months–18
years G6 months–7 years
Fees: Day £21,672 WB £42,408
FB £45,234
🌐 A 🏫 £ 16+

St Dunstan's College
Stanstead Road, London SE6 4TY
Tel: 020 8516 7200
Head of School: Mr Nick Hewlett
Age range: 3–18 years
🌐 16+

South-West London

Centre Academy London
92 St John's Hill, Battersea,
London SW11 1SH
Tel: 020 7738 2344
Head of School:
Mrs. Kas Lee-Douglas
Age range: 9–19 years
🌐 16+

Collingham College
23 Collingham Gardens,
London SW5 0HL
Tel: 020 7244 7414
Principal: Ms Sally Powell
Age range: 13–19 years
🌐 16+ A

École Primaire Marie D'Orliac
60 Clancarty Road,
London SW6 3AA
Tel: +44 (0)20 7736 5863
Director: Mr Blaise Fenart
Age range: 4–11 years
🌐

Hill House
17 Hans Place, Chelsea,
London SW1X 0EP
Tel: 020 7584 1331
Headmaster: Mr Richard Townend
Age range: 4–13 years
🌐 £

King's College School
Southside, Wimbledon
Common, London SW19 4TT
Tel: 020 8255 5300
Head: Dr Anne Cotton
Age range: B7–18 years
G16–18 years
No. of pupils: 1478
🌐 A IB 16+

L'ECOLE DE BATTERSEA
For further details see p. 52
Trott Street, Battersea,
London SW11 3DS
Tel: 020 7371 8350
Email:
admin@lecoledespetits.co.uk
Website:
www.lecoledebattersea.co.uk
Principal: Mrs F Brisset
Age range: 3–11 years
No. of pupils: 250
Fees: Day £5,075
🌐

L'ECOLE DES PETITS
For further details see p. 53
2 Hazlebury Road, Fulham,
London SW6 2NB
Tel: 020 7371 8350
Email:
admin@lecoledespetits.co.uk
Website:
www.lecoledespetits.co.uk
Principal: Mrs F Brisset
Age range: 3–6 years
No. of pupils: 120
Fees: Day £4,935
🌐

LYCÉE FRANÇAIS CHARLES DE GAULLE DE LONDRES
For further details see p. 55
35 Cromwell Road,
London SW7 2DG
Tel: 020 7584 6322
Email:
inscription@lyceefrancais.org.uk
Website:
www.lyceefrancais.org.uk
Head of School: TBC
Age range: 3–18 years
No. of pupils: 3450
Fees: Day £7,631–£15,965
🌐 £ 16+

St Paul's School
Lonsdale Road, Barnes,
London SW13 9JT
Tel: 020 8748 9162
High Master: Ms Sally-Anne Huang
Age range: B7–18 years
🌐 A 🏫 £ 16+

Westminster School
17A Dean's Yard, Westminster,
London SW1P 3PB
Tel: 020 7963 1000
Head Master: Dr Gary Savage
Age range: B13–18 years
G16–18 years
🌐 A 🏫 16+

West London

Bales College
2 Kilburn Lane, London W10 4AA
Tel: 020 8960 5899
Principal: Mr William Moore
Age range: 11–18 years
🌐 16+ A £

Ecole Française de Londres Jacques Prévert
59 Brook Green, Hammersmith,
London W6 7BE
Tel: 020 7602 6871
Director: Ms Sylvie Wanin
Age range: 4–11 years
🌐

FULHAM SCHOOL
For further details see p. 47
1-3 Chesilton Road,
London SW6 5AA
Tel: 020 8154 6751
Email:
senioradmin@fulham.school
Website: fulham.school
Executive Head of Fulham:
Bex Tear
Age range: 3–18 years
No. of pupils: 650
Fees: Day £19,158–£22,431

**Godolphin and
Latymer School**
Iffley Road, Hammersmith,
London W6 0PG
Tel: +44 (0)20 8741 1936
Head Mistress: Dr Frances Ramsey
Age range: G11–18 years
No. of pupils: 800
Fees: Day £25,185

**Halcyon London
International School**
33 Seymour Place, London W1H 5AU
Tel: +44 (0)20 7258 1169
Director: Mr Barry Mansfield
Age range: 11–18 years

ICS London
7B Wyndham Place,
London W1H 1PN
Tel: +44 (0)20 729 88800
Head of School: Alec Jiggins
Age range: 3–18 years
No. of pupils: 175
Fees: Day £19,770–£28,920

**Instituto Español Vicente
Cañada Blanch**
317 Portobello Road,
London W10 5SZ
Tel: +44 (0) 20 8969 2664
Head of School:
Mr Antonio Simón Saiz
Age range: 3–18 years

**International School
of London (ISL)**
139 Gunnersbury Avenue,
London W3 8LG
Tel: +44 (0)20 8992 5823
Principal: Mr Richard Parker
Age range: 3–18 years
No. of pupils: 420
Fees: Day £20,850–£28,850

King Fahad Academy
Bromyard Avenue, Acton,
London W3 7HD
Tel: 020 8743 0131
Director General: Dr Tahani Aljafari
Age range: 3–18 years

**Southbank International
School – Kensington**
36-38 Kensington Park
Road, London W11 3BU
Tel: +44 (0)20 7243 3803
Principal: Siobhan McGrath
Age range: 3–18 years

**Southbank International
School – Westminster**
63-65 Portland Place,
London W1B 1QR
Tel: 020 7243 3803
Principal: Dr Paul Wood
Age range: 11–19 years

Berkshire

Bradfield College
Bradfield, Berkshire RG7 6AU
Tel: 0118 964 4516
Headmaster:
Dr Christopher Stevens
Age range: 13–18 years
No. of pupils: 820
Fees: Day £33,732 FB £42,165

Eton College
Windsor, Berkshire SL4 6DW
Tel: +44 (0)1753 370 611
Head Master:
Mr Simon Henderson MA
Age range: B13–18 years
No. of pupils: 1342
Fees: FB £44,094

Heathfield School
London Road, Ascot,
Berkshire SL5 8BQ
Tel: 01344 898343
Head of School: Ms Sarah Wilson
Age range: G11–18 years
(boarding from 11)
Fees: Day £7,840–£8,000
FB £12,650–£12,950

LEIGHTON PARK SCHOOL
For further details see p. 90
Shinfield Road, Reading,
Berkshire RG2 7ED
Tel: 0118 987 9600
Email:
admissions@leightonpark.com
Website:
www.leightonpark.com
Head:
Mr Matthew L S Judd BA, PGCE
Age range: 11–18 years
No. of pupils: 550

Luckley House School
Luckley Road, Wokingham,
Berkshire RG40 3EU
Tel: 0118 978 4175
Head: Mrs Areti Bizior
Age range: 11–18 years

LVS ASCOT
For further details see p. 92
London Road, Ascot,
Berkshire SL5 8DR
Tel: 01344 882770
Email:
enquiries@lvs.ascot.sch.uk
Website: www.lvs.ascot.sch.uk
Principal: Mrs Christine Cunniffe
BA (Hons), MMus, MBA
Age range: 4–18 years
No. of pupils: 833
Fees: Day £11,640–£20,985
FB £29,760–£36,660

Padworth College
Sopers Lane, Reading,
Berkshire RG7 4NR
Tel: 0118 983 2644
Principal: Lorraine Atkins
Age range: 14–19 years

Pangbourne College
Pangbourne, Reading,
Berkshire RG8 8LA
Tel: 0118 984 2101
Headmaster: Thomas J C Garnier
Age range: 11–18 years
No. of pupils: 458
Fees: Day £6,300–£8,540 WB
£8,210–£11,510 FB £9,050–£12,680

Queen Anne's School
6 Henley Road, Caversham,
Reading, Berkshire RG4 6DX
Tel: 0118 918 7300
Head: Ms Elaine Purves
Age range: G11–18 years
(boarding from 11)
No. of pupils: G450
Fees: Day £8,370 FB £13,590

**REDDAM HOUSE
BERKSHIRE**
For further details see p. 94
Bearwood Road, Sindlesham,
Wokingham, Berkshire RG41 5BG
Tel: +44 (0)118 974 8300
Email:
registrar@reddamhouse.org.uk
Website:
www.reddamhouse.org.uk
Principal: Mr Rick Cross
Age range: 3 months–18 years
No. of pupils: 675
Fees: Day £12,006–£19,248
WB £29,241–£33,696 FB
£30,855–£35,310

St George's Ascot
Wells Lane, Ascot, Berkshire SL5 7DZ
Tel: 01344 629900
Headmistress: Mrs Liz Hewer MA
(Hons) (Cantab) PGCE
Age range: G11–18 years
(boarding from 11)

St Mary's School Ascot
St Mary's Road, Ascot,
Berkshire SL5 9JF
Tel: 01344 296614
Headmistress: Mrs Danuta Staunton
Age range: G11–18 years
(boarding from 11)

The Abbey School
Kendrick Road, Reading,
Berkshire RG1 5DZ
Tel: 0118 987 2256
Head: Mr Will le Fleming
Age range: G3–18 years
No. of pupils: 1000
Fees: Day £11,535–£19,830

The Oratory School
Woodcote, Reading,
Berkshire RG8 0PJ
Tel: 01491 683500
Head Master: Mr Joe Smith
BA(Hons), MEd, PGCE
Age range: 11–18 years

Wellington College
Duke's Ride, Crowthorne,
Berkshire RG45 7PU
Tel: +44 (0)1344 444000
Master: Mr James Dahl
Age range: 13–18 years
No. of pupils: 1100 VIth485
Fees: Day £32,940–£35,760
FB £45,090

Buckinghamshire

International School of Creative Arts (ISCA)
Framewood Road, Wexham, Buckinghamshire SL2 4QS
Tel: +44 (0)1753 208820
Head of School: Mr Robert Hunter
Age range: 15–19 years
No. of pupils: 85

Stowe School
Buckingham, Buckinghamshire MK18 5EH
Tel: 01280 818000
Headmaster: Dr Anthony Wallersteiner
Age range: 13–18 years

Teikyo School UK
Framewood Road, Wexham, Buckinghamshire SL2 4QS
Tel: 01753 663711
Age range: 15–18 years

Thornton College
College Lane, Thornton, Milton Keynes, Buckinghamshire MK17 0HJ
Tel: 01280 812610
Headteacher: Dr Louise Shaw
Age range: G3–18 years (boarding from 8)
No. of pupils: 402
Fees: Day £11,190–£17,835 WB £19,830–£25,095 FB £24,660–£30,585

Wycombe Abbey
Frances Dove Way, High Wycombe, Buckinghamshire HP11 1PE
Tel: +44 (0)1494 520381
Headmistress: Mrs Jo Duncan MA (St Andrews), PGCE (Cantab)
Age range: G11–18 years
No. of pupils: 660
Fees: Day £33,150 FB £44,100

East Sussex

Battle Abbey School
High Street, Battle, East Sussex TN33 0AD
Tel: 01424 772385
Headmaster: Mr David Clark BA, M Phil (Cantab)
Age range: 3 months–18 years (boarding from 11)

BEDE'S SENIOR SCHOOL
For further details see p. 82
Upper Dicker, Hailsham, East Sussex BN27 3QH
Tel: 01323 356609
Email: admissions@bedes.org
Website: www.bedes.org/senior
Head: Mr Peter Goodyer
Age range: 13–18 years (boarding from 13)
No. of pupils: 832
Fees: Day £8,300 WB £12,240 FB £12,990

Brighton College
Eastern Road, Brighton, East Sussex BN2 0AL
Tel: 01273 704200
Head Master: Richard Cairns
Age range: 3–18 years

Brighton International School
5 Old Steine, Brighton, East Sussex BN1 1EJ
Tel: 07796 997780
Head of School: Ms Juliet Cassells
Age range: 15–17 years

Buckswood School
Broomham Hall, Rye Road, Guestling, Hastings, East Sussex TN35 4LT
Tel: 01424 813 813
Co-Principals: Michael Shaw & Kevin Samson
Age range: 10–19 years

Eastbourne College
Old Wish Road, Eastbourne, East Sussex BN21 4JX
Tel: 01323 452323 (Admissions)
Headmaster: Mr Tom Lawson MA (Oxon)
Age range: 13–18 years

Greenfields Independent Day & Boarding School
Priory Road, Forest Row, East Sussex RH18 5JD
Tel: +44 (0)1342 822189
Executive Head: Mr. Jeff Smith
Age range: 2–18 years (boarding from 10)

MAYFIELD SCHOOL
For further details see p. 93
The Old Palace, Mayfield, East Sussex TN20 6PH
Tel: 01435 874642
Email: registrar@mayfieldgirls.org
Website: www.mayfieldgirls.org
Head: Ms Antonia Beary MA, MPhil (Cantab), PGCE
Age range: G11–18 years (boarding from 11)
No. of pupils: 425

Michael Hall School
Kidbrooke Park, Priory Road, Forest Row, East Sussex RH18 5JA
Tel: 01342 822275
Head of School: Emmeline Hawker
Age range: 0–19 years

ROEDEAN SCHOOL
For further details see p. 95
Roedean Way, Brighton, East Sussex BN2 5RQ
Tel: 01273 667500
Email: info@roedean.co.uk
Website: www.roedean.co.uk
Head of School: Niamh Green
Age range: G11–18 years (boarding from 11)
No. of pupils: 700
Fees: Day £6,290–£8,220 WB £11,120–£12,400 FB £12,180–£14,745

Essex

Brentwood School
Middleton Hall Lane,
Brentwood, Essex CM15 8EE
Tel: 01277 243243
Headmaster: Mr Michael Bond
Age range: 3–18 years
No. of pupils: 1968
Fees: Day £21,783 FB £42,687

CHIGWELL SCHOOL
For further details see p. 74
High Road, Chigwell,
Essex IG7 6QF
Tel: 020 8501 5700
Email:
admissions@chigwell-school.org
Website:
www.chigwell-school.org
Head Teacher: Mr Damian King
Age range: 4–18 years
No. of pupils: 1057

Felsted School
Felsted, Great Dunmow,
Essex CM6 3LL
Tel: +44 (0)1371 822600
Headmaster: Mr Chris Townsend
Age range: 4–18 years

Gosfield School
Cut Hedge Park, Halstead Road,
Gosfield, Halstead, Essex CO9 1PF
Tel: 01787 474040
Head of School: Mr Rod Jackson
Age range: 2–18 years
Fees: Day £7,680–£17,250

New Hall School
The Avenue, Boreham,
Chelmsford, Essex CM3 3HS
Tel: 01245 467588
Principal: Mrs Katherine Jeffrey MA,
BA, PGCE, MA(Ed Mg), NPQH
Age range: 1–18 years
No. of pupils: 1400
Fees: Day £9,621–£20,502 WB
£18,234–£28,026 FB £21,177–£32,472

Hampshire

Bedales School
Church Road, Steep, Petersfield,
Hampshire GU32 2DG
Tel: 01730 300100
Head of School: Mr Will Goldsmith
Age range: 13–18 years

Brockwood Park School
Brockwood Park, Bramdean,
Alresford, Hampshire SO24 0LQ
Tel: +44 (0)1962 771744
Principal: Mr Antonio Autor
Age range: 14–19 years

Embley
Embley Park, Romsey,
Hampshire SO51 6ZE
Tel: 01794 512206
Headteacher: Mr Cliff Canning
Age range: 2–18 years
No. of pupils: 600
Fees: Day £9,165–£17,004
WB £29,310 FB £9,598–£33,636

Lord Wandsworth College
Long Sutton, Hook,
Hampshire RG29 1TA
Tel: 01256 862201
Head of School: Mr Adam Williams
Age range: 11–18 years

Moyles Court School
Moyles Court, Ringwood,
Hampshire BH24 3NF
Tel: 01425 472856
Headmaster:
Mr Richard Milner-Smith
Age range: 2–16 years

Rookwood School
Weyhill Road, Andover,
Hampshire SP10 3AL
Tel: 01264 325900
Headmaster: Mr A Kirk-Burgess BSc,
PGCE, MSc (Oxon)
Age range: 2–18 years
(boarding from 7)

Sherfield School
South Drive, Sherfield-on-Loddon,
Hook, Hampshire RG27 0HU
Tel: 01256 884800
Headmaster: Mr Nick Brain
BA(Hons), PGCE, MA, NPQH
Age range: 3 months–18
years (boarding from 9)
No. of pupils: 625

ST SWITHUN'S SCHOOL
For further details see p. 97
Alresford Road, Winchester,
Hampshire SO21 1HA
Tel: 01962 835700
Email: office@stswithuns.com
Website: www.stswithuns.com
Head of School: Jane Gandee
MA(Cantab)
Age range: G11–18 years
No. of pupils: 492 VIth137
Fees: Day £23,478 FB £39,492

The Portsmouth Grammar School
High Street, Portsmouth,
Hampshire PO1 2LN
Tel: +44 (0)23 9236 0036
Age range: 2.5–18 years

Winchester College
College Street, Winchester,
Hampshire SO23 9NA
Tel: 01962 621100
Headmaster: Dr. T R Hands
Age range: B13–18 years
(boarding from 13)

Hertfordshire

Aldenham School
Elstree, Hertfordshire WD6 3AJ
Tel: 01923 858122
Headmaster: Mr James Fowler
Age range: 3–18 years

BERKHAMSTED SCHOOL
For further details see p. 84
Overton House, 131 High
Street, Berkhamsted,
Hertfordshire HP4 2DJ
Tel: 01442 358001
Email:
admissions@berkhamsted.com
Website:
www.berkhamsted.com
Principal: Mr Richard Backhouse
MA(Cantab)
Age range: 3–18 years
No. of pupils: 1883 VIth411
Fees: Day £10,110–£23,175
WB £31,500 FB £37,575

Bishop's Stortford College
School House, Maze Green
Road, Bishop's Stortford,
Hertfordshire CM23 2PQ
Tel: +44 (0)1279 838575
College Head:
Ms Kathy Crewe-Read
Age range: 13–18 years

Bishop's Stortford College Prep School
School House, Maze Green
Road, Bishop's Stortford,
Hertfordshire CM23 2PQ
Tel: +44 (0)1279 838583
Head of the Prep School:
Mr Bill Toleman
Age range: 4–13 years

Haileybury
Haileybury, Hertford,
Hertfordshire SG13 7NU
Tel: +44 (0)1992 706353
The Master:
Mr Martin Collier MA BA PGCE
Age range: 11–18 years
(boarding from 11)
No. of pupils: 902 VIth357
Fees: Day £6,595–£9,920
FB £8,615–£13,580

St Christopher School
Barrington Road, Letchworth
Garden City, Hertfordshire SG6 3JZ
Tel: 01462 650 850
Head of School:
Ms Emma-Kate Henry
Age range: 3–18 years

St Edmund's College & Prep School
Old Hall Green, Nr Ware,
Hertfordshire SG11 1DS
Tel: 01920 824247
Headmaster: Mr Matthew Mostyn
BA (Hons) MA (Ed)
Age range: 3–18 years
(boarding from 11)

St Francis' College
Broadway, Letchworth Garden
City, Hertfordshire SG6 3PJ
Tel: 01462 670511
Headmistress: Mrs B Goulding
Age range: G3–18 years
(boarding from 10)

St Margaret's School, Bushey
Merry Hill Road, Bushey,
Hertfordshire WD23 1DT
Tel: +44 (0)20 8416 4400
Headteacher: Lara Péchard
Age range: 2–18 years
No. of pupils: 650

Stanborough Secondary School
Stanborough Park, Garston,
Watford, Hertfordshire WD25 9JT
Tel: 01923 673268
Interim Head: Mr K. James
Age range: 11–18 years

The Purcell School, London
Aldenham Road, Bushey,
Hertfordshire WD23 2TS
Tel: 01923 331100
Principal: Mr Paul Bambrough
Age range: 10–18 years

The Royal Masonic School for Girls
Rickmansworth Park,
Rickmansworth,
Hertfordshire WD3 4HF
Tel: 01923 773168
Headmaster: Mr Kevin Carson
M.Phil (Cambridge)
Age range: B2–4 years G2–18 years

Tring Park School for the Performing Arts
Mansion Drive, Tring,
Hertfordshire HP23 5LX
Tel: 01442 824255
Principal: Mr Stefan Anderson MA,
ARCM, ARCT
Age range: 8–19 years
No. of pupils: 370 VIth171
Fees: Day £15,405–£24,885
FB £26,190–£37,605

Kent

Ashford School
East Hill, Ashford, Kent TN24 8PB
Tel: +44 (0)1233 625171
Head: Mr Michael Hall
Age range: 3 months–18 years
(boarding from 11)
No. of pupils: 1034 VIth140
Fees: Day £9,030–£19,026
WB £27,846 FB £38,778

Ashgrove School
116 Widmore Road,
Bromley, Kent BR1 3BE
Tel: 020 8460 4143
Head of School: Dr Patricia Ash
Age range: 3–11 years

Benenden School
Cranbrook, Kent TN17 4AA
Tel: 01580 240592
Headmistress: Ms Samantha Price
Age range: G11–18 years
(boarding from 11)

Bethany School
Curtisden Green, Goudhurst,
Cranbrook, Kent TN17 1LB
Tel: 01580 211273
Headmaster: Mr Francie Healy BSc,
HDipEd, NPQH
Age range: 11–18 years
No. of pupils: 346 VIth77
Fees: Day £18,795–£20,760 WB
£29,175–£32,205 FB £31,455–£35,400

COBHAM HALL SCHOOL
For further details see p. 85
Brewers Road, Cobham,
Kent DA12 3BL
Tel: 01474 823371
Email:
admissions@cobhamhall.com
Website: www.cobhamhall.com
Headteacher:
Mrs Wendy Barrett
Age range: B16–18 years G11–18
years (boarding from 11)
No. of pupils: 150
Fees: Day £7,100–£8,250
FB £11,500–£13,250

Dover College
Effingham Crescent,
Dover, Kent CT17 9RH
Tel: 01304 205969
Head of School: Mr Simon Fisher
Age range: 3–18 years

EARLSCLIFFE
For further details see p. 87
29 Shorncliffe Road,
Folkestone, Kent CT20 2NB
Tel: 01303 253951
Email:
admissions@earlscliffe.co.uk
Website: www.earlscliffe.co.uk
Headteacher: Mr Joss Williams
Age range: 15–19 years
No. of pupils: 130
Fees: Day £9,100 WB £11,745
FB £13,650

Farringtons School
Perry Street, Chislehurst,
Kent BR7 6LR
Tel: 020 8467 0256
Head: Mr David Jackson
Age range: 3–18 years
No. of pupils: 700 VIth100
Fees: Day £16,260 WB £27,120
FB £34,050

Kent College Pembury
Old Church Road, Pembury,
Tunbridge Wells, Kent TN2 4AX
Tel: +44 (0)1892 822006
Head of School:
Miss Katrina Handford
Age range: G3–18 years
(boarding from 8)
No. of pupils: 500
Fees: Day £22,575 WB £28,200
FB £35,700

Kent College, Canterbury
Whitstable Road, Canterbury,
Kent CT2 9DT
Tel: +44 (0)1227 763 231
Head of Kent College:
Mr Mark Turnbull
Age range: 3 months–18 years
(boarding from 8 years)
No. of pupils: 800
Fees: Day £6,029–£6,932
FB £9,326–£12,883

King's School Rochester
Satis House, Boley Hill,
Rochester, Kent ME1 1TE
Tel: 01634 888555
Principal: Mr B Charles
Age range: 3–18 years
No. of pupils: 638 VIth101
Fees: Day £3,770–£7,175
FB £8,175–£11,775

Rochester Independent College
254 St Margaret's Banks,
Rochester, Kent ME1 1HY
Tel: +44 (0)163 482 8115
Head of School:
Mr Alistair Brownlow
Age range: 11–18 years

Sevenoaks School
High Street, Sevenoaks,
Kent TN13 1HU
Tel: +44 (0)1732 455133
Head of School:
Mr Jesse R Elzinga AB MSt FCCT
Age range: 11–18 years
No. of pupils: 1189
Fees: Day £26,721–£30,348
FB £42,921–£46,566

St Edmund's School
St Thomas Hill, Canterbury,
Kent CT2 8HU
Tel: 01227 475601
Head:
Mr Edward O'Connor MA (Cantab),
MPhil (Oxon), MEd (Cantab)
Age range: 2–18 years
(boarding from 11)
No. of pupils: 602

St Lawrence College
College Road, Ramsgate,
Kent CT11 7AE
Tel: 01843 572931
Head of College: Mr Barney Durrant
Age range: 3–18 years
No. of pupils: 585
Fees: Day £8,394–£18,558
FB £29,454–£38,952

Sutton Valence School
North Street, Sutton
Valence, Kent ME17 3HL
Tel: 01622 845200
Headmaster: Mr James A Thomas
MA (Cantab) MA (London) NPQH
Age range: 11–18 years
(boarding from 11)
No. of pupils: 557

The King's School, Canterbury
Lattergate Office, 25 The Precincts,
Canterbury, Kent CT1 2ES
Tel: 01227 595501
Head of School: Ms Jude Lowson
Age range: 13–18 years

The Worthgate School
68 New Dover Road,
Canterbury, Kent CT1 3LQ
Tel: +44 (0)1227 866540
Acting Principal:
Dr Nicola Robinson
Age range: 13–21 years
No. of pupils: 450
Fees: Day £17,370–£27,990
FB £13,230–£19,140

TONBRIDGE SCHOOL
For further details see p. 100
High Street, Tonbridge,
Kent TN9 1JP
Tel: 01732 304297
Email:
admissions@tonbridge-school.org
Website:
www.tonbridge-school.co.uk
Headmaster:
Mr James Priory MA (Oxon)
Age range: B13–18 years
No. of pupils: 795
Fees: Day £35,067 FB £46,740

Middlesex

ACS Hillingdon International School
108 Vine Lane, Hillingdon,
Uxbridge, Middlesex UB10 0BE
Tel: +44 (0) 1895 259771
Head of School: Mr Martin Hall
Age range: 4–18 years

North London Collegiate School
Canons, Canons Drive,
Edgware, Middlesex HA8 7RJ
Tel: +44 (0)20 8952 0912
Interim Headmistress:
Dr Hazel Bagworth-Mann
Age range: G4–18 years
No. of pupils: 1080
Fees: Day £6,283–£7,436

Radnor House
Pope's Villa, Cross Deep,
Twickenham, Middlesex TW1 4QG
Tel: +44 (0)20 8891 6264
Head: Mr Darryl Wideman MA
Oxon, PGCE
Age range: 9–18 years

St Helen's School
Eastbury Road, Northwood,
Middlesex HA6 3AS
Tel: +44 (0)1923 843210
Headmistress: Mrs Alice Lucas
Age range: G3–18 years
No. of pupils: 1150

Surrey

ACS Cobham International School
Heywood, Portsmouth Road,
Cobham, Surrey KT11 1BL
Tel: +44 (0) 1932 867251
Head of School:
Mr Barnaby Sandow
Age range: 2–18 years

ACS Egham International School
London Road, Egham,
Surrey TW20 0HS
Tel: +44 (0) 1784 430800
Head of School: Mr Jeremy Lewis
Age range: 4–18 years

Box Hill School
London Road, Mickleham,
Dorking, Surrey RH5 6EA
Tel: 01372 373382
Headmaster: Cory Lowde
Age range: 11–18 years
No. of pupils: 410
Fees: Day £21,585 WB £31,635

Caterham School
Harestone Valley Road,
Caterham, Surrey CR3 6YA
Tel: 01883 343028
Headmaster:
Mr C. W. Jones MA(Cantab)
Age range: 3–18 years

Charterhouse
Godalming, Surrey GU7 2DX
Tel: +44 (0)1483 291501
Head: Dr Alex Peterken
Age range: B13–18 years
(boarding from 13) G16–18 years
No. of pupils: 940
Fees: Day £12,180 FB £14,740

City of London Freemen's School
Ashtead Park, Ashtead,
Surrey KT21 1ET
Tel: +44 (0)1372 822400
Headmaster: Mr Roland J. Martin
Age range: 7–18 years

Cranleigh School
Horseshoe Lane, Cranleigh,
Surrey GU6 8QQ
Tel: +44 (0) 1483 273666
Headmaster:
Mr Martin Reader MA, MPhil, MBA
Age range: 7–18 years
(including Prep School)
No. of pupils: 683 VIth256
Fees: Day £35,175 FB £42,720

Duke of Kent School
Peaslake Road, Ewhurst,
Surrey GU6 7NS
Tel: 01483 277313
Head:
Mrs Sue Knox BA(Hons) MBA MEd
Age range: 3–16 years
No. of pupils: 316
Fees: Day £2,740–£6,540

Epsom College
College Road, Epsom,
Surrey KT17 4JQ
Tel: 01372 821000
Acting Headmaster:
Mr Paul Williams
Age range: 11–18 years
(boarding from 13)

Frensham Heights
Rowledge, Farnham,
Surrey GU10 4EA
Tel: 01252 792561
Head: Mr Rick Clarke
Age range: 3–18 years
(boarding from 11)

KING EDWARD'S WITLEY
For further details see p. 88
Petworth Road, Godalming,
Surrey GU8 5SG
Tel: 01428 686700
Email: admissions@kesw.org
Website: www.kesw.org
Head: Mrs Joanna Wright
Age range: 11–18 years
No. of pupils: 435
Fees: Day £5,960–£7,555
WB £11,195–£11,630
FB £11,790–£12,250

MARYMOUNT INTERNATIONAL SCHOOL LONDON
For further details see p. 78
George Road, Kingston upon
Thames, Surrey KT2 7PE
Tel: +44 (0)20 8949 0571
Email:
admissions@marymountlondon.com
Website:
www.marymountlondon.com
Headmistress:
Mrs Margaret Giblin
Age range: G11–18 years
No. of pupils: 248
Fees: Day £28,830
WB £46,740 FB £48,810

Prior's Field
Priorsfield Road, Godalming,
Surrey GU7 2RH
Tel: 01483 810551
Head of School: Mrs Tracey Kirnig
Age range: G11–18 years
(boarding from 11)

Reed's School
Sandy Lane, Cobham,
Surrey KT11 2ES
Tel: 01932 869001
Headmaster: Mr Mark Hoskins
Age range: B11–18 years
(boarding from 11) G16–18 years

Royal Russell School
Coombe Lane, Croydon,
Surrey CR9 5BX
Tel: +44 (0)20 8657 4433
Headmaster:
Mr Christopher Hutchinson
Age range: 11–18 years

St Catherine's, Bramley
Station Road, Bramley,
Guildford, Surrey GU5 0DF
Tel: 01483 899609
Headmistress: Ms Alice Phillips
Age range: G4–18 years
(boarding from 11)

St James Senior Boys' School
Church Road, Ashford,
Surrey TW15 3DZ
Tel: 01784 266930
Headmaster: Mr David Brazier
Age range: B11–18 years

St John's School
Epsom Road, Leatherhead,
Surrey KT22 8SP
Tel: 01372 373000
Acting Head: Mrs Rebecca Evans
Age range: 11–18 years
(boarding from 11)
Fees: Day £22,500–£25,560
WB £32,441

St Teresa's Effingham (Senior School)
Effingham, Surrey RH5 6ST
Tel: +44 (0)1372 452037
Headmistress: Ms Claire McShane
Age range: G11–18 years
(boarding from 11)

TASIS THE AMERICAN SCHOOL IN ENGLAND
For further details see p. 98
Coldharbour Lane,
Thorpe, Surrey TW20 8TE
Tel: +44 (0)1932 582316
Email:
ukadmissions@tasisengland.org
Website: www.tasisengland.org
Head of School: Mr Bryan Nixon
Age range: 3–18 years
(boarding from 13)
No. of pupils: 650
Fees: Day £13,280–£29,080
FB £54,510

The Royal School, Haslemere
Farnham Lane, Haslemere,
Surrey GU27 1HQ
Tel: 01428 605805
Head: Mrs Pippa Smithson BA
(Hons), PGCE, MEd
Age range: 6 weeks–18 years
(boarding from 11)
No. of pupils: 315
Fees: Day £3,681–£6,414
WB £9,435 FB £10,731

Whitgift School
Haling Park, South Croydon,
Surrey CR2 6YT
Tel: +44 20 8633 9935
Headmaster:
Mr Christopher Ramsey
Age range: B10–18 years
No. of pupils: 1550
Fees: Day £22,269
WB £35,973 FB £43,629

Woldingham School
Marden Park, Woldingham,
Surrey CR3 7YA
Tel: 01883 349431
Head of School:
Dr James Whitehead
Age range: G11–18 years
(boarding from 11)
No. of pupils: 626
Fees: Day £23,160–£25,365
FB £34,170–£42,330

Yehudi Menuhin School
Stoke Road, Stoke d'Abernon,
Cobham, Surrey KT11 3QQ
Tel: 01932 864739
Headmaster: Mr Ben Gudgeon
Age range: 8–19 years

West Berkshire

Downe House School
Downe House, Cold Ash,
Thatcham, West Berkshire RG18 9JJ
Tel: +44 (0)1635 200286
Headmistress: Mrs Emma
McKendrick BA(Liverpool)
Age range: G11–18 years
(boarding from 11)
No. of pupils: 590
Fees: Day £10,960 FB £14,740

West Sussex

Ardingly College
College Road, Ardingly, Haywards
Heath, West Sussex RH17 6SQ
Tel: +44 (0)1444 893320
Headmaster: Mr Ben Figgis
Age range: 13–18 years

Burgess Hill Girls
Keymer Road, Burgess Hill,
West Sussex RH15 0EG
Tel: 01444 241050
Head of School: Lars Fox
Age range: B2.5–4 years
G2.5–18 years
No. of pupils: 557 VIth70
Fees: Day £9,825–£22,410
FB £34,560–£39,900

Christ's Hospital
Horsham, West Sussex RH13 0LJ
Tel: 01403 211293
Head Teacher: Mr Simon Reid
Age range: 11–18 years

Farlington School
Strood Park, Horsham,
West Sussex RH12 3PN
Tel: 01403 254967
Headmaster: Mr James Passam
Age range: 4–18 years
No. of pupils: 340
Fees: Day £2,050–£6,350
WB £10,500 FB £11,300

Hurst College
College Lane, Hurstpierpoint,
West Sussex BN6 9JS
Tel: 01273 833636
Headmaster: Mr. Dominic Mott
Age range: 4–18 years
(boarding from 13)
No. of pupils: 1295

Lancing College
Lancing, West Sussex BN15 0RW
Tel: 01273 452213
Head Master:
Mr Dominic T Oliver MPhil
Age range: 13–18 years

Rikkyo School in England
Guildford Road, Rudgwick,
Horsham, West Sussex RH12 3BE
Tel: +44 (0)1403 822107
Principal: Mr Tohru Okano
Age range: 10–18 years

Seaford College
Lavington Park, Petworth,
West Sussex GU28 0NB
Tel: 01798 867392
Headmaster: J P Green MA BA
Age range: 5–18 years
No. of pupils: 943 VIth264
Fees: Day £3,960–£8,210
WB £8,245–£11,115 FB £12,690

Slindon College
Slindon House, Top Road, Slindon,
Arundel, West Sussex BN18 0RH
Tel: 01243 814320
Headteacher:
Mrs Sotiria Vlahodimou
Age range: B8–18 years
(boarding from 11)

Worth School
Paddockhurst Road, Turners Hill,
Crawley, West Sussex RH10 4SD
Tel: +44 (0)1342 710200
Head Master: Mr Stuart McPherson
Age range: 11–18 years
(boarding from 13)

Specialist schools and sixth form colleges

London

Central London

City of London School
Queen Victoria Street,
London EC4V 3AL
Tel: 020 3680 6300
Head: Mr A R Bird MSc
Age range: B10–18 years
No. of pupils: 950 VIth250
Fees: Day £21,057
(icons)

City of London School for Girls
St Giles' Terrace, Barbican,
London EC2Y 8BB
Tel: 020 7847 5500
Headmistress: Ms Jenny Brown
Age range: G11–18 years
(icons)

École Jeannine Manuel – London
43-45 Bedford Square,
London WC1B 3DN
Tel: 020 3829 5970
Head of School: Pauline Prévot
Age range: 3–18 years
No. of pupils: 585
Fees: Day £20,760
(icons)

Guildhouse School
43-45 Bloomsbury Square,
London WC1A 2RA
Tel: +44 (0)1223 341300
Headmaster: Mr James Slocombe
Age range: 15–24 years
(icons)

Italia Conti Academy of Theatre Arts
Italia Conti House, 23 Goswell
Road, London EC1M 7AJ
Tel: 020 7608 0047
Director: Chris White
Age range: 10–21 years
(icons)

The Royal Ballet School (Covent Garden)
46 Floral Street, Covent
Garden, London WC2E 9DA
Tel: 020 7836 8899
Head of School:
Mr David Gajadharsingh
Age range: 11–19 years
(boarding from 11)
(icons)

East London

Darul Hadis Latifiah
1 Cornwall Avenue, Bethnal
Green, London E2 0HW
Tel: 020 8980 2673
Principal: Mr Maulana Muhammad
Hasan Chowdhury
Age range: B11–18 years
(icons)

Forest School
College Place, Snaresbrook,
London E17 3PY
Tel: 020 8520 1744
Warden: Mr Marcus Cliff Hodges
Age range: 4–18 years
(icons)

Madani Girls School
Myrdle Street, London E1 1HL
Tel: 020 7377 1992
Principal: Muhammad S. Rahman
Age range: G11–18 years
(icons)

UK Community College (UKCC)
566 Romford Road, London E12 5AF
Tel: 07979 547727
Age range: 7–18 years

North London

Beis Rochel D'Satmar Girls School
51-57 Amhurst Park, London N16 5DL
Tel: 020 8800 9060
Head of School: Mrs Elka Katz
Age range: G2–18 years
(icons)

Channing School
The Bank, Highgate, London N6 5HF
Tel: 020 8340 2328
Headmistress: Mrs Lindsey Hughes
Age range: G4–18 years
(icons)

Dwight School London
6 Friern Barnet Lane,
London N11 3LX
Tel: 020 8920 0600
Head: Chris Beddows
Age range: 2–18 years
(icons)

Greek Secondary School of London
22 Trinity Road, London N22 8LB
Tel: +44 (0)20 8881 9320
Headteacher:
Ms Sandra Doropoulou
Age range: 12–18 years

Highgate
North Road, Highgate,
London N6 4AY
Tel: 020 8340 1524
Head Master: Mr Adam Pettitt MA
Age range: 4–18 years
No. of pupils: 1935
(icons)

Lubavitch House School (Senior Girls)
107-115 Stamford Hill,
Hackney, London N16 5RP
Tel: 020 8800 0022
Headmaster:
Rabbi Shmuel Lew FRSA
Age range: G11–18 years
No. of pupils: 102
Fees: Day £3,900
(icons)

North Bridge House Senior Canonbury
6-9 Canonbury Place,
Islington, London N1 2NQ
Tel: 020 7428 1520
Head of School: Mr Brendan Pavey
Age range: 11–18 years
No. of pupils: 220
Fees: Day £19,230–£21,735
(icons)

North London Grammar School
110 Colindeep Lane, Hendon,
London NW9 6HB
Tel: 0208 205 0052
Headteacher: Mr Fatih Adak
Age range: 7–18 years

Phoenix Academy
85 Bounces Road, Edmonton,
London N9 8LD
Tel: 020 8887 6888
Head Teacher: Mr Paul Kelly
Age range: 5–18 years

Tayyibah Girls School
88 Filey Avenue, Hackney,
London N16 6JJ
Tel: 020 8880 0085
Head Teacher: Mrs Sumeya Patel
Age range: G4–18 years
(icons)

North-West London

Brampton College
Lodge House, Lodge Road,
Hendon, London NW4 4DQ
Tel: 020 8203 5025
Principal: Mr Bernard Canetti
Age range: 15–19 years
(icons)

Francis Holland School, Regent's Park, NW1
Clarence Gate, Ivor Place,
Regent's Park, London NW1 6XR
Tel: 020 7723 0176
Head of School:
Mrs Katharine Woodcock
Age range: G11–18 years
No. of pupils: 556 VIth120
Fees: Day £22,890
(icons)

Hampstead Fine Arts College
Centre Studios, 41-43 England's
Lane, London NW3 4YD
Tel: +44 (0)207 586 0312
Principal: Ms Candida Cave
Age range: 13–19 years
(icons)

Lakefield Catering & Educational Centre
Maresfield Gardens,
Hampstead, London NW3 5RY
Tel: 020 7794 5669
Course Director: Mrs Maria Brown
Age range: G16–24
No. of pupils: 16
Fees: FB £1,160
(icons)

Mill Hill School
The Ridgeway, Mill Hill
Village, London NW7 1QS
Tel: 020 8959 1176
Head:
Mrs Jane Sanchez BSc (Hons) PGCE
Age range: 13–18 years
(boarding from 13)
No. of pupils: 876 VIth312
Fees: Day £21,987 WB £31,140
FB £36,900
(icons)

NORTH BRIDGE HOUSE SENIOR HAMPSTEAD
For further details see p. 61
65 Rosslyn Hill, London NW3 5UD
Tel: 020 7428 1520
Email: admissionsenquiries@
northbridgehouse.com
Website:
www.northbridgehouse.com
Executive Headteacher:
Brendan Pavey
Age range: 2–18 years
No. of pupils: 1430

South Hampstead High School GDST
3 Maresfield Gardens,
London NW3 5SS
Tel: 020 7435 2899
Headmistress:
Mrs Victoria Bingham MA (Oxon)
Age range: G4–18 years
(icons)

The American School in London
One Waverley Place,
London NW8 0NP
Tel: +44 (0)20 7449 1200
Head of School:
Ms Coreen R. Hester
Age range: 4–18 years
(icons)

Specialist schools and sixth form colleges

London

Central London

City of London School
Queen Victoria Street,
London EC4V 3AL
Tel: 020 3680 6300
Head: Mr A R Bird MSc
Age range: B10–18 years
No. of pupils: 950 VIth250
Fees: Day £21,057
(†)(A)(£)(✐)(16+)

City of London School for Girls
St Giles' Terrace, Barbican,
London EC2Y 8BB
Tel: 020 7847 5500
Headmistress: Ms Jenny Brown
Age range: G11–18 years
(♣)(A)(£)(✐)(16+)

École Jeannine Manuel – London
43-45 Bedford Square,
London WC1B 3DN
Tel: 020 3829 5970
Head of School: Pauline Prévot
Age range: 3–18 years
No. of pupils: 585
Fees: Day £20,760
(🌐)(£)(IB)

Guildhouse School
43-45 Bloomsbury Square,
London WC1A 2RA
Tel: +44 (0)1223 341300
Headmaster: Mr James Slocombe
Age range: 15–24 years
(🌐)(🏛)(£)(16+)

Italia Conti Academy of Theatre Arts
Italia Conti House, 23 Goswell
Road, London EC1M 7AJ
Tel: 020 7608 0047
Director: Chris White
Age range: 10–21 years
(16+)(A)(16+)

The Royal Ballet School (Covent Garden)
46 Floral Street, Covent
Garden, London WC2E 9DA
Tel: 020 7836 8899
Head of School:
Mr David Gajadharsingh
Age range: 11–19 years
(boarding from 11)
(🏛)

East London

Darul Hadis Latifiah
1 Cornwall Avenue, Bethnal
Green, London E2 0HW
Tel: 020 8980 2673
Principal: Mr Maulana Muhammad
Hasan Chowdhury
Age range: B11–18 years
(†)

Forest School
College Place, Snaresbrook,
London E17 3PY
Tel: 020 8520 1744
Warden: Mr Marcus Cliff Hodges
Age range: 4–18 years
(A)(£)(✐)(16+)

Madani Girls School
Myrdle Street, London E1 1HL
Tel: 020 7377 1992
Principal: Muhammad S. Rahman
Age range: G11–18 years
(♣)

UK Community College (UKCC)
566 Romford Road, London E12 5AF
Tel: 07979 547727
Age range: 7–18 years

North London

Beis Rochel D'Satmar Girls School
51-57 Amhurst Park, London N16 5DL
Tel: 020 8800 9060
Head of School: Mrs Elka Katz
Age range: G2–18 years
(♣)

Channing School
The Bank, Highgate, London N6 5HF
Tel: 020 8340 2328
Headmistress: Mrs Lindsey Hughes
Age range: G4–18 years
(♣)(£)(✐)(16+)

Dwight School London
6 Friern Barnet Lane,
London N11 3LX
Tel: 020 8920 0600
Head: Chris Beddows
Age range: 2–18 years
(🌐)(£)(IB)(✐)(16+)

Greek Secondary School of London
22 Trinity Road, London N22 8LB
Tel: +44 (0)20 8881 9320
Headteacher:
Ms Sandra Doropoulou
Age range: 12–18 years

Highgate
North Road, Highgate,
London N6 4AY
Tel: 020 8340 1524
Head Master: Mr Adam Pettitt MA
Age range: 4–18 years
No. of pupils: 1935
(A)(£)(✐)(16+)

Lubavitch House School (Senior Girls)
107-115 Stamford Hill,
Hackney, London N16 5RP
Tel: 020 8800 0022
Headmaster:
Rabbi Shmuel Lew FRSA
Age range: G11–18 years
No. of pupils: 102
Fees: Day £3,900
(♣)(A)

North Bridge House Senior Canonbury
6-9 Canonbury Place,
Islington, London N1 2NQ
Tel: 020 7428 1520
Head of School: Mr Brendan Pavey
Age range: 11–18 years
No. of pupils: 220
Fees: Day £19,230–£21,735
(£)(✐)

North London Grammar School
110 Colindeep Lane, Hendon,
London NW9 6HB
Tel: 0208 205 0052
Headteacher: Mr Fatih Adak
Age range: 7–18 years

Phoenix Academy
85 Bounces Road, Edmonton,
London N9 8LD
Tel: 020 8887 6888
Head Teacher: Mr Paul Kelly
Age range: 5–18 years

Tayyibah Girls School
88 Filey Avenue, Hackney,
London N16 6JJ
Tel: 020 8880 0085
Head Teacher: Mrs Sumeya Patel
Age range: G4–18 years
(♣)

North-West London

Brampton College
Lodge House, Lodge Road,
Hendon, London NW4 4DQ
Tel: 020 8203 5025
Principal: Mr Bernard Canetti
Age range: 15–19 years
(16+)(A)

Francis Holland School, Regent's Park, NW1
Clarence Gate, Ivor Place,
Regent's Park, London NW1 6XR
Tel: 020 7723 0176
Head of School:
Mrs Katharine Woodcock
Age range: G11–18 years
No. of pupils: 556 VIth120
Fees: Day £22,890
(♣)(A)(£)(16+)

Hampstead Fine Arts College
Centre Studios, 41-43 England's
Lane, London NW3 4YD
Tel: +44 (0)207 586 0312
Principal: Ms Candida Cave
Age range: 13–19 years
(16+)

Lakefield Catering & Educational Centre
Maresfield Gardens,
Hampstead, London NW3 5RY
Tel: 020 7794 5669
Course Director: Mrs Maria Brown
Age range: G16–24
No. of pupils: 16
Fees: FB £1,160
(♣)(16+)(🏛)(£)(✐)(16+)(🐾)

Mill Hill School
The Ridgeway, Mill Hill
Village, London NW7 1QS
Tel: 020 8959 1176
Head:
Mrs Jane Sanchez BSc (Hons) PGCE
Age range: 13–18 years
(boarding from 13)
No. of pupils: 876 VIth312
Fees: Day £21,987 WB £31,140
FB £36,900
(♣)(A)(🏛)(£)(✐)(16+)

**NORTH BRIDGE HOUSE
SENIOR HAMPSTEAD**
For further details see p. 61
65 Rosslyn Hill, London NW3 5UD
Tel: 020 7428 1520
Email: admissionsenquiries@
northbridgehouse.com
Website:
www.northbridgehouse.com
Executive Headteacher:
Brendan Pavey
Age range: 2–18 years
No. of pupils: 1430
(✐)

South Hampstead High School GDST
3 Maresfield Gardens,
London NW3 5SS
Tel: 020 7435 2899
Headmistress:
Mrs Victoria Bingham MA (Oxon)
Age range: G4–18 years
(♣)(A)(£)(✐)(16+)

The American School in London
One Waverley Place,
London NW8 0NP
Tel: +44 (0)20 7449 1200
Head of School:
Ms Coreen R. Hester
Age range: 4–18 years
(🌐)(16+)

The King Alfred School
North End Road, London NW11 7HY
Tel: 020 8457 5200
Head: Robert Lobatto MA (Oxon)
Age range: 4–18 years
No. of pupils: 670
Ⓐ 🖊 16⁺

The Mount, Mill Hill International
Milespit Hill, London NW7 2RX
Tel: +44 (0)20 3826 33
Head of School: Ms Sarah Bellotti
Age range: 13–17 years
No. of pupils: 80
Fees: Day £27,000 WB £37,500
FB £44,250
🏃 £

University College School Hampstead (UCS) Senior
Frognal, Hampstead,
London NW3 6XH
Tel: 020 7435 2215
Headmaster: Mr Mark J Beard
Age range: B11–18 years
G16–18 years
🏃 Ⓐ £ 🖊 16⁺

Wentworth College
6-10 Brentmead Place,
London NW11 9LH
Tel: 020 8458 8524
Principal: Mr Manuel Guimaraes
Age range: 14–19 years
16⁺ Ⓐ 16⁺

South-East London

Alleyn's School
Townley Road, Dulwich,
London SE22 8SU
Tel: 020 8557 1500
Head of School: Ms Jane Lunnon
Age range: 4–18 years
Ⓐ 🖊 16⁺

Blackheath High School GDST
Vanbrugh Park, Blackheath,
London SE3 7AG
Tel: 020 8853 2929
Acting Head: Ms Natalie Argile
Age range: G3–18 years
🏃 Ⓐ £ 🖊 16⁺

Colfe's School
Horn Park Lane, London SE12 8AW
Tel: 020 8852 2283
Head of School: Mr R Russell
Age range: 3–18 years
Ⓐ £ 🖊 16⁺

DLD College London
199 Westminster Bridge
Road, London SE1 7FX
Tel: +44 (0)20 7935 8411
Principal: Mr Irfan H Latif
Age range: 13–19 years
🌐 16⁺ Ⓐ 🏛 £ 🖊

Dulwich College
Dulwich Common,
London SE21 7LD
Tel: 020 8693 3601
Master: Dr J A F Spence
Age range: B6 months–18
years G6 months–7 years
Fees: Day £21,672 WB £42,408
FB £45,234
🏃 🌐 Ⓐ 🏛 £ 🖊 16⁺

Eltham College
Grove Park Road, Mottingham,
London SE9 4QF
Tel: 0208 857 1455
Headmaster: Mr Guy R Sanderson
Age range: 7–18 years
Ⓐ £ 🖊 16⁺

Greenwich Steiner School
90 Mycenae Road, London SE3 7SE
Tel: 020 8858 4404
Executive Principal:
Mr Allan Osborne
Age range: 3–18 years

James Allen's Girls' School
144 East Dulwich Grove,
Dulwich, London SE22 8TE
Tel: 020 8693 1181
Head of School:
Mrs Alex Hutchinson
Age range: G4–18 years
🏃 Ⓐ £ 🖊 16⁺

Marathon Science School
1-9 Evelyn Street, Surrey
Quays, London SE8 5RQ
Tel: 020 7231 3232
Headteacher: Mr Mehmet Yilmaz
Age range: B11–18 years
🏃 🏛

Riverston School
63/69 Eltham Road, Lee,
London SE12 8UF
Tel: 020 8318 4327
Headmaster:
Mr David A T Ward MA
Age range: 9 months–19 years

St Dunstan's College
Stanstead Road, London SE6 4TY
Tel: 020 8516 7200
Head of School: Mr Nick Hewlett
Age range: 3–18 years
🌐 16⁺

Sydenham High School GDST
15 & 19 Westwood Hill,
London SE26 6BL
Tel: 020 8557 7004
Head of School:
Ms Antonia Geldeard
Age range: G4–18 years
🏃 Ⓐ £ 🖊 16⁺

The Cedars School
147 Central Hill, Upper
Norwood, London SE19 1RS
Tel: 020 8185 7770
Headmaster: Mr Robert Teague
Age range: B11–18 years
🏃

The Laurels School
1 Our Lady's Close, Upper
Norwood, London SE19 3FA
Tel: 020 8674 7229
Headmistress: Mrs Linda Sanders
BA Hons (Bristol), MA (Madrid)
Age range: G11–18 years
🏃

South-West London

Centre Academy London
92 St John's Hill, Battersea,
London SW11 1SH
Tel: 020 7738 2344
Head of School:
Mrs. Kas Lee-Douglas
Age range: 9–19 years
🌐 🖊 16⁺

Collingham College
23 Collingham Gardens,
London SW5 0HL
Tel: 020 7244 7414
Principal: Ms Sally Powell
Age range: 13–19 years
🌐 16⁺ Ⓐ

Emanuel School
Battersea Rise, London SW11 1HS
Tel: 020 8870 4171
Headmaster: Mr Robert Milne
Age range: 10–18 years
Ⓐ £ 16⁺

Francis Holland School, Sloane Square, SW1
39 Graham Terrace,
London SW1W 8JF
Tel: 020 7730 2971
Head: Mrs Lucy Elphinstone
MA(Cantab)
Age range: G4–18 years
🏃 Ⓐ £ 16⁺

Hall School Wimbledon
17, The Downs, Wimbledon,
London SW20 8HF
Tel: 020 8879 9200
Headmaster: Mr. A Hammond
Age range: 5–18 years
No. of pupils: 160
Fees: Day £4,570–£6,140
🖊

Harrodian
Lonsdale Road, London SW13 9QN
Tel: 020 8748 6117
Headmaster: Mr James R Hooke
Age range: 4–18 years
Ⓐ £ 🖊 16⁺

Ibstock Place School
Clarence Lane, Roehampton,
London SW15 5PY
Tel: 020 8876 9991
Head of School:
Mr Christopher J Wolsey
Age range: 4–18 years
Ⓐ £ 16⁺

Kensington Park School
40-44 Bark Place, Bayswater,
London W2 4AT
Tel: +44 (0)20 7616 4400
Headmaster: Mr Stephen Mellor
Age range: 11–18 years
Ⓐ 🏛

King's College School
Southside, Wimbledon
Common, London SW19 4TT
Tel: 020 8255 5300
Head: Dr Anne Cotton
Age range: B7–18 years
G16–18 years
No. of pupils: 1478
🏃 🌐 Ⓐ £ IB 16⁺

LONDON PARK SCHOOL, CLAPHAM
For further details see p. 54
7-11 Nightingale Lane, Clapham
South, London SW4 9AH
Tel: 020 8161 0301
Email: admissions@
londonparkschools.com
Website:
www.londonparkschools.com
Head: Mr Paul Vanni
Age range: 11–16 (plus 16-18
in standalone Sixth Form)
No. of pupils: 250
Fees: Day £7,535

LYCÉE FRANÇAIS CHARLES DE GAULLE DE LONDRES
For further details see p. 55
35 Cromwell Road,
London SW7 2DG
Tel: 020 7584 6322
Email:
inscription@lyceefrancais.org.uk
Website:
www.lyceefrancais.org.uk
Head of School: TBC
Age range: 3–18 years
No. of pupils: 3450
Fees: Day £7,631–£15,965
🌐 £ 🖊 16⁺

MANDER PORTMAN WOODWARD – MPW LONDON
For further details see p. 58
90-92 Queen's Gate,
London SW7 5AB
Tel: 020 7835 1355
Email: london@mpw.ac.uk
Website: www.mpw.ac.uk
Principal:
Mr Steve Boyes BA, MSc, PGCE
Age range: 14–19 years
No. of pupils: 600
Fees: Day £10,765
16⁺ Ⓐ 🏛 £ 🖊

MORE HOUSE SCHOOL
For further details see p. 60
22-24 Pont Street, Knightsbridge,
London SW1X 0AA
Tel: 020 7235 2855
Email:
registrar@morehousemail.org.uk
Website:
www.morehouse.org.uk
Head: Ms Faith Hagerty
Age range: G11–18 years
No. of pupils: 145
Fees: Day £7,750
🚶 Ⓐ £ ✎ 16•

Putney High School GDST
35 Putney Hill, London SW15 6BH
Tel: 020 8788 4886
Headmistress:
Mrs Suzie Longstaff BA, MA, PGCE
Age range: G4–18 years
🚶 Ⓐ £ ✎ 16•

Queen's Gate School
133 Queen's Gate, London SW7 5LE
Tel: 020 7589 3587
Principal: Miss Amy Wallace MA
MPhil (Cantab), PGCE (Oxon)
Age range: G4–18 years
No. of pupils: 500 VIth81
🚶 Ⓐ £ ✎ 16•

St Paul's School
Lonsdale Road, Barnes,
London SW13 9JT
Tel: 020 8748 9162
High Master: Ms Sally-Anne Huang
Age range: B7–18 years
🚶 🌐 Ⓐ £ ✎ 16•

**Streatham & Clapham
High School GDST**
42 Abbotswood Road,
London SW16 1AW
Tel: 020 8677 8400
Executive Head: Mrs Isabel Tobias
MA (Cantab), PGCE
Age range: G3–18 years
🚶 Ⓐ £ ✎ 16•

Swedish School in London
82 Lonsdale Road, Barnes,
London SW13 9JS
Tel: 020 8741 1751
Head of School:
Ms. Jenny Abrahamsson
Age range: 3–18 years
16•

Thomas's Outdoors
Stroud Crescent, London SW15 3EQ
Tel: 020 7751 8200
Head of School: Mr Paul Wild
Age range: 4–18 years

Westminster School
17A Dean's Yard, Westminster,
London SW1P 3PB
Tel: 020 7963 1000
Head Master: Dr Gary Savage
Age range: B13–18 years
G16–18 years
🚶 🌐 Ⓐ £ ✎ 16•

Westminster Tutors
86 Old Brompton Road, South
Kensington, London SW7 3LQ
Tel: 020 7584 1288
Principal: Joe Mattei
Age range: 14+ years
No. of pupils: VIth40
Fees: Day £4,000–£25,000
16• Ⓐ £ ✎

**Wimbledon High
School GDST**
Mansel Road, Wimbledon,
London SW19 4AB
Tel: 020 8971 0900
Head of School:
Ms Fionnuala Kennedy
Age range: G4–18 years
🚶 Ⓐ £ ✎ 16•

West London

**Albemarle Independent
College**
18 Dunraven Street, Mayfair,
London W1K 7FE
Tel: 02074 097273
Co-Principals:
Beverley Mellon & James Eytle
Age range: 14–19 years
16• Ⓐ 16•

**ArtsEd Day School
& Sixth Form**
14 Bath Road, Chiswick,
London W4 1LY
Tel: 020 8987 6666
Headteacher: Mr Matthew Bulmer
Age range: 11–18 years

Ashbourne College
17 Old Court Place,
Kensington, London W8 4PL
Tel: 020 7937 3858
Principal: Mr Michael Kirby MSc,
BApSc, MInstD
Age range: 13–21 years
16• Ⓐ £

Bales College
2 Kilburn Lane, London W10 4AA
Tel: 020 8960 5899
Principal: Mr William Moore
Age range: 11–18 years
🌐 16• Ⓐ 🏛 £

David Game College
31 Jewry Street, London EC3N 2ET
Tel: 02072 216665
Principal: D T P Game MA, MPhil
Age range: 13–22 years
16• Ⓐ 🏛 16•

**Ealing Independent
College**
83 New Broadway, Ealing,
London W5 5AL
Tel: 020 8579 6668
Headteacher: Allan Cairns
Age range: 13–19 years
No. of pupils: 96
16• Ⓐ 16•

**Eaton Square
Senior School**
106 Piccadilly, Mayfair,
London W1J 7NL
Tel: +44 (0)20 7491 7393
Headteacher: Dr Adrian Rainbow
Age range: 11–18 years

FULHAM SCHOOL
For further details see p. 47
1-3 Chesilton Road,
London SW6 5AA
Tel: 020 8154 6751
Email: senioradmin@
fulham.school
Website: fulham.school
Executive Head of Fulham:
Bex Tear
Age range: 3–18 years
No. of pupils: 650
Fees: Day £19,158–£22,431
🌐 Ⓐ ✎

**Godolphin and
Latymer School**
Iffley Road, Hammersmith,
London W6 0PG
Tel: +44 (0)20 8741 1936
Head Mistress: Dr Frances Ramsey
Age range: G11–18 years
No. of pupils: 800
Fees: Day £25,185
🚶 🌐 Ⓐ £ IB ✎ 16•

**Halcyon London
International School**
33 Seymour Place, London W1H 5AU
Tel: +44 (0)20 7258 1169
Director: Mr Barry Mansfield
Age range: 11–18 years
🌐 £ IB

ICS London
7B Wyndham Place,
London W1H 1PN
Tel: +44 (0)20 729 88800
Head of School: Alec Jiggins
Age range: 3–18 years
No. of pupils: 175
Fees: Day £19,770–£28,920
🌐 IB 16•

**Instituto Español Vicente
Cañada Blanch**
317 Portobello Road,
London W10 5SZ
Tel: +44 (0) 20 8969 2664
Head of School:
Mr Antonio Simón Saiz
Age range: 3–18 years
🌐

**International School
of London (ISL)**
139 Gunnersbury Avenue,
London W3 8LG
Tel: +44 (0)20 8992 5823
Principal: Mr Richard Parker
Age range: 3–18 years
No. of pupils: 420
Fees: Day £20,850–£28,850
🌐 IB 16•

King Fahad Academy
Bromyard Avenue, Acton,
London W3 7HD
Tel: 020 8743 0131
Director General: Dr Tahani Aljafari
Age range: 3–18 years
🌐 Ⓐ £ IB 16•

Latymer Upper School
King Street, Hammersmith,
London W6 9LR
Tel: 020 8629 2024
Head: Mr David Goodhew
Age range: 11–18 years
Ⓐ £ ✎ 16•

**Leiths School of
Food & Wine**
16-20 Wendell Road, Shepherd's
Bush, London W12 9RT
Tel: 020 8749 6400
Age range: 17+ years
16•

MAIDA VALE SCHOOL
For further details see p. 56
18 Saltram Crescent,
London W9 3HR
Tel: 020 4511 6000
Email: admissions@
maidavaleschool.com
Website:
www.maidavaleschool.com
Headmaster:
Mr Magnus Bashaarat
Age range: 11–18 years
No. of pupils: 160
Fees: Day £8,073

**Notting Hill & Ealing
High School GDST**
2 Cleveland Road, West
Ealing, London W13 8AX
Tel: (020) 8799 8400
Headmaster: Mr Matthew Shoults
Age range: G4–18 years
🚶 Ⓐ £ 16•

Queen's College
43-49 Harley Street,
London W1G 8BT
Tel: 020 7291 7000
Principal: Mr Richard Tillet
Age range: G11–18 years
🚶 16•

**Ray Cochrane
Beauty School**
118 Baker Street, London W1U 6TT
Tel: 02033 896888
Heads of Education:
Xubin Yuan & Eleonora Androva
Age range: 16+ years
16• 16• 🌸

Sassoon Academy
5 Ave Maria Lane,
London EC4M 7AQ
Tel: 02080 163812
Academy Principal & Educator:
Mr Joshua Gibson
Age range: 16+ years
16• 16• 🌸

Southbank International School – Kensington
36-38 Kensington Park Road, London W11 3BU
Tel: +44 (0)20 7243 3803
Principal: Siobhan McGrath
Age range: 3–18 years

Southbank International School – Westminster
63-65 Portland Place, London W1B 1QR
Tel: 020 7243 3803
Principal: Dr Paul Wood
Age range: 11–19 years

St Augustine's Priory
Hillcrest Road, Ealing, London W5 2JL
Tel: 020 8997 2022
Headteacher: Mrs Sarah Raffray M.A., N.P.Q.H
Age range: B3–4 years G3–18 years

ST BENEDICT'S SCHOOL
For further details see p. 64
54 Eaton Rise, Ealing, London W5 2ES
Tel: 020 8862 2000
Email: admissions@stbenedicts.org.uk
Website: www.stbenedicts.org.uk
Headmaster: Mr A Johnson BA
Age range: 3–18 years
No. of pupils: 1083 VIth185
Fees: Day £14,940–£19,575

St James Senior Girls' School
Earsby Street, London W14 8SH
Tel: 02073 481777
Headmistress: Mrs Sarah Labram BA
Age range: G11–18 years

St Paul's Girls' School
Brook Green, Hammersmith, London W6 7BS
Tel: 020 7603 2288
High Mistress: Mrs Sarah Fletcher
Age range: G11–18 years

Wetherby Senior School
100 Marylebone Lane, London W1U 2QU
Tel: 020 7535 3530
Headmaster: Mr Joe Silvester
Age range: B11–18 years

Berkshire

Bradfield College
Bradfield, Berkshire RG7 6AU
Tel: 0118 964 4516
Headmaster: Dr Christopher Stevens
Age range: 13–18 years
No. of pupils: 820
Fees: Day £33,732 FB £42,165

Claires Court Nursery, Girls and Sixth Form
1 College Avenue, Maidenhead, Berkshire SL6 6AW
Tel: 01628 327500
Head of Juniors: Ms Leanne Kirby
Age range: B16–18 years G2–18 years

Eton College
Windsor, Berkshire SL4 6DW
Tel: +44 (0)1753 370 611
Head Master: Mr Simon Henderson MA
Age range: B13–18 years
No. of pupils: 1342
Fees: FB £44,094

Heathfield School
London Road, Ascot, Berkshire SL5 8BQ
Tel: 01344 898343
Head of School: Ms Sarah Wilson
Age range: G11–18 years (boarding from 11)
Fees: Day £7,840–£8,000 FB £12,650–£12,950

Langley Hall Arts Academy
Symphony House, 4 Waterside Court, Langley, Berkshire SL3 6EZ
Tel: 01753 900470
Principal: Mr Claudio Di Meo
Age range: 12–18 years

LEIGHTON PARK SCHOOL
For further details see p. 90
Shinfield Road, Reading, Berkshire RG2 7ED
Tel: 0118 987 9600
Email: admissions@leightonpark.com
Website: www.leightonpark.com
Head: Mr Matthew L S Judd BA, PGCE
Age range: 11–18 years
No. of pupils: 550

Luckley House School
Luckley Road, Wokingham, Berkshire RG40 3EU
Tel: 0118 978 4175
Head: Mrs Areti Bizior
Age range: 11–18 years

LVS ASCOT
For further details see p. 92
London Road, Ascot, Berkshire SL5 8DR
Tel: 01344 882770
Email: enquiries@lvs.ascot.sch.uk
Website: www.lvs.ascot.sch.uk
Principal: Mrs Christine Cunniffe BA (Hons), MMus, MBA
Age range: 4–18 years
No. of pupils: 833
Fees: Day £11,640–£20,985 FB £29,760–£36,660

OneSchool Global UK Reading Campus (Senior)
The Quad, 14 Arkwright Road, Reading, Berkshire RG2 0LU
Tel: 03000 700421
Age range: 11–18 years

Padworth College
Sopers Lane, Reading, Berkshire RG7 4NR
Tel: 0118 983 2644
Principal: Lorraine Atkins
Age range: 14–19 years

Pangbourne College
Pangbourne, Reading, Berkshire RG8 8LA
Tel: 0118 984 2101
Headmaster: Thomas J C Garnier
Age range: 11–18 years
No. of pupils: 458
Fees: Day £6,300–£8,540 WB £8,210–£11,510 FB £9,050–£12,680

Queen Anne's School
6 Henley Road, Caversham, Reading, Berkshire RG4 6DX
Tel: 0118 918 7300
Head: Ms Elaine Purves
Age range: G11–18 years (boarding from 11)
No. of pupils: G450
Fees: Day £8,370 FB £13,590

Reading Blue Coat School
Holme Park, Sonning Lane, Sonning, Reading, Berkshire RG4 6SU
Tel: 0118 944 1005
Headmaster: Mr Peter Thomas
Age range: B11–18 years G16–18 years

REDDAM HOUSE BERKSHIRE
For further details see p. 94
Bearwood Road, Sindlesham, Wokingham, Berkshire RG41 5BG
Tel: +44 (0)118 974 8300
Email: registrar@reddamhouse.org.uk
Website: www.reddamhouse.org.uk
Principal: Mr Rick Cross
Age range: 3 months–18 years
No. of pupils: 675
Fees: Day £12,006–£19,248 WB £29,241–£33,696 FB £30,855–£35,310

St George's Ascot
Wells Lane, Ascot, Berkshire SL5 7DZ
Tel: 01344 629900
Headmistress: Mrs Liz Hewer MA (Hons) (Cantab) PGCE
Age range: G11–18 years (boarding from 11)

St Joseph's College
Upper Redlands Road,
Reading, Berkshire RG1 5JT
Tel: 0118 966 1000
Head of School:
Mrs Laura Stotesbury
Age range: 3–18 years
(A) (£) 🖊 (16)

St Mary's School Ascot
St Mary's Road, Ascot,
Berkshire SL5 9JF
Tel: 01344 296614
Headmistress: Mrs Danuta Staunton
Age range: G11–18 years
(boarding from 11)
🏃 🌐 (A) 🏛 (£) (16)

The Abbey School
Kendrick Road, Reading,
Berkshire RG1 5DZ
Tel: 0118 987 2256
Head: Mr Will le Fleming
Age range: G3–18 years
No. of pupils: 1000
Fees: Day £11,535–£19,830
🏃 🌐 (A) 🏛 (£) (IB) 🖊 (16)

The Marist School
King's Road, Sunninghill,
Ascot, Berkshire SL5 7PS
Tel: 01344 624291
Principal: Ms Jo Smith
Age range: G2–18 years
🏃 (A) (16)

The Oratory School
Woodcote, Reading,
Berkshire RG8 0PJ
Tel: 01491 683500
Head Master: Mr Joe Smith
BA(Hons), MEd, PGCE
Age range: 11–18 years
🌐 (A) 🏛 (£) 🖊 (16)

The Vine Christian School
Three Mile Cross Church,
Basingstoke Road, Three Mile
Cross, Reading, Berkshire RG7 1HF
Tel: 0118 988 6464
Head of School:
Mrs René Esterhuizen
Age range: 3–18 years

Wellington College
Duke's Ride, Crowthorne,
Berkshire RG45 7PU
Tel: +44 (0)1344 444000
Master: Mr James Dahl
Age range: 13–18 years
No. of pupils: 1100 VIth485
Fees: Day £32,940–£35,760
FB £45,090
🌐 (A) 🏛 (£) (IB) 🖊 (16)

Buckinghamshire

Akeley Wood School
Akeley Wood House, Buckingham,
Buckinghamshire MK18 5AE
Tel: 01280 814110
Headmaster: Mr Simon Antwis
Age range: 12 months–18 years
No. of pupils: 700 VIth100
Fees: Day £10,665–£15,900
(A) (£) 🖊 (16)

**International School of
Creative Arts (ISCA)**
Framewood Road, Wexham,
Buckinghamshire SL2 4QS
Tel: +44 (0)1753 208820
Head of School: Mr Robert Hunter
Age range: 15–19 years
No. of pupils: 85
🌐 🏛

Pipers Corner School
Pipers Lane, Great
Kingshill, High Wycombe,
Buckinghamshire HP15 6LP
Tel: 01494 718 255
Headmistress: Mrs H J Ness-Gifford
BA(Hons), PGCE
Age range: G4–18 years
🏃 (A) 🏛 (£) 🖊 (16) 🌸

St Mary's School
94 Packhorse Road, Gerrards
Cross, Buckinghamshire SL9 8JQ
Tel: 01753 883370
Head of School: Mrs Patricia Adams
Age range: G3–18 years
🏃 (A) (£) 🖊 (16)

Stowe School
Buckingham, Buckinghamshire
MK18 5EH
Tel: 01280 818000
Headmaster:
Dr Anthony Wallersteiner
Age range: 13–18 years
🌐 (A) 🏛 (£) 🖊 (16)

Teikyo School UK
Framewood Road, Wexham,
Buckinghamshire SL2 4QS
Tel: 01753 663711
Age range: 15–18 years
🌐 🏛 (IB)

Thornton College
College Lane, Thornton, Milton
Keynes, Buckinghamshire MK17 0HJ
Tel: 01280 812610
Headteacher: Dr Louise Shaw
Age range: G3–18 years
(boarding from 8)
No. of pupils: 402
Fees: Day £11,190–£17,835 WB
£19,830–£25,095 FB £24,660–£30,585
🏃 🌐 (A) 🏛 🖊

Wycombe Abbey
Frances Dove Way, High Wycombe,
Buckinghamshire HP11 1PE
Tel: +44 (0)1494 520381
Headmistress: Mrs Jo Duncan MA
(St Andrews), PGCE (Cantab)
Age range: G11–18 years
No. of pupils: 660
Fees: Day £33,150 FB £44,100
🏃 🌐 (A) 🏛 (£) 🖊 (16)

East Sussex

**Bartholomews
Tutorial College**
22-23 Prince Albert Street,
Brighton, East Sussex BN1 1HF
Tel: 01273 205965/205141
Age range: 14+ years
No. of pupils: 40
Fees: Day £22,000
(16) (A) 🖊

Battle Abbey School
High Street, Battle, East
Sussex TN33 0AD
Tel: 01424 772385
Headmaster:
Mr David Clark BA, M Phil (Cantab)
Age range: 3 months–18 years
(boarding from 11)
🌐 (A) 🏛 (£) 🖊 (16)

BEDE'S SENIOR SCHOOL
For further details see p. 82
Upper Dicker, Hailsham,
East Sussex BN27 3QH
Tel: 01323 356609
Email: admissions@bedes.org
Website: www.bedes.org/senior
Head: Mr Peter Goodyer
Age range: 13–18 years
(boarding from 13)
No. of pupils: 832
Fees: Day £8,300 WB £12,240
FB £12,990
🌐 (A) 🏛 (£) 🖊 (16)

Brighton College
Eastern Road, Brighton,
East Sussex BN2 0AL
Tel: 01273 704200
Head Master: Richard Cairns
Age range: 3–18 years
🌐 (A) 🏛 (£) 🖊 (16)

Brighton Girls GDST
Montpelier Road, Brighton,
East Sussex BN1 3AT
Tel: 01273 280280
Head: Ms Rosie McColl
Age range: G4–18 years
🏃 (A) (£) 🖊 (16)

Buckswood School
Broomham Hall, Rye
Road, Guestling, Hastings,
East Sussex TN35 4LT
Tel: 01424 813 813
Co-Principals:
Michael Shaw & Kevin Samson
Age range: 10–19 years
🌐 (A) 🏛 (£) (IB) 🖊 (16)

Claremont School
Bodiam, Nr Robertsbridge,
East Sussex TN32 5UJ
Tel: 01580 830396
Age range: 3 months–18
years (boarding from 10)
🏛

Eastbourne College
Old Wish Road, Eastbourne,
East Sussex BN21 4JX
Tel: 01323 452323 (Admissions)
Headmaster:
Mr Tom Lawson MA (Oxon)
Age range: 13–18 years
🌐 (A) 🏛 (£) 🖊 (16)

**Greenfields Independent
Day & Boarding School**
Priory Road, Forest Row,
East Sussex RH18 5JD
Tel: +44 (0)1342 822189
Executive Head: Mr. Jeff Smith
Age range: 2–18 years
(boarding from 10)
🌐 (A) 🏛 🖊 (16)

Lewes Old Grammar School
140 High Street, Lewes,
East Sussex BN7 1XS
Tel: 01273 472634
Headmaster: Mr Robert Blewitt
Age range: 3–18 years
🖋 16+

MAYFIELD SCHOOL
For further details see p. 93
The Old Palace, Mayfield,
East Sussex TN20 6PH
Tel: 01435 874642
Email:
registrar@mayfieldgirls.org
Website: www.mayfieldgirls.org
Head: Ms Antonia Beary MA,
MPhil (Cantab), PGCE
Age range: G11–18 years
(boarding from 11)
No. of pupils: 425
👤 🌐 Ⓐ 🏛 £ 🖋 16+

ROEDEAN SCHOOL
For further details see p. 95
Roedean Way, Brighton,
East Sussex BN2 5RQ
Tel: 01273 667500
Email: info@roedean.co.uk
Website: www.roedean.co.uk
Head of School: Niamh Green
Age range: G11–18 years
(boarding from 11)
No. of pupils: 700
Fees: Day £6,290–£8,220
WB £11,120–£12,400
FB £12,180–£14,745
👤 🌐 Ⓐ 🏛 £ 🖋 16+

The Montessori Place
45 Cromwell Road, Hove,
East Sussex BN3 3ER
Tel: 01273 773 764
Head of School:
Mr Rob Gueterbock
Age range: 15 months–18 years

Michael Hall School
Kidbrooke Park, Priory Road,
Forest Row, East Sussex RH18 5JA
Tel: 01342 822275
Head of School: Emmeline Hawker
Age range: 0–19 years
🌐 🖋 16+

Essex

Bancroft's School
High Road, Woodford
Green, Essex IG8 0RF
Tel: 020 8505 4821
Head: Mr Simon Marshall MA, PGCE
(Cantab), MA, MPhil (Oxon)
Age range: 7–18 years
Ⓐ £ 🖋 16+

Brentwood School
Middleton Hall Lane,
Brentwood, Essex CM15 8EE
Tel: 01277 243243
Headmaster: Mr Michael Bond
Age range: 3–18 years
No. of pupils: 1968
Fees: Day £21,783 FB £42,687
🌐 Ⓐ 🏛 £ IB 🖋 16+

CHIGWELL SCHOOL
For further details see p. 74
High Road, Chigwell,
Essex IG7 6QF
Tel: 020 8501 5700
Email:
admissions@chigwell-school.org
Website:
www.chigwell-school.org
Head Teacher: Mr Damian King
Age range: 4–18 years
🌐 Ⓐ 🏛 £ 🖋 16+
No. of pupils: 1057

Felsted School
Felsted, Great Dunmow,
Essex CM6 3LL
Tel: +44 (0)1371 822600
Headmaster: Mr Chris Townsend
Age range: 4–18 years
🌐 Ⓐ 🏛 £ IB 🖋 16+

Gosfield School
Cut Hedge Park, Halstead Road,
Gosfield, Halstead, Essex CO9 1PF
Tel: 01787 474040
Head of School: Mr Rod Jackson
Age range: 2–18 years
Fees: Day £7,680–£17,250
🌐 🖋

Guru Gobind Singh Khalsa College
Roding Lane, Chigwell,
Essex IG7 6BQ
Tel: 020 8559 9160
Principal: Mr Amarjit Singh Toor
BSc(Hons), BSc, BT
Age range: 3–19 years

New Hall School
The Avenue, Boreham,
Chelmsford, Essex CM3 3HS
Tel: 01245 467588
Principal: Mrs Katherine Jeffrey MA,
BA, PGCE, MA(Ed Mg), NPQH
Age range: 1–18 years
No. of pupils: 1400
Fees: Day £9,621–£20,502 WB
£18,234–£28,026 FB £21,177–£32,472
🌐 🏛 £ 🖋 16+

Hampshire

Alton School
Anstey Lane, Alton,
Hampshire GU34 2NG
Tel: 01420 82070
Headmaster: Mr Karl Guest
Age range: 0–18 years
No. of pupils: 400
Ⓐ Ⓔ ⑯

Bedales School
Church Road, Steep, Petersfield,
Hampshire GU32 2DG
Tel: 01730 300100
Head of School: Mr Will Goldsmith
Age range: 13–18 years

Brockwood Park School
Brockwood Park, Bramdean,
Alresford, Hampshire SO24 0LQ
Tel: +44 (0)1962 771744
Principal: Mr Antonio Autor
Age range: 14–19 years

Churcher's College
Petersfield, Hampshire GU31 4AS
Tel: 01730 263033
Headmaster:
Mr Simon Williams , MA, BSc
Age range: 3–18 years
Fees: Day £11,535–£17,265
Ⓐ Ⓔ ⑯

Embley
Embley Park, Romsey,
Hampshire SO51 6ZE
Tel: 01794 512206
Headteacher: Mr Cliff Canning
Age range: 2–18 years
No. of pupils: 600
Fees: Day £9,165–£17,004
WB £29,310 FB £9,598–£33,636

Farnborough Hill
Farnborough Road, Farnborough,
Hampshire GU14 8AT
Tel: 01252 545197
Head: Mrs A Neil BA, MEd, PGCE
Age range: G11–18 years

Hurst Lodge School
Yateley Hall, Firgrove Road,
Yateley, Hampshire GU46 6HJ
Tel: 01252 227002
Principal: Ms Victoria Smit
Age range: 4–19 years

King Edward VI School
Wilton Road, Southampton,
Hampshire SO15 5UQ
Tel: 023 8070 4561
Head Master: Mr N T Parker
Age range: 11–18 years
No. of pupils: 965
Fees: Day £18,645
Ⓐ Ⓔ ⑯

Lord Wandsworth College
Long Sutton, Hook,
Hampshire RG29 1TA
Tel: 01256 862201
Head of School: Mr Adam Williams
Age range: 11–18 years

Portsmouth High School GDST
Kent Road, Southsea, Portsmouth,
Hampshire PO5 3EQ
Tel: 023 9282 6714
Headmistress:
Mrs Jane Prescott BSc NPQH
Age range: G3–18 years
No. of pupils: 500
Fees: Day £2,574–£4,800

Ringwood Waldorf School
Folly Farm Lane, Ashley,
Ringwood, Hampshire BH24 2NN
Tel: 01425 472664
Age range: 3–18 years

Rookwood School
Weyhill Road, Andover,
Hampshire SP10 3AL
Tel: 01264 325900
Headmaster: Mr A Kirk-Burgess BSc,
PGCE, MSc (Oxon)
Age range: 2–18 years
(boarding from 7)

Salesian College
119 Reading Road, Farnborough,
Hampshire GU14 6PA
Tel: 01252 893000
Headmaster: Mr Gerard Owens
Age range: B11–18 years
G16–18 years

Sherfield School
South Drive, Sherfield-on-Loddon,
Hook, Hampshire RG27 0HU
Tel: 01256 884800
Headmaster: Mr Nick Brain
BA(Hons), PGCE, MA, NPQH
Age range: 3 months–18
years (boarding from 9)
No. of pupils: 625

ST SWITHUN'S SCHOOL
For further details see p. 97
Alresford Road, Winchester,
Hampshire SO21 1HA
Tel: 01962 835700
Email: office@stswithuns.com
Website: www.stswithuns.com
Head of School:
Jane Gandee MA(Cantab)
Age range: G11–18 years
No. of pupils: 492 VIth137
Fees: Day £23,478 FB £39,492

The Portsmouth Grammar School
High Street, Portsmouth,
Hampshire PO1 2LN
Tel: +44 (0)23 9236 0036
Age range: 2.5–18 years

Winchester College
College Street, Winchester,
Hampshire SO23 9NA
Tel: 01962 621100
Headmaster: Dr. T R Hands
Age range: B13–18 years
(boarding from 13)

Hertfordshire

Aldenham School
Elstree, Hertfordshire WD6 3AJ
Tel: 01923 858122
Headmaster: Mr James Fowler
Age range: 3–18 years

BERKHAMSTED SCHOOL
For further details see p. 84
Overton House, 131 High
Street, Berkhamsted,
Hertfordshire HP4 2DJ
Tel: 01442 358001
Email:
admissions@berkhamsted.com
Website:
www.berkhamsted.com
Principal: Mr Richard Backhouse
MA(Cantab)
Age range: 3–18 years
No. of pupils: 1883 VIth411
Fees: Day £10,110–£23,175
WB £31,500 FB £37,575

Bishop's Stortford College
School House, Maze Green
Road, Bishop's Stortford,
Hertfordshire CM23 2PQ
Tel: +44 (0)1279 838575
College Head:
Ms Kathy Crewe-Read
Age range: 13–18 years

Egerton Rothesay School
Durrants Lane, Berkhamsted,
Hertfordshire HP4 3UJ
Tel: 01442 865275
Headteacher:
Mr Colin Parker BSc(Hons), Dip.Ed
(Oxon), PGCE, C.Math MIMA
Age range: 6–19 years

**Haberdashers'
Boys' School**
Butterfly Lane, Elstree,
Borehamwood,
Hertfordshire WD6 3AF
Tel: 020 8266 1700
Headmaster: Mr Gus Lock
Age range: B4–18 years
No. of pupils: 1500

**Haberdashers'
Girls' School**
Aldenham Road,
Elstree, Borehamwood,
Hertfordshire WD6 3BT
Tel: 020 8266 2300
Headmistress: Mrs Rose Hardy
Age range: G4–18 years
No. of pupils: 1200

Haileybury
Haileybury, Hertford,
Hertfordshire SG13 7NU
Tel: +44 (0)1992 706353
The Master:
Mr Martin Collier MA BA PGCE
Age range: 11–18 years
(boarding from 11)
No. of pupils: 902 VIth357
Fees: Day £6,595–£9,920
FB £8,615–£13,580

Immanuel College
87/91 Elstree Road, Bushey,
Hertfordshire WD23 4EB
Tel: 020 8950 0604
Head: Mr Mike Buchanan
Age range: 4–18 years

Mount House School
Camlet Way, Hadley Wood,
Barnet, Hertfordshire EN4 0NJ
Tel: 020 8449 6889
Head: Mrs Sarah Richardson
Age range: 11–18 years

Queenswood
Shepherd's Way, Brookmans Park,
Hatfield, Hertfordshire AL9 6NS
Tel: 01707 602500
Principal: Mrs Jo Cameron
Age range: G11–18 years
(boarding from 11)
No. of pupils: 418
Fees: Day £7,115–£8,440
WB 7,325–10,615 FB £8,395–£11,810

Sherrardswood School
Lockleys, Welwyn,
Hertfordshire AL6 0BJ
Tel: 01438 714282
Headmistress: Mrs Anna Wright
Age range: 2–18 years

**St Albans High
School for Girls**
Townsend Avenue, St Albans,
Hertfordshire AL1 3SJ
Tel: 01727 853800
Head: Ms Amber Waite
Age range: G4–18 years

**St Albans Independent
College**
69 London Road, St Albans,
Hertfordshire AL1 1LN
Tel: 01727 842348
Principals:
Mr. A N Jemal & Mr Elvis Cotena
Age range: 14–19 years

St Albans School
Abbey Gateway, St Albans,
Hertfordshire AL3 4HB
Tel: 01727 855521
Headmaster:
Mr JWJ Gillespie MA(Cantab), FRSA
Age range: B11–18 years
G16–18 years

St Christopher School
Barrington Road, Letchworth
Garden City, Hertfordshire SG6 3JZ
Tel: 01462 650 850
Head of School:
Ms Emma-Kate Henry
Age range: 3–18 years

St Columba's College
King Harry Lane, St Albans,
Hertfordshire AL3 4AW
Tel: 01727 892040
Head: Mr David Shannon-Little
Age range: 4–18 years
No. of pupils: 805

**St Edmund's College
& Prep School**
Old Hall Green, Nr Ware,
Hertfordshire SG11 1DS
Tel: 01920 824247
Headmaster: Mr Matthew Mostyn
BA (Hons) MA (Ed)
Age range: 3–18 years
(boarding from 11)

St Francis' College
Broadway, Letchworth Garden
City, Hertfordshire SG6 3PJ
Tel: 01462 670511
Headmistress: Mrs B Goulding
Age range: G3–18 years
(boarding from 10)

**St Margaret's
School, Bushey**
Merry Hill Road, Bushey,
Hertfordshire WD23 1DT
Tel: +44 (0)20 8416 4400
Headteacher: Lara Péchard
Age range: 2–18 years
No. of pupils: 650

**Stanborough
Secondary School**
Stanborough Park, Garston,
Watford, Hertfordshire WD25 9JT
Tel: 01923 673268
Interim Head: Mr K. James
Age range: 11–18 years

The Purcell School, London
Aldenham Road, Bushey,
Hertfordshire WD23 2TS
Tel: 01923 331100
Principal: Mr Paul Bambrough
Age range: 10–18 years

**The Royal Masonic
School for Girls**
Rickmansworth Park,
Rickmansworth,
Hertfordshire WD3 4HF
Tel: 01923 773168
Headmaster: Mr Kevin Carson
M.Phil (Cambridge)
Age range: B2–4 years G2–18 years

**Tring Park School for
the Performing Arts**
Mansion Drive, Tring,
Hertfordshire HP23 5LX
Tel: 01442 824255
Principal: Mr Stefan Anderson MA,
ARCM, ARCT
Age range: 8–19 years
No. of pupils: 370 VIth171
Fees: Day £15,405–£24,885
FB £26,190–£37,605

Kent

Ashford School
East Hill, Ashford, Kent TN24 8PB
Tel: +44 (0)1233 625171
Head: Mr Michael Hall
Age range: 3 months–18 years
(boarding from 11)
No. of pupils: 1034 VIth140
Fees: Day £9,030–£19,026
WB £27,846 FB £38,778
Ⓐ Ⓐ ⓐ Ⓔ ☞ 16⁺

BABINGTON HOUSE SCHOOL
For further details see p. 72
Grange Drive, Chislehurst,
Kent BR7 5ES
Tel: 020 8467 5537
Email:
sjames@babingtonhouse.com
Website:
www.babingtonhouse.com
Headmaster:
Mr Tim Lello MA, FRSA, NPQH
Age range: 3–18 years
No. of pupils: 466
Ⓐ Ⓔ ☞

Beech Grove School
Forest Drive, Nonington,
Dover, Kent CT15 4FB
Tel: 01304 843 707
Headteacher: Timothy Maas
Age range: 6–18 years

Beechwood School
12 Pembury Road, Tunbridge
Wells, Kent TN2 3QD
Tel: 01892 532747
Headmaster:
Mr Justin Foster-Gandey
Age range: 3–18 years
ⓐ ☞ 16⁺

Benenden School
Cranbrook, Kent TN17 4AA
Tel: 01580 240592
Headmistress: Ms Samantha Price
Age range: G11–18 years
(boarding from 11)
ⓐ Ⓐ ☞ 16⁺

Bethany School
Curtisden Green, Goudhurst,
Cranbrook, Kent TN17 1LB
Tel: 01580 211273
Headmaster: Mr Francie Healy BSc,
HDipEd, NPQH
Age range: 11–18 years
No. of pupils: 346 VIth77
Fees: Day £18,795–£20,760 WB
£29,175–£32,205 FB £31,455–£35,400
Ⓐ Ⓐ ⓐ Ⓔ ☞ 16⁺

Bishop Challoner School
228 Bromley Road, Shortlands,
Bromley, Kent BR2 0BS
Tel: 020 8460 3546
Headteacher:
Mr Mark Wallace BA (Hons), MBA
Age range: 3–18 years
Ⓐ Ⓔ ☞ 16⁺

Bromley High School GDST
Blackbrook Lane, Bickley,
Bromley, Kent BR1 2TW
Tel: 020 8781 7000/1
Head: Mrs A M Drew BA(Hons), MBA
(Dunelm)
Age range: G4–18 years
ⓐ Ⓐ Ⓔ ☞ 16⁺

COBHAM HALL SCHOOL
For further details see p. 85
Brewers Road, Cobham,
Kent DA12 3BL
Tel: 01474 823371
Email:
admissions@cobhamhall.com
Website: www.cobhamhall.com
Headteacher:
Mrs Wendy Barrett
Age range: B16–18 years G11–18
years (boarding from 11)
No. of pupils: 150
Fees: Day £7,100–£8,250
FB £11,500–£13,250
ⓐ Ⓐ Ⓐ Ⓔ ☞ 16⁺

Darul Uloom London
Foxbury Avenue, Perry Street,
Chislehurst, Kent BR7 6SD
Tel: 020 8295 0637
Principal:
Mufti Muhammed Kamil Sheikh
Age range: B11–19 years
ⓐ ⓐ

Dover College
Effingham Crescent,
Dover, Kent CT17 9RH
Tel: 01304 205969
Head of School: Mr Simon Fisher
Age range: 3–18 years
Ⓐ ⓐ ☞ 16⁺

EARLSCLIFFE
For further details see p. 87
29 Shorncliffe Road,
Folkestone, Kent CT20 2NB
Tel: 01303 253951
Email:
admissions@earlscliffe.co.uk
Website: www.earlscliffe.co.uk
Headteacher: Mr Joss Williams
Age range: 15–19 years
No. of pupils: 130
Fees: Day £9,100 WB £11,745
FB £13,650
Ⓐ Ⓐ ⓐ

Farringtons School
Perry Street, Chislehurst,
Kent BR7 6LR
Tel: 020 8467 0256
Head: Mr David Jackson
Age range: 3–18 years
No. of pupils: 700 VIth100
Fees: Day £16,260 WB £27,120
FB £34,050
Ⓐ Ⓐ ⓐ Ⓔ ☞ 16⁺

Kent College Pembury
Old Church Road, Pembury,
Tunbridge Wells, Kent TN2 4AX
Tel: +44 (0)1892 822006
Head of School:
Miss Katrina Handford
Age range: G3–18 years
(boarding from 8)
No. of pupils: 500
Fees: Day £22,575 WB £28,200
FB £35,700
Ⓐ Ⓐ Ⓐ Ⓐ Ⓔ ☞ 16⁺

Kent College, Canterbury
Whitstable Road, Canterbury,
Kent CT2 9DT
Tel: +44 (0)1227 763 231
Head of Kent College:
Mr Mark Turnbull
Age range: 3 months–18 years
(boarding from 8 years)
No. of pupils: 800
Fees: Day £6,029–£6,932
FB £9,326–£12,883
ⓐ Ⓐ ⓐ Ⓔ ⒾⒷ ☞ 16⁺

King's School Rochester
Satis House, Boley Hill,
Rochester, Kent ME1 1TE
Tel: 01634 888555
Principal: Mr B Charles
Age range: 3–18 years
No. of pupils: 638 VIth101
Fees: Day £3,770–£7,175
FB £8,175–£11,775
ⓐ Ⓐ ⓐ Ⓔ ☞ 16⁺

OneSchool Global UK Maidstone Campus
Heath Road, Maidstone,
Kent ME17 4HT
Tel: 03000 700 507
Age range: 7–18 years

Radnor House, Sevenoaks
Combe Bank Drive,
Sevenoaks, Kent TN14 6AE
Tel: 01959 563720
Head of School: Mr Fraser Halliwell
Age range: 2–18 years
☞ 16⁺

Rochester Independent College
254 St Margaret's Banks,
Rochester, Kent ME1 1HY
Tel: +44 (0)163 482 8115
Head of School:
Mr Alistair Brownlow
Age range: 11–18 years
ⓐ 16⁺

Sackville School
Tonbridge Road, Hildenborough,
Tonbridge, Kent TN11 9HN
Tel: 01732 838888
Headteacher: Ms Leoni Ellis
Age range: 11–18 years
☞ 16⁺

Sevenoaks School
High Street, Sevenoaks,
Kent TN13 1HU
Tel: +44 (0)1732 455133
Head of School:
Mr Jesse R Elzinga AB MSt FCCT
Age range: 11–18 years
No. of pupils: 1189
Fees: Day £26,721–£30,348
FB £42,921–£46,566
ⓐ ⓐ Ⓔ ⒾⒷ ☞ 16⁺

St Edmund's School
St Thomas Hill, Canterbury,
Kent CT2 8HU
Tel: 01227 475601
Head: Mr Edward O'Connor MA
(Cantab), MPhil (Oxon), MEd
(Cantab)
Age range: 2–18 years
(boarding from 11)
No. of pupils: 602
ⓐ Ⓐ ⓐ Ⓔ ☞ 16⁺

St Lawrence College
College Road, Ramsgate,
Kent CT11 7AE
Tel: 01843 572931
Head of College: Mr Barney Durrant
Age range: 3–18 years
No. of pupils: 585
Fees: Day £8,394–£18,558
FB £29,454–£38,952
ⓐ Ⓐ ⓐ Ⓔ ☞ 16⁺

Sutton Valence School
North Street, Sutton
Valence, Kent ME17 3HL
Tel: 01622 845200
Headmaster: Mr James A Thomas
MA (Cantab) MA (London) NPQH
Age range: 11–18 years
(boarding from 11)
No. of pupils: 557
ⓐ Ⓐ ⓐ Ⓔ ☞ 16⁺

The King's School, Canterbury
Lattergate Office, 25 The Precincts,
Canterbury, Kent CT1 2ES
Tel: 01227 595501
Head of School: Ms Jude Lowson
Age range: 13–18 years

The Worthgate School
68 New Dover Road,
Canterbury, Kent CT1 3LQ
Tel: +44 (0)1227 866540
Acting Principal:
Dr Nicola Robinson
Age range: 13–21 years
No. of pupils: 450
Fees: Day £17,370–£27,990
FB £13,230–£19,140

TONBRIDGE SCHOOL
For further details see p. 100
High Street, Tonbridge,
Kent TN9 1JP
Tel: 01732 304297
Email: admissions@
tonbridge-school.org
Website:
www.tonbridge-school.co.uk
Headmaster:
Mr James Priory MA (Oxon)
Age range: B13–18 years
No. of pupils: 795
Fees: Day £35,067 FB £46,740

Walthamstow Hall School
Holly Bush Lane, Sevenoaks,
Kent TN13 3UL
Tel: 01732 451334
Headmistress: Miss Stephanie Ferro
Age range: G3–18 years

Middlesex

ACS Hillingdon International School
108 Vine Lane, Hillingdon,
Uxbridge, Middlesex UB10 0BE
Tel: +44 (0) 1895 259771
Head of School: Mr Martin Hall
Age range: 4–18 years

Halliford School
Russell Road, Shepperton,
Middlesex TW17 9HX
Tel: 01932 223593
Headmaster:
Mr James Davies BMus (Hons) LGSM
FASC ACertCM PGCE
Age range: B11–18 years
G16–18 years
No. of pupils: 450
Fees: Day £19,200

Hampton School
Hanworth Road, Hampton,
Middlesex TW12 3HD
Tel: 020 8979 5526
Headmaster:
Mr Kevin Knibbs MA (Oxon)
Age range: B11–18 years

Harrow School
5 High Street, Harrow on the
Hill, Middlesex HA1 3HP
Tel: 020 8872 8000
Head Master: Mr Alastair Land
Age range: B13–18 years

John Lyon School
Middle Road, Harrow on the
Hill, Middlesex HA2 0HN
Tel: 020 8515 9443
Head: Miss Katherine Haynes BA,
MEd, NPQH
Age range: 11–18 years
No. of pupils: 600

KEW HOUSE SCHOOL
For further details see p. 77
Kew House, 6 Capital
Interchange Way, London,
Middlesex TW8 0EX
Tel: 0208 742 2038
Email: admissions@
kewhouseschool.com
Website:
www.kewhouseschool.com
Headmaster: Mr Will Williams
Age range: 11–18 years
No. of pupils: 595
Fees: Day £8,073

Lady Eleanor Holles
Hanworth Road, Hampton,
Middlesex TW12 3HF
Tel: 020 8979 1601
Head of School:
Mrs Heather Hanbury
Age range: G7–18 years
No. of pupils: 970
Fees: Day £21,738

Menorah Foundation School
Abbots Road, Edgware,
Middlesex HA8 0QS
Tel: 020 8906 9992
Headteacher: Karen Kent
Age range: B11–21 years

Merchant Taylors' School
Sandy Lodge, Northwood,
Middlesex HA6 2HT
Tel: 01923 820644
Head Master:
Mr S J Everson MA (Cantab)
Age range: B11–18 years

North London Collegiate School
Canons, Canons Drive,
Edgware, Middlesex HA8 7RJ
Tel: +44 (0)20 8952 0912
Interim Headmistress:
Dr Hazel Bagworth-Mann
Age range: G4–18 years
No. of pupils: 1080
Fees: Day £6,283–£7,436

Northwood College for Girls GDST
Maxwell Road, Northwood,
Middlesex HA6 2YE
Tel: 01923 825446
Head of School:
Mrs Rebecca Brown
Age range: G3–18 years
No. of pupils: 844

Radnor House
Pope's Villa, Cross Deep,
Twickenham, Middlesex TW1 4QG
Tel: +44 (0)20 8891 6264
Head: Mr Darryl Wideman MA
Oxon, PGCE
Age range: 9–18 years

Regent College London
Regent House, 167 Imperial Drive,
Harrow, Middlesex HA2 7HD
Tel: +44 (0)20 3870 6666
Co-Principals: Dr Selva Pankaj &
Mrs Tharshiny Pankaj
Age range: 14–24 years

St Helen's School
Eastbury Road, Northwood,
Middlesex HA6 3AS
Tel: +44 (0)1923 843210
Headmistress: Mrs Alice Lucas
Age range: G3–18 years
No. of pupils: 1150

St. Catherine's School
Cross Deep, Twickenham,
Middlesex TW1 4QJ
Tel: 020 8891 2898
Headmistress:
Mrs Johneen McPherson MA
Age range: G5–18 years
No. of pupils: 434
Fees: Day £13,395–£16,875

St. John's Senior School
North Lodge, The Ridgeway,
Enfield, Middlesex EN2 8BE
Tel: +44 (0)20 8366 0035
Head Teacher: Mr A Tardios
Age range: 11–18 years

The St Michael Steiner School
Park Road, Hanworth Park,
London, Middlesex TW13 6PN
Tel: 0208 893 1299
Age range: 3–18 years

Surrey

ACS Cobham International School
Heywood, Portsmouth Road, Cobham, Surrey KT11 1BL
Tel: +44 (0) 1932 867251
Head of School:
Mr Barnaby Sandow
Age range: 2–18 years
Ⓐ Ⓔ ⒾⒷ Ⓔ ⒗

ACS Egham International School
London Road, Egham, Surrey TW20 0HS
Tel: +44 (0) 1784 430800
Head of School: Mr Jeremy Lewis
Age range: 4–18 years
Ⓐ ⒾⒷ Ⓔ ⒗

Box Hill School
London Road, Mickleham, Dorking, Surrey RH5 6EA
Tel: 01372 373382
Headmaster: Cory Lowde
Age range: 11–18 years
No. of pupils: 410
Fees: Day £21,585 WB £31,635
Ⓐ Ⓔ Ⓔ Ⓔ Ⓔ ⒗

Cambridge Tutors College
Water Tower Hill, Croydon, Surrey CR0 5SX
Tel: 020 8688 5284/7363
Principal: Dr Chris Drew
Age range: 14–23 years
⒗ Ⓐ Ⓔ ⒗

Canbury School
Kingston Hill, Kingston upon Thames, Surrey KT2 7LN
Tel: 020 8549 8622
Headmistress: Ms Carolyn Yates
Age range: 11–18 years
Ⓔ

Caterham School
Harestone Valley Road, Caterham, Surrey CR3 6YA
Tel: 01883 343028
Headmaster:
Mr C. W. Jones MA(Cantab)
Age range: 3–18 years
Ⓐ Ⓐ Ⓔ Ⓔ ⒗

Charterhouse
Godalming, Surrey GU7 2DX
Tel: +44 (0)1483 291501
Head: Dr Alex Peterken
Age range: B13–18 years (boarding from 13) G16–18 years
No. of pupils: 940
Fees: Day £12,180 FB £14,740
Ⓐ Ⓐ Ⓐ Ⓔ ⒾⒷ Ⓔ ⒗

City of London Freemen's School
Ashtead Park, Ashtead, Surrey KT21 1ET
Tel: +44 (0)1372 822400
Headmaster: Mr Roland J. Martin
Age range: 7–18 years
Ⓐ Ⓐ Ⓔ Ⓔ ⒗

Claremont Fan Court School
Claremont Drive, Esher, Surrey KT10 9LY
Tel: 01372 473794
Head: Mr William Brierly
Age range: 2.5–18 years
No. of pupils: 1100
Ⓐ Ⓔ ⒗

Cranleigh School
Horseshoe Lane, Cranleigh, Surrey GU6 8QQ
Tel: +44 (0) 1483 273666
Headmaster:
Mr Martin Reader MA, MPhil, MBA
Age range: 7–18 years (including Prep School)
No. of pupils: 683 VIth256
Fees: Day £35,175 FB £42,720
Ⓐ Ⓐ Ⓐ Ⓔ Ⓔ ⒗

Cranmore School
Epsom Road, West Horsley, Surrey KT24 6AT
Tel: 01483 280340
Headmaster: Mr Barry Everitt
Age range: 2–18 years
Ⓐ Ⓔ

Croydon High School GDST
Old Farleigh Road, Selsdon, South Croydon, Surrey CR2 8YB
Tel: 02082 607543
Head: Ms Annabel Davies
Age range: G3–18 years
Ⓐ Ⓐ Ⓔ Ⓔ ⒗

Dunottar School
High Trees Road, Reigate, Surrey RH2 7EL
Tel: 01737 761945
Headmaster: Mr Mark Tottman
Age range: 11–18 years
Ⓐ Ⓔ ⒗

Epsom College
College Road, Epsom, Surrey KT17 4JQ
Tel: 01372 821000
Acting Headmaster:
Mr Paul Williams
Age range: 11–18 years (boarding from 13)
Ⓐ Ⓐ Ⓔ Ⓔ ⒗

Ewell Castle School
Church Street, Ewell, Epsom, Surrey KT17 2AW
Tel: 020 8393 1413
Principal: Mr Silas Edmonds
Age range: 3–18 years
No. of pupils: 670
Fees: Day £5,382–£18,141
Ⓐ Ⓔ Ⓔ ⒗

Frensham Heights
Rowledge, Farnham, Surrey GU10 4EA
Tel: 01252 792561
Head: Mr Rick Clarke
Age range: 3–18 years (boarding from 11)
Ⓐ Ⓐ Ⓔ Ⓔ ⒗

Gordon's School
West End, Woking, Surrey GU24 9PT
Tel: 01276 858084
Head Teacher: Andrew Moss MEd
Age range: 11–18 years
No. of pupils: 938 VIth317
Fees: Day £9,081 WB £18,222 FB £19,446
Ⓐ Ⓐ Ⓔ ⒗

Guildford High School
London Road, Guildford, Surrey GU1 1SJ
Tel: 01483 561440
Headmistress:
Mrs F J Boulton BSc, MA
Age range: G4–18 years
Ⓐ Ⓐ ⒗

HAMPTON COURT HOUSE
For further details see p. 73
Hampton Court Road, Richmond upon Thames, London, Surrey KT8 9BS
Tel: 020 8614 0865
Email: reception@hchnet.co.uk
Website: www.hamptoncourthouse.co.uk
Headteacher: Katherine Vintiner
Age range: 2–18 years
No. of pupils: 300
Fees: Day £15,075–£22,044
Ⓐ

Hurtwood House
Holmbury St. Mary, Dorking, Surrey RH5 6NU
Tel: 01483 279000
Principal: Mr Cosmo Jackson
Age range: 16–18 years
No. of pupils: 360
Fees: Day £29,748 FB £44,622
⒗ Ⓐ Ⓐ

KING EDWARD'S WITLEY
For further details see p. 88
Petworth Road, Godalming, Surrey GU8 5SG
Tel: 01428 686700
Email: admissions@kesw.org
Website: www.kesw.org
Head: Mrs Joanna Wright
Age range: 11–18 years
No. of pupils: 435
Fees: Day £5,960–£7,555 WB £11,195–£11,630 FB £11,790–£12,250
Ⓐ Ⓐ Ⓐ Ⓔ ⒾⒷ Ⓔ ⒗

Kingston Grammar School
London Road, Kingston upon Thames, Surrey KT2 6PY
Tel: 02085 465875
Head Master: Mr Stephen Lehec
Age range: 11–18 years
Ⓐ Ⓔ Ⓔ ⒗

Lingfield College
Racecourse Road, Lingfield, Surrey RH7 6PH
Tel: 01342 832407
Headmaster:
Mr R Bool B.A. Hons, MBA
Age range: 2–18 years
Ⓐ Ⓔ Ⓔ ⒗

MARYMOUNT INTERNATIONAL SCHOOL LONDON
For further details see p. 78
George Road, Kingston upon Thames, Surrey KT2 7PE
Tel: +44 (0)20 8949 0571
Email: admissions@marymountlondon.com
Website: www.marymountlondon.com
Headmistress:
Mrs Margaret Giblin
Age range: G11–18 years
No. of pupils: 248
Fees: Day £28,830 WB £46,740 FB £48,810
Ⓐ Ⓐ Ⓐ Ⓔ ⒾⒷ Ⓔ ⒗

Notre Dame School
Cobham, Surrey KT11 1HA
Tel: 01932 869990
Head of Seniors: Mrs Anna King MEd, MA (Cantab), PGCE
Age range: B2–7 years G2–18 years
Ⓐ Ⓐ Ⓔ Ⓔ ⒗

Old Palace of John Whitgift School
Old Palace Road, Croydon, Surrey CR0 1AX
Tel: 02086 882027
Head of School: Mrs Jane Burton
Age range: G3–18 years
No. of pupils: 650
Fees: Day £3,300–£5,536
Ⓐ Ⓔ ⒗

OneSchool Global UK Hindhead Campus
Tilford Road, Hindhead, Surrey GU26 6SJ
Tel: 01428 601800
Age range: 7–18 years

OneSchool Global UK Kenley Campus
Victor Beamish Avenue, Kenley, Surrey CR3 5FX
Tel: 01883 338634
Age range: 7–18 years

Prior's Field
Priorsfield Road, Godalming, Surrey GU7 2RH
Tel: 01483 810551
Head of School: Mrs Tracey Kirnig
Age range: G11–18 years (boarding from 11)
Ⓐ Ⓐ Ⓐ Ⓔ Ⓔ ⒗

Reed's School
Sandy Lane, Cobham,
Surrey KT11 2ES
Tel: 01932 869001
Headmaster: Mr Mark Hoskins
Age range: B11–18 years
(boarding from 11) G16–18 years

Reigate Grammar School
Reigate Road, Reigate,
Surrey RH2 0QS
Tel: 01737 222231
Headmaster: Mr Shaun Fenton MA
(Oxon) MEd (Oxon)
Age range: 11–18 years

RGS Guildford
High Street, Guildford,
Surrey GU1 3BB
Tel: 01483 880600
Headmaster: Dr J M Cox BSc, PhD
Age range: B11–18 years

Royal Russell School
Coombe Lane, Croydon,
Surrey CR9 5BX
Tel: +44 (0)20 8657 4433
Headmaster:
Mr Christopher Hutchinson
Age range: 11–18 years

Sir William Perkins's School
Guildford Road, Chertsey,
Surrey KT16 9BN
Tel: 01932 574900
Head: Mr C C Muller
Age range: G11–18 years
No. of pupils: 600
Fees: Day £6,246

St Catherine's, Bramley
Station Road, Bramley,
Guildford, Surrey GU5 0DF
Tel: 01483 899609
Headmistress: Ms Alice Phillips
Age range: G4–18 years
(boarding from 11)

St George's College
Weybridge Road, Addlestone,
Weybridge, Surrey KT15 2QS
Tel: 01932 839300
Headmistress: Mrs Rachel Owens
Age range: 11–18 years

St James Senior Boys' School
Church Road, Ashford,
Surrey TW15 3DZ
Tel: 01784 266930
Headmaster: Mr David Brazier
Age range: B11–18 years

St John's School
Epsom Road, Leatherhead,
Surrey KT22 8SP
Tel: 01372 373000
Acting Head: Mrs Rebecca Evans
Age range: 11–18 years
(boarding from 11)
Fees: Day £22,500–
£25,560 WB £32,441

**St Teresa's Effingham
(Senior School)**
Effingham, Surrey RH5 6ST
Tel: +44 (0)1372 452037
Headmistress: Ms Claire McShane
Age range: G11–18 years
(boarding from 11)

Surbiton High School
13-15 Surbiton Crescent, Kingston
upon Thames, Surrey KT1 2JT
Tel: 02085 465245
Principal: Mrs Rebecca Glover
Age range: B4–11 years G4–18 years

Sutton High School GDST
55 Cheam Road, Sutton,
Surrey SM1 2AX
Tel: 020 8642 0594
Head of School: Ms Beth Dawson
Age range: G3–18 years

**TASIS THE AMERICAN
SCHOOL IN ENGLAND**
For further details see p. 98
Coldharbour Lane,
Thorpe, Surrey TW20 8TE
Tel: +44 (0)1932 582316
Email:
ukadmissions@tasisengland.org
Website: www.tasisengland.org
Head of School: Mr Bryan Nixon
Age range: 3–18 years
(boarding from 13)
No. of pupils: 650
Fees: Day £13,280–£29,080
FB £54,510

**The Royal Ballet School
(White Lodge)**
White Lodge, Richmond Park,
Richmond, Surrey TW10 5HR
Tel: 020 8392 8440
Head of School:
Mr David Gajadharsingh
Age range: 11–19 years
(boarding from 11)

**The Royal School,
Haslemere**
Farnham Lane, Haslemere,
Surrey GU27 1HQ
Tel: 01428 605805
Head: Mrs Pippa Smithson BA
(Hons), PGCE, MEd
Age range: 6 weeks–18
years (boarding from 11)
No. of pupils: 315
Fees: Day £3,681–£6,414
WB £9,435 FB £10,731

Tormead School
Cranley Road, Guildford,
Surrey GU1 2JD
Tel: 01483 575101
Head of School: Mr David Boyd
Age range: G4–18 years

Trinity School
Shirley Park, Croydon,
Surrey CR9 7AT
Tel: 020 8656 9541
Head: Mr Alasdair Kennedy
Age range: B10–18 years
G16–18 years

Whitgift School
Haling Park, South Croydon,
Surrey CR2 6YT
Tel: +44 20 8633 9935
Headmaster:
Mr Christopher Ramsey
Age range: B10–18 years
No. of pupils: 1550
Fees: Day £22,269 WB £35,973
FB £43,629

Woldingham School
Marden Park, Woldingham,
Surrey CR3 7YA
Tel: 01883 349431
Head of School:
Dr James Whitehead
Age range: G11–18 years
(boarding from 11)
No. of pupils: 626
Fees: Day £23,160–£25,365
FB £34,170–£42,330

Yehudi Menuhin School
Stoke Road, Stoke d'Abernon,
Cobham, Surrey KT11 3QQ
Tel: 01932 864739
Headmaster: Mr Ben Gudgeon
Age range: 8–19 years

West Berkshire

Downe House School
Downe House, Cold Ash,
Thatcham, West Berkshire RG18 9JJ
Tel: +44 (0)1635 200286
Headmistress: Mrs Emma
McKendrick BA(Liverpool)
Age range: G11–18 years
(boarding from 11)
No. of pupils: 590
Fees: Day £10,960 FB £14,740

St Gabriel's
Sandleford Priory, Newbury,
West Berkshire RG20 9BD
Tel: 01635 555680
Principal: Mr Ricki Smith
Age range: 6 months–18 years

St. Michael's School
Harts Lane, Burghclere, Newbury,
West Berkshire RG20 9JW
Tel: 01635 278137
Headmaster: Rev. Fr. John Brucciani
Age range: B4–18 years
(boarding from 11) G4–11 years

West Sussex

Ardingly College
College Road, Ardingly, Haywards Heath, West Sussex RH17 6SQ
Tel: +44 (0)1444 893320
Headmaster: Mr Ben Figgis
Age range: 13–18 years
Ⓐ Ⓐ 🏫 £ ⒾⒷ ✎ 16·

Burgess Hill Girls
Keymer Road, Burgess Hill, West Sussex RH15 0EG
Tel: 01444 241050
Head of School: Lars Fox
Age range: B2.5–4 years G2.5–18 years
No. of pupils: 557 VIth70
Fees: Day £9,825–£22,410 FB £34,560–£39,900
🏃 Ⓐ Ⓐ 🏫 £ ✎ 16·

Christ's Hospital
Horsham, West Sussex RH13 0LJ
Tel: 01403 211293
Head Teacher: Mr Simon Reid
Age range: 11–18 years
Ⓐ Ⓐ 🏫 £ ⒾⒷ 16·

Farlington School
Strood Park, Horsham, West Sussex RH12 3PN
Tel: 01403 254967
Headmaster: Mr James Passam
Age range: 4–18 years
No. of pupils: 340
Fees: Day £2,050–£6,350 WB £10,500 FB £11,300
Ⓐ Ⓐ 🏫 £ ✎ 16·

Hurst College
College Lane, Hurstpierpoint, West Sussex BN6 9JS
Tel: 01273 833636
Headmaster: Mr. Dominic Mott
Age range: 4–18 years (boarding from 13)
No. of pupils: 1295
Ⓐ Ⓐ 🏫 £ 16·

Lancing College
Lancing, West Sussex BN15 0RW
Tel: 01273 452213
Head Master: Mr Dominic T Oliver MPhil
Age range: 13–18 years
Ⓐ Ⓐ 🏫 £ ✎ 16·

Our Lady of Sion School
Gratwicke Road, Worthing, West Sussex BN11 4BL
Tel: 01903 204063
Headmaster: Mr Steven Jeffery
Age range: 3–18 years
Ⓐ £ 16·

Rikkyo School in England
Guildford Road, Rudgwick, Horsham, West Sussex RH12 3BE
Tel: +44 (0)1403 822107
Principal: Mr Tohru Okano
Age range: 10–18 years
Ⓐ 🏫

Seaford College
Lavington Park, Petworth, West Sussex GU28 0NB
Tel: 01798 867392
Headmaster: J P Green MA BA
Age range: 5–18 years
No. of pupils: 943 VIth264
Fees: Day £3,960–£8,210 WB £8,245–£11,115 FB £12,690
Ⓐ Ⓐ 🏫 £ ✎ 16·

Slindon College
Slindon House, Top Road, Slindon, Arundel, West Sussex BN18 0RH
Tel: 01243 814320
Headteacher: Mrs Sotiria Vlahodimou
Age range: B8–18 years (boarding from 11)
🏃 Ⓐ Ⓐ 🏫 £ ✎

Worth School
Paddockhurst Road, Turners Hill, Crawley, West Sussex RH10 4SD
Tel: +44 (0)1342 710200
Head Master: Mr Stuart McPherson
Age range: 11–18 years (boarding from 13)
Ⓐ Ⓐ 🏫 £ ⒾⒷ ✎ 16·

Examinations and qualifications

Common Entrance

What is Common Entrance?

The Common Entrance examinations are used in UK independent schools (and some independent schools overseas) for transfer from junior to senior schools at the ages of 11+ and 13+. They were first introduced in 1904 and are internationally recognised as being a rigorous form of assessment following a thorough course of study. The examinations are produced by the Independent Schools Examinations Board and backed by HMC (Headmasters' and Headmistresses' Conference), GSA (Girls' Schools Association), and IAPS (Independent Association of Prep Schools) which together represent the leading independent schools in the UK, and many overseas.

Common Entrance is not a public examination as, for example, GCSE, and candidates may normally be entered only in one of the following circumstances:

a) they have been offered a place at a senior school subject to their passing the examination, or

b) they are entered as a 'trial run', in which case the papers are marked by the junior school concerned.

Candidates normally take the examination in their own junior or preparatory schools, either in the UK or overseas.

How does Common Entrance fit into the progression to GCSEs?

Rapid changes in education nationally and internationally have resulted in regular reviews of the syllabuses for all the Common Entrance examinations. Reviews of the National Curriculum, in particular, have brought about a number of changes, with the Board wishing to ensure that it continues to set high standards. It is also a guiding principle that Common Entrance should be part of the natural progression from 11-16, and not a diversion from it.

Common Entrance at 11+

At 11+, the examination consists of papers in English, mathematics and science. It is designed so that it can be taken by candidates either from independent preparatory schools or by candidates from schools in the maintained sector or overseas who have had no special preparation. The examination is normally taken in January for entrance to senior schools in the following September.

Common Entrance at 13+

At 13+, most candidates come from independent preparatory schools. The compulsory subjects are English, mathematics and science. Papers in French, geography, German, Classical Greek, history, Latin, religious studies and Spanish are also available and candidates usually offer as many subjects as they can. In most subjects, papers are available at more than one level to cater for candidates of different abilities. There are three examination sessions each year, with the majority of candidates sitting in the summer prior to entry to their senior schools in September.

Marking and grading

The papers are set centrally but the answers are marked by the senior school for which a candidate is entered. Mark schemes are provided by the Board but senior schools are free to set their own grade boundaries. Results are available within two weeks of the examinations taking place.

Pre-Testing and the ISEB Common Pre-Tests

A number of senior independent schools 'pre-test' pupils for entry, prior to them taking their main entrance examinations at a later date. Usually, these pre-tests take place when a pupil is in Year 6 or Year 7 of his or her junior school and will then be going on to sit Common Entrance in Year 8. The tests are designed to assess a pupil's academic potential and suitability for a particular senior school so that the child, the parents and the school know well in advance whether he/she is going to be offered a place at the school, subject to a satisfactory performance in the entrance examinations. The tests enable senior schools to manage their lists and help to ensure that pupils are not entered for examinations in which they are unlikely to be successful. In short, it reduces uncertainty for all concerned.

Pre-tests may be written specifically for the senior school for which the candidate is entered but a growing number of schools are choosing to use the Common Pre-Tests provided by the Independent Schools Examinations Board. These online tests are usually taken in the candidate's own junior school and one of their main advantages is that a pupil need sit the tests only once, with the results then made available to any senior school which wishes to use them. The multiple-choice tests cover verbal reasoning, non-verbal reasoning, English and mathematics, with the results standardised according to the pupil's age when they are taken. Further information is available on the ISEB website at www.iseb.co.uk.

Parents are advised to check the entrance requirements for senior schools to see if their child will be required to sit a pre-test.

Further information

Details of the Common Entrance examinations and how to register candidates are available on the ISEB website www.iseb.co.uk. Copies of past papers and a wide range of textbooks and other resources can be purchased from Galore Park Publishing Ltd at www.galorepark.co.uk. Support materials are also available from Hodder Education and other publishers; see the Resources section of the ISEB website for details.

Independent Schools Examinations Board
Endeavour House, Crow Arch Lane,
Ringwood, Hampshire BH24 1HP

Telephone: 01425 470555
Email: enquiries@iseb.co.uk
Web: www.iseb.co.uk

7+ Entrance Exams

What is the 7+?

The 7+ is the descriptive name given to the entrance exams set by an increasing number of independent schools for pupils wishing to gain admission into their Year 3.

7+ entrance exams may be simply for admission into a selective preparatory school, which will then prepare the child for Common Entrance exams to gain a place at senior school. Alternatively, the 7+ can be a route into a school with both prep and senior departments, therefore often effectively bypassing the 11+ or 13+ Common Entrance exams.

The Independent Schools Examinations Board provides Common Entrance examinations and assessments for pupils seeking entry to independent senior schools at 11+ and 13+, but there is as yet no equivalent for the 7+. The testing is largely undertaken by the individual schools, although some schools might commission the test from external agencies. Many schools in the incredibly competitive London area offer entrance exams at 7+ and some share specimen papers on their website to clarify what 7+ children will face.

Who sits the 7+?

The 7+ is sat by Year 2 children, who may be moving from a state primary school or a stand-alone pre-prep school to an independent prep school (although many prep schools now have their own pre-prep department, with a cohort of children poised to pass into Year 3 there).

Registration for 7+ entrance exams usually closes in the November of Year 2, with the exams then sat in January or February, for entry that September.

How is the 7+ assessed?

Written exam content will be primarily English and maths based, whilst spelling, dictation, mental arithmetic and more creative skills may be assessed verbally on a one-to-one basis. Group exercises are also sometimes used to look at a child's initiative and their ability to work with others.

Schools will not only be looking for academic potential, but also good citizens and a mixture of personalities to produce a well-rounded year group. For this reason, children are often asked to attend an interview. Some schools interview all candidates, whilst others may call back a limited number with good test results. They will be looking for a child's ability to look an adult in the eye and think on their feet, but also simply to show some spark and personality.

After the assessments, children will be told if they have been successful in gaining a firm place, or a place on a waiting list.

Further Information

As the 7+ is not centrally regulated, it is best for parents to seek accurate admissions and testing information direct from the schools in which they are interested. In addition to a school's facilities and ethos, choosing a school for admission at 7+ will probably also involve whether the school has a senior department and if not, the prep school's record in gaining its students places at target senior schools.

Experienced educational consultants may be able to help parents decide which independent prep school is best suited for their child, based on their personality, senior school ambitions and academic potential. Many parents enlist the help of tutors to prepare children for the 7+, if only to reduce the fear of the unknown in these very young children. This is achieved by teaching them the required curriculum, what to expect on their test and interview days, and giving them the opportunity to practice tackling the type of assessments they will face.

The Pre-Senior Baccalaureate

What is the Pre-Senior Baccalaureate?

The Pre-Senior Baccalaureate (PSB) is part of the Learning Skills Trust (LST) which operates 2 frameworks of study. The PSB is designed for Years 2 – 8 and the Skills Development Framework (SDF) for Years 9 – 11. The frameworks focus on the active development and assessment of 6 core skills: Communication, Collaboration, Leadership, Independence, Reviewing and Improving and Thinking and Learning. Member schools promote the core skills across all areas of school life, and provide guidance for pupils in progressing these skills, which are seen as essential for developing capable and balanced adults, able to make the most of the opportunities of a fast-changing world. A strong but appropriate knowledge base compliments this, with the use of focused tutoring, pastoral care and Well Being programmes.

Schools do not work to a prescribed curriculum and the emphasis is upon promoting an independent approach which works for each individual school. There are subject INSET days for LST school staff annually, supported by specialist colleagues, to ensure that work done in LST schools compliments the demands of education at higher levels.

The development of skills is recognised as essential by the Independent Schools Inspectorate (ISI), and recent ISI reports on PSB schools highlight the excellent contribution the PSB has in schools achieving excellence.

Assessment

The PSB has a 10-point scale for all subjects studied with a compulsory spine covering: English, Maths, Science, Modern Languages, The Humanities, Art, Design Technology, Music, Sport and PE with each pupil additionally completing a cross curricular project – The Pre-Senior Project Qualification. Optional subjects are agreed with schools, but these must be supported by a scheme of work clearly identifying appropriate core skills which are assessed on a narrative scale. The 10-point scale cross references both ISEB and National Curriculum assessment levels. Pupils moving on to senior school do so via individual senior school pre-testing arrangements, the award of the PSB certificate, core ISEB papers or a combination of the above.

The SDF is a commitment to enable students across 3 years to experience authentic interdisciplinary experiences through extended project work. Schools have freedom to work within the framework and adapt it to their specific setting and existing programmes can be adapted to the SDF. The assessment of core skills is across all aspects of school life and not focused on academic subjects, which have their own particular demands. Time is given for students to reflect on the development of core skills, progression academically and contributions more widely to school life. A particular emphasis is given to the successful transition to independent study and away from closed learning tasks assessed on knowledge retention rather than student reflection.

Membership categories

All schools join as Partner Members and progress to full membership following an audit.

Affiliated membership is for schools that have developed their own skills-based approach, in line with LST principles; staff can participate in training opportunities and the Heads of Affiliated Schools join committee meetings as guests.

Membership of the above categories is dependent upon strong ISI reports, the development of a skills-based curriculum, with skills clearly identified in schemes of work, and excellent teaching.

Foundation membership is for organisations that actively support the LST by providing funding which enables the charity to invest in research, IT, etc. They also provide staff for meetings and conferences and offer a valuable perspective on the operation of the charity.

Further details

The LST is an entirely independent charity overseen by a Board of Trustees who have expertise in both primary and secondary education. Details of the LST can be found on the website – psbacc.org – together with contact details for the Operations Manager who can provide further details on request.

General Certificate of Secondary Education (GCSE)

What are the GCSE qualifications?

GCSE qualifications were first introduced in 1986 and are the principal means of assessment at Key Stage 4 across a range of academic subject areas. They command respect and have status not only in the UK but worldwide.

Main features of the GCSE

There are four unitary awarding organisations for GCSEs in England. WJEC and CCEA also offer GCSE qualifications in Wales and Northern Ireland. Each examining group designs its own specifications but they are required to conform to set criteria. For some aspects of the qualification system, the exam boards adopt common ways of working. When the exam boards work together in this way they generally do so through the Joint Council of Qualifications (JCQ). The award of a grade is intended to indicate that a candidate has met the required level of skills, knowledge and understanding.

New, reformed GCSEs have been introduced in recent years. Assessment in these reformed GCSEs consists primarily of formal examinations taken at the end of the student's two-year course. Other types of assessment, non-exam assessment (NEA), is used where there are skills and knowledge which cannot be assessed through exams. Ofqual have set the percentage of the total marks that will come from NEA.

The reformed GCSEs feature new and more demanding content, as required by the government and developed by the exam boards. Courses are designed for two years of study (linear assessment) and no longer divided into different modules.

Exams can only be split into 'foundation tier' and 'higher tier' if one exam paper does not give all students the opportunity to show their knowledge and their abilities. Such tiering is only available in maths, science and modern foreign languages; other subjects do not have tiers. Resit opportunities will only be available each November in English language and maths, and then only for students who have turned 16 by the 31st of August in the year of the November assessment.

Summer 2022 marked the return of GCSE exams for the first time since 2019. Exams in 2020 and 2021 were replaced by alternatives due to constraints imposed following the pandemic. Grades were awarded through teachers' assessments based on mock exams, coursework and other available evidence.

Grading

The basic principle that exam boards follow when setting grade boundaries is that if the group of students (the cohort) taking a qualification in one year is of similar ability to the cohort in the previous year then the overall results (outcomes) should be comparable.

The reformed exams taken in summer 2017 were the first to show a new grading system, with the A* to G grades being phased out.

The new grading system is 9 to 1, with 9 being the top grade. Ofqual says this allows greater differentiation between students. It expects that broadly the same proportion of students will achieve a grade 4 and above as currently achieve a grade C and above, that broadly the same proportion of students will achieve a grade 7 and above as currently achieve a grade A and above. There are three anchor points between the new grading system and the old one: the bottom of the new 1 grade is the same as the bottom of the old G grade, the bottom of the new 4 grade is the bottom of the old C grade, and the bottom of the 7 grade is the same as the bottom of the old A grade. Grade 9 will be set using the tailored approach formula in the first award.

Grades 2, 3, 5 and 6 will be awarded arithmetically so that the grade boundaries are equally spaced in terms of marks from neighbouring grades.

The government's definition of a 'strong pass' will be set at grade 5 for reformed GCSEs. A grade 4 – or 'standard pass' – will continue to be a level 2 achievement. The DfE does not expect employers, colleges or universities to raise the bar to a grade 5 if a grade 4 would meet their requirements.

Can anyone take GCSE qualifications?

GCSEs are intended mainly for 16-year-old pupils, but are open to anyone of any age, whether studying full-time or part-time at a school, college or privately. There are no formal entry requirements.

Students normally study up to ten subjects over a two-year period. Short course GCSEs are available in some subjects (including PE and religious studies) – these include half the content of a full GCSE, so two short course GCSEs are equivalent to one full GCSE.

The English Baccalaureate

The English Baccalaureate (EBacc) is a school performance measure. It allows people to see how many pupils get a grade C or above (current grading) in the core academic subjects at Key Stage 4 in any government-funded school. The DfE introduced the EBacc measure in 2010.

Progress 8 and Attainment 8

Progress 8 aims to capture the progress a pupil makes from the end of primary school to the end of secondary school. It is a type of value added measure, which means that pupils' results are compared to the actual achievements of other pupils with the same prior attainment.

The new performance measures are designed to encourage schools to offer a broad and balanced curriculum with a focus on an academic core at Key Stage 4, and reward schools for the teaching of all their pupils, measuring performance across 8 qualifications. Every increase in every grade a pupil achieves will attract additional points in the performance tables.

Progress 8 will be calculated for individual pupils solely in order to calculate a school's Progress 8 score, and there will be no need for schools to share individual Progress 8 scores with their pupils. Schools should continue to focus on which qualifications are most suitable for individual pupils, as the grades pupils achieve will help them reach their goals for the next stage of their education or training.

Attainment 8 will measure the achievement of a pupil across 8 qualifications including mathematics (double weighted) and English (double weighted), 3 further qualifications that count in the English Baccalaureate (EBacc) measure and 3 further qualifications that can be GCSE qualifications (including EBacc subjects) or any other non-GCSE qualification on the DfE approved list.

General Certificate of Education (GCE) Advanced level (A level)

Typically, A level qualifications are studied over a two-year period. There are no lower or upper age limits. Schools and colleges usually expect students aged 16-18 to have obtained grades A*-C (grade 5 in the new criteria) in five subjects at GCSE level before taking an advanced level course. This requirement may vary between centres and according to which specific subjects are to be studied. Mature students may be assessed on different criteria as to their suitability to embark on the course.

GCE Qualifications

Over the past few years, AS level and A level qualifications have been in a process of reform. New subjects have been introduced gradually, with the first wave taught from September 2015. Subjects that have not been reformed are no longer available for teaching.

GCE qualifications are available at two levels: the Advanced Subsidiary (AS), which is generally delivered over one year and is seen as half an A level; and the A level (GCE). Nearly 70 titles are available, covering a wide range of subject areas, including humanities, sciences, language, business, arts, mathematics and technology.

One of the major reforms is that AS level results no longer count towards an A level (they previously counted for 50%). The two qualifications are linear, with AS assessments typically taking place after one year and A levels after two.

New-style AS and A levels were first taught from September 2015 for: art and design, biology, business studies, chemistry, computer studies, economics, English language, English language and literature, English literature, history, physics, psychology, and sociology.

Subjects first taught from September 2016 include: ancient languages such as Latin or Greek, dance, drama (theatre studies), geography, modern languages such as Spanish or French, music, physical education, religious studies.

Those introduced for first teaching from September 2017: accounting, design and technology, music technology, history of art, environmental science, philosophy, maths, further maths, archaeology, accounting, electronics, ancient history, law, classical civilisation, film studies, media studies, politics, geology, statistics, Chinese, Italian, Russian. In 2018 Biblical Hebrew, Modern Hebrew & languages such as Bengali, Polish and Urdu were available for first teaching.

Some GCE AS and A levels, particularly the practical ones, contain a proportion of coursework. All GCE A levels that contain one or more types of assessment will have an element of synoptic assessment that tests students' understanding of the whole specification. GCE AS are graded A-E and A levels are graded A*-E.

Overall the amount of coursework at A level has been reduced in the reforms. In some subjects, such as the sciences, practical work will not contribute to the final A level but will be reported separately in a certificate of endorsement. In the sciences, students will do at least 12 practical activities, covering apparatus and techniques. Exam questions about practical work will make up at least 15% of the total marks for the qualification and students will be assessed on their knowledge, skills and understanding of practical work.

Summer 2022 marked the return of exams for the first time since 2019. Exams in 2020 and 2021 were replaced by alternatives due to constraints imposed following the pandemic. Grades were awarded through teachers' assessments based on mock exams, coursework and other available evidence.

Cambridge International AS & A Level

Cambridge International AS & A Level is an internationally benchmarked qualification, taught in over 130 countries worldwide. It is typically for learners aged 16 to 19 years who need advanced study to prepare for university. It was created specifically for an international audience and the content has been devised to suit the wide variety of schools worldwide and avoid any cultural bias.

Cambridge International A Level is typically a two-year course, and Cambridge International AS Level is typically one year. Some subjects can be started as a Cambridge International AS Level and extended to a Cambridge International A Level. Students can either follow a broad course of study, or specialise in one particular subject area.

Learners use Cambridge International AS & A Levels to gain places at leading universities worldwide, including the UK, Ireland, USA, Canada, Australia, New Zealand, India, Singapore, Egypt, Jordan, South Africa, the Netherlands, Germany and Spain. In places such as the US and Canada, good grades in carefully chosen Cambridge International A Level subjects can result in up to one year of university course credit.

Assessment options:

Cambridge International AS & A Levels have a linear structure with exams at the end of the course. Students can choose from a range of assessment options:
Option 1: take Cambridge International AS Levels only. The Cambridge International AS Level syllabus content is half a Cambridge International A Level.
Option 2: staged assessment, which means taking the Cambridge International AS Level in one exam session and the Cambridge International A Level at a later session. However, this route is not possible in all subjects.
Option 3: take all Cambridge International A Level papers in the same examination session, usually at the end of the course.

Grades and subjects

Cambridge International A Levels are graded from A* to E. Cambridge International AS Levels are graded from A to E.

Subjects: available in 55 subjects including accounting, Afrikaans, Afrikaans – first language (AS only), Afrikaans language (AS only), applied information and communication technology, Arabic, Arabic language (AS only), art and design, biology, business, chemistry, Chinese, Chinese language (AS only), classical studies, computing, design and technology, design and textiles, digital media & design, divinity, economics, English language, English literature, environmental management, food studies, French, French language (AS only), French literature (AS only), general paper, geography, German, German language (AS only), Global Perspectives & Research, Hindi, Hindi language (AS only), Hindi literature (AS only), Hinduism, history, Islamic studies, Japanese language (AS only), English language and literature (AS only), law, Marathi, Marathi language (AS only), marine science, mathematics, further mathematics, media studies, music, physical education, physical science, physics, Portuguese, Portuguese language (AS only), Portuguese literature (AS only), psychology, sociology, Spanish, Spanish first language (AS only), Spanish language (AS only), Spanish literature (AS only), Tamil, Tamil language (AS only), Telugu, Telugu language (AS only), thinking skills, travel and tourism, Urdu, Urdu language (AS only).
Website: www.cambridgeinternational.org/alevel

Cambridge IGCSE

Cambridge IGCSE is the world's most popular international qualification for 14 to 16 year olds. It develops skills in creative thinking, enquiry and problem solving, in preparation for the next stage in a student's education. Cambridge IGCSE is taken in over 150 countries, and is widely recognised by employers and higher education institutions worldwide.

Cambridge IGCSE is graded from A*-G. In the UK, Cambridge IGCSE is accepted as equivalent to the GCSE. It can be used as preparation for Cambridge International A & AS Levels, UK A and AS levels, IB or AP and in some instances entry into university. Cambridge IGCSE First Language English and Cambridge IGCSE English Language qualifications are recognised by a significant number of UK universities as evidence of competence in the language for university entrance.

Subjects: available in over 70 subjects including accounting, Afrikaans – first language, Afrikaans – second language, agriculture, Arabic – first language, Arabic – foreign language, art and design, Baha Indonesia, Bangladesh studies, biology, business studies, chemistry, child development, Chinese – first language, Chinese – second language, Chinese (Mandarin) – foreign language, computer studies, Czech – first language, design and technology, development studies, drama, Dutch – first language, Dutch – foreign language, economics, English – additional language , English – first language, English – literature, English – second language, enterprise, environmental management, food and nutrition, French – first language, French – foreign language, geography, German – first language, German – foreign language, global perspectives, Greek – foreign language, Hindi as a second language, Italian – foreign language, history, India studies, Indonesian – foreign language, information and communication technology, IsiZulu as a second language, Japanese – first language, Japanese – foreign language, Kazakh as a second language, Korean (first language), Latin, Malay – first language, Malay – foreign language, mathematics, mathematics – additional, international mathematics, music, Pakistan studies, physical education, physical science, physics, Portuguese – first language, Portuguese – foreign language, religious studies, Russian – first language, science – combined, sciences – co-ordinated (double), sociology, Spanish – first language, Spanish – foreign language, Spanish – literature, Thai – first language, travel and tourism, Turkish – first language, Urdu – second language, world literature.
Website: www.cambridgeinternational.org/igcse

Edexcel International GCSEs

Pearson's Edexcel International GCSEs are academic qualifications aimed at learners aged 14 to 16. They're equivalent to a UK General Certificate of Secondary Education (GCSE), and are the main requirement for Level 3 studies, including progression to GCE AS or A levels, BTECs or employment. International GCSEs are linear qualifications, meaning that students take all of the exams at the end of the course. They are available at Level 1 (grades 3-1) and Level 2 (grades 9-4). There are currently more than 100,000 learners studying Edexcel International GCSEs, in countries throughout Asia, Africa, Europe, the Middle East and Latin America. Developed by subject specialists and reviewed regularly, many of Pearson's Edexcel International GCSEs include specific international content to make them relevant to students worldwide.

Pearson's Edexcel International GCSEs were initially developed for international schools. They have since become popular among independent schools in the UK, but are not approved for use in UK state schools.

OCR Free Standing Maths Qualifications (FSMQ)

Aimed at those students wishing to acquire further qualifications in maths, specifically additional mathematics and foundations of advanced mathematics (MEI). Further UCAS points can be earned upon completion of the advanced FSMQ in additional mathematics.

AQA Certificate in Mathematical Studies (Core Maths)

This Level 3 qualification has been available since September 2015. It is designed for students who achieved a Grade 4 or above at GCSE and want to continue studying Maths. The qualification carries UCAS points equivalent to an AS level qualification.

AQA Certificate in Further Maths

This level 2 qualification has been designed to provide stretch and challenge to the most able mathematicians. This will be best suited to students who either already have, or are expected to achieve the top grades in GCSE Mathematics and are likely to progress to A level Mathematics and Further Mathematics.

Scottish qualifications

Information supplied by the Scottish Qualifications Authority

In Scotland, qualifications are awarded by the Scottish Qualifications Authority (SQA), the national accreditation and awarding body. A variety of qualifications are offered in schools, including:

- National Qualifications (National Units, National Courses, Skills for Work Courses and Scottish Baccalaureates)

- National Qualification Group Awards (National Certificates and National Progression Awards)

- Awards

National Qualifications cover subjects to suit everyone's interests and skills – from Chemistry to Construction, History to Hospitality, and Computing to Care.

Qualifications in the Scottish qualifications system sit at various levels on the Scottish Credit and Qualifications Framework (SCQF). There are 12 levels on the SCQF and each level represents the difficulty of learning involved. Qualifications in schools span SCQF levels 1 to 7.

National Qualifications (NQ)

National Qualifications are among the most important types of qualification in Scotland.

National Qualifications range from SCQF levels 1 to 7 and include National Units, National Courses, Skills for Work Courses, Scottish Baccalaureates and National Qualification Group Awards.

They are taught in the senior phase of secondary school and they are also offered in colleges, and by some training providers.

They are designed to help young people to demonstrate the skills, knowledge and understanding they have developed at school or college and enable them to prepare for further learning, training and employment.

National Courses

National Courses are available in over 60 subjects, at the following levels: National 2 (SCQF level 2), National 3 (SCQF level 3), National 4 (SCQF level 4), National 5 (SCQF level 5), Higher (SCQF level 6), and Advanced Higher (SCQF level 7).

National 2, National 3 and National 4 courses consist of units and unit assessments, which are internally assessed by teachers and lecturers, and quality assured by SQA. Students complete the unit assessments during class time. National 4 courses also include an Added Value Unit assessment that assesses students' performance across the whole course. This is usually in the form of an assignment, performance, practical activity or class test. National 2 to National 4 courses are not graded but are assessed as pass or fail.

National 5, Higher and Advanced Higher courses do not include units. They involve a course assessment that takes place at the end of the course. For most subjects, the course assessment is a combination of one or more formal exams and one or more coursework assessments (such as an assignment, performance, project or practical activity). SQA marks all exams and the majority of coursework. In some subjects, coursework is internally assessed by the teacher or lecturer and quality assured by SQA, while performances and practical activities may be subject to visiting assessment by an SQA examiner.

National 5, Higher and Advanced Higher courses are graded A to D or 'no award'.

National Units

National Units are the building blocks of National 2 to National 4 Courses and National Qualification Group Awards. They are also qualifications in their own right and can be done on an individual basis — such as National 1 qualifications, which are standalone units. Units are normally designed to take 40 hours of teaching to complete and each one is assessed by completing a unit assessment. Over 3500 National Units are available, including National Literacy and Numeracy Units, which assess students' literacy and numeracy skills.

Freestanding units are also available at SCQF levels 5, 6 and 7 and can be taken on an individual basis.

Skills for Work Courses

Skills for Work courses are designed to introduce students to the demands and expectations of the world of work. They are available in a variety of areas such as construction, hairdressing and hospitality. The courses involve a strong element of learning through involvement in practical and vocational activities, and develop knowledge, skills and experience that are related to employment. They consist of units and unit assessments, which are internally assessed by teachers and lecturers, and quality assured by SQA. Skills for Work courses are not graded but are assessed as pass or fail. They are available at National

4, National 5 and Higher levels (SCQF levels 4 to 6) and are often delivered in partnership between schools and colleges.

Scottish Baccalaureates

Scottish Baccalaureates consist of a coherent group of Higher and Advanced Higher qualifications, with the addition of an interdisciplinary project. They are available in four subject areas: Expressive Arts, Languages, Science and Social Sciences. The interdisciplinary project is marked and awarded at Advanced Higher level (SCQF level 7). It provides students with a platform to apply their knowledge in a realistic context, and to demonstrate initiative, responsibility and independent working. Aimed at high-achieving sixth year students, the Scottish Baccalaureate encourages personalised, in-depth study and interdisciplinary learning in their final year of secondary school.

National Qualification Group Awards

National Certificates (NCs) and National Progression Awards (NPAs) are referred to as National Qualification Group Awards. These qualifications provide students preparing for work with opportunities to develop skills that are sought after by employers. They are available at SCQF levels 2 to 6.

NCs prepare students for employment, career development or progression to more advanced study at HNC/HND level. They are available in a range of subjects, including: Sound Production, Technical Theatre, and Child, Health and Social Care.

NPAs develop specific skills and knowledge in specialist vocational areas, including Journalism, Architecture and Interior Design, and Legal Services. They link to National Occupational Standards, which are the basis of Scottish Vocational Qualifications (SVQs) and are taught in partnership between schools, colleges, employers and training providers.

Awards

SQA Awards provide students with opportunities to acquire skills, recognise achievement and promote confidence through independent thinking and positive attitudes, while motivating them to be successful and participate positively in the wider community.

A variety of different awards are offered at a number of SCQF levels and cover subjects including leadership, employability and enterprise. These awards are designed to recognise the life, learning and work skills that students gain from taking part in activities both in and out of school, such as sports, volunteering and fundraising.

For more information on SQA and its portfolio of qualifications, visit www.sqa.org.uk

Additional and Alternative

Cambridge Primary

Cambridge Primary is typically for learners aged 5 to 11 years. It develops learner skills and understanding in 10 subjects: English as a first or second language, mathematics, science, art & design, digital literacy, music, physical education, Cambridge Global Perspectives and ICT. The flexible curriculum frameworks include optional assessment tools to help schools monitor learners' progress and give detailed feedback to parents. At the end of Cambridge Primary, schools can enter students for Cambridge Primary Checkpoint tests which are marked in Cambridge.
Website: www.cambridgeinternational.org/primary

Cambridge ICT Starters introduces learners, typically aged 5 to 14 years, to the key ICT applications they need to achieve computer literacy and to understand the impact of technology on our daily lives. It can be taught and assessed in English or Spanish.

Cambridge Lower Secondary

Cambridge Lower Secondary is typically for learners aged 11 to 14 years. It develops learner skills and understanding in 10 subjects: English, English as a second language, mathematics, science, art & design, digital literacy, music, physical education, Cambridge Global Perspectives and ICT, and includes assessment tools. At the end of Cambridge Lower Secondary, schools can enter students for Cambridge Lower Secondary Checkpoint tests which are marked in Cambridge and provide an external international benchmark for student performance.
Website: www.cambridgeinternational.org/lowersecondary

European Baccalaureate (EB)

Not to be confused with the International Baccalaureate (IB) or the French Baccalaureate, this certificate is available in European schools and recognised in all EU countries.

To obtain the baccalaureate, a student must obtain a minimum score of 50%, which is made up from: coursework, oral participation in class and tests (50%); five written examinations (35%) – mother-tongue, first foreign language and maths are compulsory for all candidates; three oral examinations (15%) – mother tongue and first foreign language are compulsory (history or geography may also be compulsory here, dependant on whether the candidate has taken a written examination in these subjects).

Subjects taught in different languages have the same syllabi, regardless of the language, and the same is valid for examinations – the content is simply translated into different languages. In case of languages, the syllabi vary, but nevertheless, they are harmonized and the examinations have to follow an agreed structure. The EB has been specifically designed to meet, at the very least, the minimum qualification requirements of each member state.

Study for the EB begins at nursery stage (age four) and progresses through primary (age six) and on into secondary school (age 12).

Syllabus
Languages: Bulgarian, Czech, Danish, Dutch, English, Estonian, Finnish, Finnish as a second national language, French, German, Greek, Hungarian, Irish, Italian, Latvian, Lithuanian, Maltese, Polish, Portuguese, Romanian, Slovak, Slovenian, Spanish, Swedish, Swedish for Finnish pupils.

Literary: art education, non-confessional ethics, geography, ancient Greek, history, human sciences, Latin, music, philosophy, physical education.

Sciences: biology, chemistry, economics, ICT, integrated science, mathematics, physics.
For more information, contact:
Office of the Secretary-General of the European Schools, rue de la Science 23 – 2nd floor, B-1040 Bruxelles, Belgique
Tel: +32 (0)2 895 26 11
Website: www.eursc.eu

The International Baccalaureate (IB)

The International Baccalaureate (IB) offers four challenging and high quality educational programmes for a worldwide community of schools, aiming to develop internationally minded people who, recognizing their common humanity and shared guardianship of the planet, help to create a better, more peaceful world.

The IB works with schools around the world (both state and privately funded) that share the commitment to international education to deliver these programmes.

Schools that have achieved the high standards required for authorization to offer one or more of the IB programmes are known as IB World Schools. There are over half a million students attending almost 5000 IB World Schools in over 150 countries and this number is growing annually.

The Primary Years, Middle Years and Diploma Programmes share a common philosophy and common characteristics. They develop the whole student, helping students to grow intellectually, socially, aesthetically and culturally. They provide a broad and balanced education that includes science and the humanities, languages and mathematics, technology and the arts. The programmes teach students to think critically, and encourage them to draw connections between areas of knowledge and to use problem-solving techniques and concepts from many disciplines. They instil in students a sense of responsibility towards others and towards the environment. Lastly, and perhaps most importantly, the programmes give students an awareness and understanding of their own culture and of other cultures, values and ways of life.

A fourth programme called the IB Career-related Programme (CP) became available to IB World Schools from September 2012. All IB programmes include:

- A written curriculum or curriculum framework

- Student assessment appropriate to the age range

- Professional development and networking opportunities for teachers

- Support, authorization and programme evaluation for the school

The IB Primary Years Programme

The IB Primary Years Programme (PYP), for students aged three to 12, focuses on the development of the whole child as an inquirer, both in the classroom and in the world outside. It is a framework consisting of five essential elements (concepts, knowledge, skills, attitude, action) and guided by six trans-disciplinary themes of global significance, explored using knowledge and skills derived from six subject areas (language, social studies, mathematics, science and technology, arts, and personal, social and physical education) with a powerful emphasis on inquiry-based learning.

The most significant and distinctive feature of the PYP is the six trans-disciplinary themes. These themes are about issues that have meaning for, and are important to, all of us. The programme offers a balance between learning about or through the subject areas, and learning beyond them. The six themes of global significance create a trans-disciplinary framework that allows students to 'step up' beyond the confines of learning within subject areas:

- Who we are

- Where we are in place and time

- How we express ourselves

- How the world works

- How we organize ourselves

- Sharing the planet

The PYP exhibition is the culminating activity of the programme. It requires students to analyse and propose solutions to real-world issues, drawing on what they have learned through the programme. Evidence of student development and records of PYP exhibitions are reviewed by the IB as part of the programme evaluation process.

Assessment is an important part of each unit of inquiry as it both enhances learning and provides opportunities for students to reflect on what they know, understand and can do. The teacher's feedback to the students provides the guidance, the tools and the incentive for them to become more competent, more skilful and better at understanding how to learn.

The IB Middle Years Programme (MYP)

The Middle Years Programme (MYP), for students aged 11 to 16, comprises eight subject groups:

- Language acquisition

- Language and literature

- Individuals and societies

- Sciences

- Mathematics

- Arts

- Physical and health education

- Design

The MYP requires at least 50 hours of teaching time for each subject group in each year of the programme. In years 4 and 5, students have the option to take courses from six of the eight subject groups within certain limits, to provide greater flexibility in meeting local requirements and individual student learning needs.

Each year, students in the MYP also engage in at least one collaboratively planned interdisciplinary unit that involves at least two subject groups.

MYP students also complete a long-term project, where they decide what they want to learn about, identify what they already know, discovering what they will need to know to complete the project, and create a proposal or criteria for completing it.

The MYP aims to help students develop their personal understanding, their emerging sense of self and their responsibility in their community.

The MYP allows schools to continue to meet state, provincial or national legal requirements for students with access needs. Schools must develop an inclusion/special educational needs (SEN) policy that explains assessment access arrangements, classroom accommodations and curriculum modification that meet individual student learning needs.

The IB Diploma Programme (IBDP)

The IB Diploma Programme, for students aged 16 to 19, is an academically challenging and motivating curriculum of international education that prepares students for success at university and in life beyond studies.

DP students choose at least one course from six subject groups, thus ensuring depth and breadth of knowledge and experience in languages, social studies, the experimental sciences, mathematics, and the arts. With more than 35 courses to choose from, students have the flexibility to further explore and learn subjects that meet their interest. Out of the six courses required, at least three and not more than four must be taken at higher level (240 teaching hours), the others at standard level (150 teaching hours). Students can take examinations in English, French or Spanish.

In addition, three unique components of the programme – the DP core – aim to broaden students' educational experience and challenge them to apply their knowledge and skills. The DP core – the extended essay (EE), theory of knowledge (TOK) and creativity, activity, service (CAS) – are compulsory and central to the philosophy of the programme.

The IB uses both external and internal assessment to measure student performance in the DP. Student results are determined by performance against set standards, not by each student's position in the overall rank order. DP assessment is unique in the way that it measures the extent to which students have mastered advanced academic skills not what they have memorized. DP assessment also encourages an international outlook and intercultural skills, wherever appropriate.

The IB diploma is awarded to students who gain at least 24 points out of a possible 45 points, subject to certain minimum levels of performance across the whole programme and to satisfactory participation in the creativity, activity, and service requirement.

Recognized and respected by leading universities globally, the DP encourages students to be knowledgeable, inquiring, caring and compassionate, and to develop intercultural understanding, open-mindedness and the attitudes necessary to respect and evaluate a range of viewpoints.

The IB Career Related Programme (IBCP)

The IB Career-related Programme, for students aged 16 to 19, offers an innovative educational framework that combines academic studies with career-related learning. Through the CP, students develop the competencies they need to succeed in the 21st century. More importantly, they have the opportunity to engage with a rigorous study programme that genuinely interests them while gaining transferable and lifelong skills that prepares them to pursue higher education, apprenticeships or direct employment.

CP students complete four core components – language development, personal and professional skills, service learning and a reflective project – in order to receive the International Baccalaureate Career-related Programme Certificate. Designed to enhance critical thinking and intercultural understanding, the CP core helps students develop the communication and personal skills, as well as intellectual habits required for lifelong learning.

Schools that choose to offer the CP can create their own distinctive version of the programme and select career pathways that suit their students and local community needs. The IB works with a variety of CRS providers around the world and schools seeking to develop career pathways with professional communities can benefit from our existing collaborations. All CRS providers undergo a rigorous curriculum evaluation to ensure that their courses align with the CP pedagogy and meet IB quality standards. The flexibility to meet the needs, backgrounds and contexts of learners allows CP schools to offer an education that is relevant and meaningful to their students.

Launched in 2012, there are 250 CP schools. Many schools with the IB Diploma Programme (DP) and the Middle Years Programme (MYP) have chosen the CP as an alternative IB pathway to offer students. CP schools often report that the programme has helped them raise student aspiration, increase student engagement and retention and encouraged learners to take responsibility for their own actions, helping them foster high levels of self-esteem through meaningful achievements.

For more information on IB programmes, visit: www.ibo.org

Africa, Europe, Middle East IB Global Centre, Churchillplein 6, The Hague, 2517JW, The Netherlands
Tel: +31 (0)70 352 6000
Email: support@ibo.org

Pearson Edexcel Mathematics Awards

Pearson's Edexcel Mathematics Awards are small, stand-alone qualifications designed to help students to develop and demonstrate proficiency in different areas of mathematics. These Awards enable students to focus on understanding key concepts and techniques, and are available across three subjects, including: Number and Measure (Levels 1 and 2), Algebra (Levels 2 and 3) and Statistical Methods (Levels 1, 2 and 3).

Designed to build students' confidence and fluency; the Awards can fit into the existing programme of delivery for mathematics in schools and colleges, prepare students for GCSE and/or GCE Mathematics, and to support further study in other subjects, training or the workplace. They offer a choice of levels to match students' abilities, with clear progression between the levels. These small, 60-70 guided learning hour qualifications are assessed through one written paper per level. Each qualification is funded and approved for pre-16 and 16-18 year old students in England and in schools and colleges in Wales.

Projects

Extended Project Qualification (EPQ)

AQA, OCR, Pearson and WJEC offer the Extended Project Qualification, which is a qualification aimed at developing a student's research and independent learning skills. The EPQ can be taken as a stand-alone qualification, and it is equivalent to half an A level in UCAS points (but only a third of performance points).

Students complete a research based written report and may produce an artefact or a practical science experiment as part of their project.

Cambridge International Project Qualification (IPQ)

Cambridge International is offering a new standalone project-based qualification, which can be taken alongside Cambridge International AS & A levels. Students complete a 5000-word research project on a topic of their choice. The qualification is assessed by Cambridge International.

For more information, go to www.cambridgeinternational.org/advanced

Entry level and basic skills

Entry Level Qualifications

If you want to take GCSE or NVQ Level 1 but have not yet reached the standard required, then entry level qualifications are for you as they are designed to get you started on the qualifications ladder.

Entry level qualifications are available in a wide range of areas. You can take an entry level certificate in most subjects where a similar GCSE exists. There are also vocational entry level qualifications – some in specific areas like retail or catering and others where you can take units in different work-related subjects to get a taster of a number of career areas. Also available are entry level certificates in life skills and the basic skills of literacy and numeracy.

Anyone can take an entry level qualification – your school or college will help you decide which qualification is right for you.

Entry level qualifications are flexible programmes so the time it takes to complete will vary according to where you study and how long you need to take the qualification.

Subjects available include: Art and Design, Computer Science, English, Geography, History, Latin, Mathematics, Physical Education and Science.

Functional Skills

Functional Skills are qualifications in English and maths that equip learners with the basic practical skills required in everyday life, education and the workplace. They are available at Entry Level, Level 1 and Level 2. Functional Skills are identified as funded 'stepping stone' qualifications to English and maths GCSE for post-16 learners who haven't previously achieved a grade 3 in these subjects. There are part of apprenticeship completion requirements.

Vocational qualifications

Applied Generals/Level 3 Certificates

Applied General qualifications are available in a wide range of subjects, they are a real alternative to A level support progression to further study or employment aimed at students aged 16-18.

Developed together with teachers, schools, colleges and higher education institutions, they help learners to develop knowledge and skills.

A mixture of assessment types means learners can apply their knowledge in a practical way. An integrated approach creates a realistic and relevant qualification for learners.

AQA Technical Award

AQA's Technical Award is a practical, vocational Level 1/2 qualification for 14- to 16-year-olds to take alongside GCSEs.

The Technical Award in Performing Arts provides an introduction to life and work, equipping learners with the practical, transferable skills and core knowledge needed to progress to further general or vocational study, including Level 3 qualifications, employment or apprenticeships.

Learners are assessed on doing rather than knowing through the project-based internal assessments, where they can apply their knowledge to practical tasks. There are two internally assessed units worth 30% each, and an externally assessed exam worth 40%.

The last time schools can enter for this qualification will be summer 2023, and there will be no resit opportunity.

BTECs

BTEC Level 2 First qualifications
ie BTEC Level 2 Diplomas, BTEC Level 2 Extended Certificates, BTEC Level 2 Certificates and BTEC Level 2 Award.

BTEC Firsts are Level 2 introductory work-related programmes covering a wide range of vocational areas including business, engineering, information technology, health and social care, media, travel and tourism, and public services.

Programmes may be taken full or part-time. They are practical programmes that provide a foundation for the knowledge and skills you will need in work. Alternatively, you can progress onto a BTEC National qualification, Applied GCE A level or equivalent.

There are no formal entry requirements and they can be studied alongside GCSEs. Subjects available include: Agriculture, Animal Care, Applied Science, Art and Design, Business, Children's Care, Learning and Development, Construction, Countryside and the Environment, Engineering, Fish Husbandry, Floristry, Health and Social care, Horse Care, Horticulture, Hospitality, IT, Land-based Technology, Business, Creative Media Production, Music, Performing Arts, Public Services, Sport, Travel and Tourism, and Vehicle Technology.

BTEC Foundation Diploma in Art and Design (QCF)
For those students preparing to go on to higher education within the field of art and design. This diploma is recognised as one of the best courses of its type in the UK, and is used in preparation for degree programmes. Units offered include researching, recording and responding in art and design, media experimentation, personal experimental studies, and a final major project.

BTEC Nationals
ie BTEC Level 3 Extended Diplomas (QCF), BTEC Level 3 Diplomas (QCF), BTEC Level 3 Subsidiary Diplomas (QCF), BTEC Level 3 Certificates (QCF)

BTEC National programmes are long-established vocational programmes. They are practical programmes that are highly valued by employers. They enable you to gain the knowledge and skills that you will need in work, or give you the choice to progress on to a BTEC Higher National, a Foundation Degree or a degree programme.

BTEC Nationals, which hold UCAS points cover a range of vocationally specialist sectors including child care, children's play, learning and development, construction, art and design, aeronautical engineering, electrical/electronic engineering, IT, business, creative and media production, performing arts, public services, sport, sport and exercise sciences and applied science. The programmes may be taken full- or part-time, and can be taken in conjunction with NVQs and/or functional skills units at an appropriate level.

There are no formal entry requirements, but if you have any of the following you are likely to be at the right level to study a BTEC national qualification.

- a BTEC Level 2 First qualification

- GCSEs – at grades A*-C in several subjects

- Relevant work experience

There are also very specialist BTEC Nationals, such as Pharmaceutical Science and Blacksmithing and Metalworking.

BTEC Higher Nationals

Known as HNDs and HNCs – ie BTEC Level 5 HND Diplomas (QCF) and BTEC Level 4 HNC Diplomas (QCF)

BTEC HNDs and HNCs are further and higher education qualifications that offer a balance of education and vocational training. They are available in over 40 work-related subjects such as Graphic Design, Business, Health and Social Care, Computing and Systems Development, Manufacturing Engineering, Hospitality Management, and Public Services.

BTEC higher national courses combine study with hands-on work experience during your course. Once completed, you can use the skills you learn to begin your career, or continue on to a related degree course.

HNDs are often taken as a full-time course over two years but can also be followed part-time in some cases.

HNCs are often for people who are working and take two years to complete on a part-time study basis by day release, evenings, or a combination of the two. Some HNC courses are done on a full-time basis.

There are no formal entry requirements, but if you have any of the following you are likely to be at the right academic level:

- at least one A level

- a BTEC Level 3 National qualification

- level 3 NVQ

BTEC specialist and professional qualifications

These qualifications are designed to prepare students for specific and specialist work activities. These are split into two distinct groups:

- Specialist qualifications (entry to Level 3)

- Professional qualifications (Levels 4-7)

Cambridge Nationals

Cambridge Nationals from exam board OCR are vocationally-related qualifications that take an engaging, practical and inspiring approach to learning and assessment.

They are industry-relevant, geared to key sector requirements and very popular with schools and colleges because they suit such a broad range of learning styles and abilities.

Cambridge Nationals are available in: Child Development, Creative iMedia, Engineering Design, Engineering Manufacture, Enterprise and Marketing, Health and Social Care, ICT, Information Technologies, Principles in Engineering and Engineering Business, Sport Science, Sport Studies, Systems Control in Engineering. They are joint Level 1 and 2 qualifications aimed at students aged 14-16 in full-time study.

Cambridge Technicals

OCR's Cambridge Technicals are practical and flexible vocationally-related qualifications, offering students in-depth study in a wide range of subjects, including business, health and social care, IT, sport, art and design, digital media, applied science, performing arts and engineering.

Cambridge Technicals are aimed at young people aged 16-19 who have completed Key Stage 4 of their education and want to study in a more practical, work-related way.

Cambridge Technicals are available at Level 2 and Level 3, and carry UCAS points at Level 3.

NVQs

NVQs reward those who demonstrate skills gained at work. They relate to particular jobs and are usefully taken while you are working. Within reason, NVQs do not have to be completed in a specified amount of time. They can be taken by full-time employees or by school and college students with a work placement or part-time job that enables them to develop the appropriate skills. There are no age limits and no special entry requirements.

NVQs are organised into levels, based on the competencies required. Levels 1-3 are the levels most applicable to learners within the 14-19 phase. Achievement of Level 4 within this age group will be rare. See the OCR website for further information.

Occupational Studies (Northern Ireland)

Targeted at learners working towards and at Level 1 and 2 in Key Stage 4 within the Northern Ireland curriculum. For further information see the CCEA website.

OCR Vocational Qualifications

These are available at different levels and different sizes. Levels 1-3 are the levels most applicable to learners within the 14-19 phase. The different sizes are indicated with the use of Award, Certificate and Diploma in the qualification title and indicate the number of hours it typically takes to complete the qualification.

Vocational qualifications are assessed according to each individual specification, but may include practical assessments and/or marked assessments. They are designed to provide evidence of a student's relevant skills and knowledge in their chosen subject. These qualifications can be used for employment or as a path towards further education. See the OCR website for further details.

SVQs (Scotland)

Scottish Vocational Qualifications (SVQs) are work-based qualifications that demonstrate someone can do their job well and to the national standards for their sector. There are over 500 SVQs that cover many occupations in Scotland – from forestry to IT, management to catering, and from journalism to construction. Experts from industry, commerce and education produce SVQs based on national standards.

Many people study for SVQs in the workplace while carrying out their day-to-day role. Each SVQ unit defines one aspect of a job and what it is to be competent in that aspect of the job. Learners can work through one unit at a time, or gather evidence for several units at the same time. There are no formal written exams, instead learners collect and submit evidence, usually from their own work. They are assessed by an SVQ assessor and the assessment can take place at the learner's place of work, at college or through a training provider.

Awarding organisations and examination dates

Awarding organisations

In England there are four awarding organisations, each offering GCSEs, AS and A levels (Eduqas offers only reformed qualifications in England, whereas WJEC offers in England, Wales, Northern Ireland and independent regions). There are separate awarding organisations in Wales (WJEC) and Northern Ireland (CCEA). The awarding organisation in Scotland (SQA) offers equivalent qualifications.

This information was supplied by the awarding bodies and was accurate at the time of going to press. It is intended as a general guide only for candidates in the United Kingdom. Dates are subject to variation and should be confirmed with the awarding organisation concerned.

AQA

Qualifications offered:
GCSE
AS and A level
Foundation Certificate of Secondary Education (FCSE)
Entry Level Certificate (ELC)
Foundation and Higher Projects
Extended Project Qualification (EPQ)
Applied Generals/AQA Level 3 Certificates and Extended Certificates
Functional Skills
AQA Certificate
Technical Award

Other assessment schemes:
Unit Award Scheme (UAS)

Contact:
Email: eos@aqa.org.uk
Website: www.aqa.org.uk
Tel: 0800 197 7162 (8am–5pm Monday to Friday)
+44 161 696 5995 (Outside the UK)

Devas Street, Manchester M15 6EX
Stag Hill House, Guildford, Surrey GU2 7XJ
Windsor House, Cornwall Road, Harrogate, HG1 2PW
2nd Floor, Lynton House, 7–12 Tavistock Square, London, WC1H 9LT

CCEA – Council for the Curriculum, Examinations and Assessment

Qualifications offered:
GCSE
GCE AS/A level
Key Skills (Levels 1-4)
Entry Level Qualifications
Occupational Studies (Levels 1 & 2)
QCF Qualifications
Applied GCSE and GCE

Contact:
Email: info@ccea.org.uk
Website: www.ccea.org.uk

29 Clarendon Road, Clarendon Dock, Belfast, BT1 3BG
Tel: (028) 9026 1200

Eduqas

Eduqas, part of WJEC, offers Ofqual reformed GCSEs, AS and A levels to secondary schools and colleges. Our qualifications are available in England, Channel Islands, Isle of Man, Northern Ireland and to the independent sector in Wales (restrictions may apply).

Qualifications offered:
GCSE (9-1)
AS
A level
Level 3

Contact:
Email: info@wjec.co.uk
Website: www.eduqas.co.uk

Eduqas (WJEC CBAC Ltd),
245 Western Avenue, Cardiff, CF5 2YX
Telephone: 029 2026 5000

IB – International Baccalaureate

Qualification offered:
IB Diploma
IB Career-related Certificate

Contact:
Email: support@ibo.org
Website: www.ibo.org

IB Global Centre, The Hague, Churchillplein 6, 2517 JW, The Hague, The Netherlands
Tel: +31 70 352 60 00

IB Global Centre, Washington DC, 7501 Wisconsin Avenue, Suite 200 West Bethesda, Maryland 20814, USA
Tel: +1 301 202 3000

IB Global Centre, Singapore, 600 North Bridge Road, #21-01 Parkview Square, Singapore 188778
Tel: +65 6 579 5000

IB Global Centre, Cardiff, Peterson House, Malthouse Avenue, Cardiff Gate, Cardiff, Wales, CF23 8GL, UK
Email: reception@ibo.org
Tel: +44 29 2054 7777

International Baccalaureate Foundation Office, Route des Morillons 15, Grand-Saconnex, Genève, CH-1218, Switzerland
Tel: +41 22 309 2540

OCR – Oxford Cambridge and RSA Examinations – and Cambridge International

Qualifications offered by OCR or sister awarding organisation Cambridge Assessment International Education (Cambridge International) include:
GCSE
GCE AS/A level
IGCSE
International AS/A level
Extended Project
Cambridge International Project Qualification
Cambridge Pre-U
Cambridge Nationals
Cambridge Technicals
Functional Skills
FSMQ – Free Standing Maths Qualification
NVQ

Contact:
OCR
OCR Head Office, The Triangle Building, Shaftesbury Road, Cambridge, CB2 8EA
Website: www.ocr.org.uk
Tel: +44 1223 553998

Cambridge International
Website: www.cambridgeinternational.org
Email: info@cambridgeinternational.org
Tel: +44 1223 553554

Pearson

Qualifications offered:

Pearson's qualifications are offered in the UK but are also available through their international centres across the world. They include:

DiDA, CiDA
GCE A levels
GCSEs
Functional Skills
International GCSEs and Edexcel Certificates
ESOL (Skills for Life)
BTEC Enterprise qualifications
BTEC Entry Level, Level 1 and Level 1 Introductory
BTEC Firsts
BTEC Foundation Diploma in Art and Design
BTEC Industry Skills
BTEC International Level 3
BTEC Level 2 Technicals
BTEC Level 3 Technical Levels in Hospitality
BTEC Nationals
BTEC Specialist and Professional qualifications
BTEC Tech Awards
Higher Nationals
T Levels

Contact:
190 High Holborn, London WC1V 7BH
See website for specific contact details:
qualifications.pearson.com

SQA – Scottish Qualifications Authority

Qualifications offered:

National Qualifications (NQs): National 1 to National 5; Higher; Advanced Higher
Skills for Work; Scottish Baccalaureates
National Certificates (NCs)
National Progression Awards (NPAs)
Awards
Core Skills
Scottish Vocational Qualifications (SVQs)
Higher National Certificates and Higher National Diplomas (HNCs/HNDs)*

*SQA offers HNCs and HNDs to centres in Scotland. Outside of Scotland, the equivalent qualifications are the SQA Advanced Certificate and SQA Advanced Diploma.

Contact:
Email: customer@sqa.org.uk Tel: 0345 279 1000
Website: www.sqa.org.uk
Glasgow – The Optima Building, 58 Robertson Street, Glasgow, G2 8DQ
Dalkeith – Lowden, 24 Wester Shawfair, Dalkeith, Midlothian, EH22 1FD

WJEC

With over 65 years' experience in delivering qualifications, WJEC is the largest provider in Wales and a leading provider in England and Northern Ireland.

Qualifications offered:
GCSE
GCE A/AS
Functional Skills
Entry Level
Welsh Baccalaureate Qualifications
Essential Skills Wales
Wider Key Skills
Project Qualifications Principal Learning
Other general qualifications such as Level 1 and Level 2 Awards and Certificates including English Language, English Literature, Latin Language, Latin Language & Roman Civilisation and Latin Literature
QCF Qualifications

Contact:
Email: info@wjec.co.uk
Website: www.wjec.co.uk

245 Western Avenue, Cardiff, CF5 2YX
Tel: 029 2026 5000

Educational organisations

Educational organisations

Artsmark

Arts Council England's Artsmark was set up in 2001, and rounds are held annually.

All schools in England can apply for an Artsmark – primary, middle, secondary, special and pupil referral units, maintained and independent – on a voluntary basis. An Artsmark award is made to schools showing commitment to the full range of arts – music, dance, drama and art and design.

Tel: 0161 934 4317
Email: artsmark@artscouncil.org.uk
Website: www.artsmark.org.uk

Association for the Education and Guardianship of International Students (AEGIS)

AEGIS brings together schools and guardianship organisations to ensure and promote the welfare of international students. AEGIS provides accreditation for all reputable guardianship organisations.

AEGIS, The Wheelhouse, Bond's Mill Estate, Bristol Road, Stonehouse, Gloucestershire GL10 3RF.
Tel: 01453 821293
Email: info@aegisuk.net
Website: www.aegisuk.net

The Association of American Study Abroad Programmes (AASAP)

Established in 1991 to represent American study abroad programmes in the UK.

Contact: Kalyn Franke, AASAP/UK,
University of Maryland in London, Connaught Hall,
36-45 Tavistock Square, London WC1H 9EX
Email: info@aasapuk.org
Website: www.aasapuk.org

The Association of British Riding Schools (ABRS)

An independent body of proprietors and principals of riding establishments, aiming to look after their interests and those of the riding public and to raise standards of management, instruction and animal welfare.

Blenheim Business Centre, Smithers Hill, Shipley,
West Sussex RH13 8PP.
Tel: 01403 741188
Email: office@abrs-info.org
Website: www.abrs-info.org

Association of Colleges (AOC)

Created in 1996 to promote the interest of further education colleges in England and Wales.

2-5 Stedham Place, London WC1A 1HU
Tel: 0207 034 9900
Email: enquiries@aoc.co.uk
Website: www.aoc.co.uk

Association of Governing Bodies of Independent Schools (AGBIS)

AGBIS supports and advises governing bodies of schools in the independent sector on all aspects of governance. Registered charity No. 1108756

Association of Governing Bodies of Independent Schools,
3 Codicote Road, Welwyn, Hertfordshire AL6 9LY
Tel: 01438 840730
Email: enquiries@agbis.org.uk
Website: www.agbis.org.uk

Association of Employment and Learning Providers (AELP)

AELP's purpose is to influence the education and training agenda. They are the voice of independent learning providers throughout England.

Association of Employment and Learning Providers,
2nd Floor, 9 Apex Court, Bradley Stoke, Bristol, BS32 4JT
Tel: 0117 986 5389
Email: enquiries@aelp.org.uk
Website: www.aelp.org.uk

The Association of School and College Leaders (ASCL)

Formerly the Secondary Heads Association, the ASCL is a professional association for secondary school and college leaders.
2nd Floor, Peat House, 1 Waterloo Way, Leicester LE1 6LP
Tel: 0116 299 1122
Fax: 0116 299 1123
Email: info@ascl.org.uk
Website: www.ascl.org.uk

Boarding Schools' Association (BSA)

For information on the BSA see editorial on page 26

The British Accreditation Council (BAC)

The British Accreditation Council (BAC) has now been the principal accrediting body for the independent further and higher education and training sector for nearly 30 years. BAC-accredited institutions in the UK now number more than 300, offering everything from website design to yoga to equine dentistry, as well as more standard qualifications in subjects such as business, IT, management and law. As well as our accreditation of institutions offering traditional teaching, BAC has developed a new accreditation scheme for providers offering online, distance and blended learning. Some students may also look to study outside the UK at one of the institutions holding BAC international accreditation.
Wax Chandlers' Hall 1st Floor, 6 Gresham Street, London EC2V 7AD
Tel: 0300 330 1400
Email: info@the-bac.org
Website: www.the-bac.org

The British Association for Early Childhood Education (BAECE)

Promotes quality provision for all children from birth to eight in whatever setting they are placed. Publishes booklets and organises conferences for those interested in early years education and care. Registered charity Nos. 313082; SC039472
Fountain Court, 2 Victoria Square, St Albans AL1 3T
Tel: 01727 884925
Email: office@early-education.org.uk
Website: www.early-education.org.uk

The Choir Schools' Association (CSA)

Represents 44 schools attached to cathedrals, churches and college chapels, which educate cathedral and collegiate choristers.
CSA Information Officer, 39 Bournside Road, Cheltenham, Gloucestershire GL51 3AL
Tel: 07903 850597
Email: ian.jones@choirschools.org.uk
Website: www.choirschools.org.uk

CIFE

CIFE is the professional association for independent sixth form and tutorial colleges accredited by the British Accreditation Council (BAC), the Independent Schools Council or the DfE (Ofsted). Member colleges specialise in preparing students for GCSE and A level (AS and A2) in particular and university entrance in general.

The aim of the association is to provide a forum for the exchange of information and ideas, and for the promotion of best practice, and to safeguard adherence to strict standards of professional conduct and ethical propriety. Further information can be obtained from CIFE:
Tel: 0208 767 8666
Email: enquiries@cife.org.uk
Website: www.cife.org.uk

Council of British International Schools (COBIS)

COBIS is a membership association of British schools of quality worldwide and is committed to a stringent process of quality assurance for all its member schools. COBIS is a member of the Independent Schools Council (ISC) of the United Kingdom.
COBIS, 55–56 Russell Square, Bloomsbury,
London WC1B 4HP
Tel: 020 3826 7190
Email: pa@cobis.org.uk
Website: www.cobis.org.uk

Council of International Schools (CIS)

CIS is a not-for-profit organisation committed to supporting its member schools and colleges in achieving and delivering the highest standards of international education. CIS provides accreditation to schools, teacher and leader recruitment and best practice development. CIS Higher Education assists member colleges and universities in recruiting a diverse profile of qualified international students.
Schipholweg 113, 2316 XC Leiden, The Netherlands.
Tel: +31 71 524 3300
Email: info@cois.org
Website: www.cois.org

Dyslexia Action (DA)

A registered, educational charity (No. 268502), which has established teaching and assessment centres and conducts teacher-training throughout the UK. The aim of the institute is to help people with dyslexia of all ages to overcome their difficulties in learning to read, write and spell and to achieve their potential.
Dyslexia Action Training and Guild, Centurion House,
London Road, Staines-upon-Thames TW18 4AX
Tel: 01784 222 304
Email: trainingcourses@dyslexiaaction.org.uk
Website: www.dyslexiaaction.org.uk

European Association for International Education (EAIE)

A not-for-profit organisation aiming for internationalisation in higher education in Europe. It has a membership of over 1800.
PO Box 11189, 1001 GD Amsterdam, The Netherlands
Tel: +31 20 344 5100
Fax: +31 20 344 5119
Email: info@eaie.org
Website: www.eaie.org

ECIS (European Collaborative for International Schools)

ECIS is a membership organisation which provides services to support professional development, good governance and leadership in international schools.
24 Greville Street,
London, EC1N 8SS
Tel: 020 7824 7040
Email: ecis@ecis.org
Website: www.ecis.org

The Girls' Day School Trust (GDST)

The Girls' Day School Trust (GDST) is one of the largest, longest-established and most successful groups of independent schools in the UK, with 4000 staff and over 20,000 students between the ages of 3 and 18. As a charity that owns and runs a family of 25 schools in England and Wales, it reinvests all its income into its schools for the benefit of the pupils. With a long history of pioneering innovation in the education of girls, the GDST now also educates boys in some of its schools, and has two coeducational sixth form colleges. Registered charity No. 306983
10 Bressenden Place, London, SW1E 5DH
Tel: 020 7393 6666
Email: info@wes.gdst.net
Website: www.gdst.net

Girls' Schools Association (GSA)

For information on the GSA see editorial on page 27

The Heads' Conference (HMC)

For information on the HMC see editorial on page 28

Human Scale Education (HSE)

An educational reform movement aiming for small education communities based on democracy, fairness and respect. Registered charity No. 1000400
Email: contact@hse.org.uk
Website: www.humanscaleeducation.com

The Independent Association of Prep Schools (IAPS)

For further information about IAPS see editorial on page 29

The Independent Schools Association (ISA)

For further information about ISA see editorial on page 30

The Independent Schools' Bursars Association (ISBA)

Exists to support and advance financial and operational performance in independent schools. The ISBA is a charitable company limited by guarantee.
Company No. 6410037; registered charity No. 1121757
Bluett House, Unit 11–12 Manor Farm, Cliddesden, nr Basingstoke, Hampshire RG25 2JB
Tel: 01256 330369
Email: office@theisba.org.uk
Website: www.theisba.org.uk

The Independent Schools Council (ISC)

The Independent Schools Council exists to promote choice, diversity and excellence in education; the development of talent at all levels of ability; and the widening of opportunity for children from all backgrounds to achieve their potential. Its 1280 member schools educate more than 500,000 children at all levels of ability and from all socioeconomic classes. Nearly a third of children in ISC schools receive help with fees. The Governing Council of ISC contains representatives from each of the eight ISC constituent associations listed below.
See also page 32.

Members:
Association of Governing Bodies of Independent Schools (AGBIS)
Girls' Schools Association (GSA)
Headmasters' and Headmistresses' Conference (HMC)
Independent Association of Prep Schools (IAPS)
Independent Schools Association (ISA)
Independent Schools Bursars' Association (ISBA)
The Society of Heads
The council also has close relations with the BSA, COBIS, SCIS and WISC.

First Floor, 27 Queen Anne's Gate, London, SW1H 9BU
Tel: 020 7766 7070
Fax: 020 7766 7071
Email: research@isc.co.uk
Website: www.isc.co.uk

The Independent Schools Examinations Board (ISEB)

Details of the Common Entrance examinations are obtainable from:
Independent Schools Examinations Board,
Endeavour House, Crow Arch Lane, Ringwood BH24 1HP
Tel: 01425 470555
Email: enquiries@iseb.co.uk
Website: www.iseb.co.uk
Copies of past papers can be purchased from Galore Park: www.galorepark.co.uk

International Baccalaureate (IB)

For full information about the IB see full entry on page 187.

International Schools Theatre Association (ISTA)

International body of teachers and students of theatre, run by teachers for teachers. Registered charity No. 1050103
Lakeside Offices, The Old Cattle Market, Coronation Park, Helston, Cornwall TR13 0SR
Tel: 01326 560398
Email: office@ista.co.uk
Website: www.ista.co.uk

Maria Montessori Institute (MMI)

Authorised by the Association Montessori Internationale (AMI) to run their training course in the UK. Further information is available from:
26 Lyndhurst Gardens, Hampstead, London NW3 5NW
Tel: 020 7435 3646
Email: info@mariamontessori.org
Website: www.mariamontessori.org

The National Association of Independent Schools & Non-Maintained Schools (NASS)

A membership organisation working with and for special schools in the voluntary and private sectors within the UK.
Registered charity No. 1083632
PO Box 705, York YO30 6WW
Tel/Fax: 01904 624446
Email: krippon@nasschools.org.uk
Website: www.nasschools.org.uk

National Day Nurseries Association (NDNA)

A national charity that aims to promote quality in early years. Registered charity No. 1078275
NDNA, National Early Years Enterprise Centre,
Longbow Close, Huddersfield, West Yorkshire HD2 1GQ
Tel: 01484 407070
Fax: 01484 407060
Email: info@ndna.org.uk
Website: www.ndna.org.uk

NDNA Cymru, Office 3, Crown House, 11 Well Street, Ruthin, Denbighshire LL15 1AE
Tel: 01824 707823
Email: wales@ndna.org.uk

NDNA Scotland, The Mansfield Traquair Centre,
15 Mansfield Place, Edinburgh EH3 6BB
Tel: 0131 516 6967
Email: scot@ndna.org.uk

National Foundation for Educational Research (NFER)

NFER is the UK's largest independent provider of research, assessment and information services for education, training and children's services. Its clients include UK government departments and agencies at both national and local levels. NFER is a not-for-profit organisation and a registered charity No. 313392
Head Office, The Mere, Upton Park,
Slough, Berkshire SL1 2DQ
Tel: 01753 574123
Fax: 01753 691632
Email: enquiries@nfer.ac.uk
Website: www.nfer.ac.uk

Potential Plus UK

Potential Plus UK is an independent charity that supports the social, emotional and learning needs of children with high learning potential of all ages and backgrounds. Registered charity No. 313182
The Open University, Vaughan Harley Building Ground Floor, Walton Hall, Milton Keynes MK7 6AA
Tel: 01908 646433
Email: amazingchildren@potentialplusuk.org
Website: www.potentialplusuk.org

Round Square

An international group of schools formed in 1967 following the principles of Dr Kurt Hahn, the founder of Salem School in Germany, and Gordonstoun in Scotland. The Round Square, named after Gordonstoun's 17th century circular building in the centre of the school, now has more than 100 member schools. Registered charity No. 327117
Round Square, First Floor, Morgan House, Madeira Walk, Windsor SL4 1EP
Tel: 01474 709843
Website: www.roundsquare.org

Royal National Children's SpringBoard Foundation

On 1 July 2017 the Royal National Children's Foundation (RNCF) merged with The SpringBoard Bursary Foundation to create the Royal National Children's SpringBoard Foundation ('Royal SpringBoard'). The newly merged charity gives life-transforming bursaries to disadvantaged and vulnerable children from across the UK.
6th Floor, Minster House, 42 Mincing Lane,
London, EC3R 7A
Tel: 01932 868622
Email: admin@royalspringboard.org.uk
Website: www.royalspringboard.org.uk

School Fees Independent Advice (SFIA)

For further information about SFIA, see editorial page 34

Schools Music Association of Great Britain (SMA)

The SMA is a national 'voice' for music in education. It is now part of the Incorporated Society of Musicians Registered charity No. 313646
Website: www.ism.org/sma

Scottish Council of Independent Schools (SCIS)

Representing more than 70 independent, fee-paying schools in Scotland, the Scottish Council of Independent Schools (SCIS) is the foremost authority on independent schools in Scotland and offers impartial information, advice and guidance to parents. Registered charity No. SC018033
1, St Colme Strreet, Edinburgh EH3 6AA
Tel: 0131 556 2316
Email: info@scis.org.uk
Website: www.scis.org.uk

Society of Education Consultants (SEC)

The Society is a professional membership organisation that supports management consultants who specialise in education and children's services. The society's membership includes consultants who work as individuals, in partnerships or in association with larger consultancies.
SEC, Bellamy House, 13 West Street, Cromer NR27 9HZ
Tel: 0330 323 0457
Email: administration@sec.org.uk
Website: www.sec.org.uk

The Society of Heads

For full information see editorial on page 31

State Boarding Forum (SBF)

For full information about the SBF see editorial on page 26

Steiner Waldorf Schools Fellowship (SWSF)

Representing Steiner education in the UK and Ireland, the SWSF has member schools and early years centres in addition to interest groups and other affiliated organisations. Member schools offer education for children within the normal range of ability, aged 3 to 18.
Registered charity No. 295104
Steiner Waldorf Schools Fellowship® Ltd, 35 Park Road, London NW1 6XT
Tel: 0204 5249933
Email: admin@steinerwaldorf.org
Website: www.steinerwaldorf.org

Support and Training in Prep Schools (SATIPS)

SATIPS aims to support teachers in the independent and maintained sectors of education. Registered charity No. 313688
West Routengill, Walden, West Burton, Leyburn, North Yorkshire, DL8 4LF
Website: www.satips.org

The Tutors' Association

The Tutors' Association is the professional body for tutoring and wider supplementary education sector in the UK. Launched in 2013, they have over 1,300 members, including Individual and Corporate Members representing some 30,000 tutors throughout the UK.
Tel: 01628 306108
Email: info@thetutorsassociation.org.uk
Website: www.thetutorsassociation.org.uk

UCAS (Universities and Colleges Admissions Service)

UCAS is the organisation responsible for managing applications to higher education courses in England, Scotland, Wales and Northern Ireland. Registered charity Nos. 1024741 and SC038598
Rosehill, New Barn Lane,
Cheltenham, Gloucestershire GL52 3LZ
Tel: 0371 468 0 468
Website: www.ucas.com

UKCISA – The Council for International Student Affairs

UKCISA is the UK's national advisory body serving the interests of international students and those who work with them. Registered charity No. 1095294
Website: www.ukcisa.org.uk

United World Colleges (UWC)

UWC was founded in 1962 and their philosophy is based on the ideas of Dr Kurt Hahn (see Round Square Schools). Registered charity No. 313690.
UWC International, Third Floor, 55 New Oxford Street, London, WC1A 1BS, UK
Tel: 020 7269 7800
Fax: 020 7405 4374
Email: info@uwcio.uwc.org
Website: www.uwc.org

World-Wide Education Service of CfBT Education Trust (WES)

A leading independent service which provides home education courses worldwide.
Waverley House, Penton,
Carlisle, Cumbria CA6 5QU
Tel: 01228 577123
Email: office@weshome.com
Website: www.weshome.com

Glossary

ACETS	Awards and Certificates in Education	COBIS	Council of British International)
AEA	Advanced Extension Award	CSA	The Choir Schools' Association
AEB	Associated Examining Board for the General Certificate of Education	CST	The Christian Schools' Trust
		DfE	Department for Education (formerly DfES and DCFS)
AEGIS	Association for the Education and Guardianship of International Students	DipEd	Diploma of Education
AGBIS	Association of Governing Bodies of Independent Schools	DipTchng	Diploma of Teaching
		EAIE	European Association for International Education
AHIS	Association of Heads of Independent Schools	ECIS	European Council of International Schools
AJIS	Association of Junior Independent Schools	EdD	Doctor of Education
ALP	Association of Learning Providers	Edexcel	GCSE Examining group, incorporating Business and Technology Education Council (BTEC) and University of London Examinations and Assessment Council (ULEAC)
ANTC	The Association of Nursery Training Colleges		
AOC	Association of Colleges		
AP	Advanced Placement		
ASCL	Association of School & College Leaders		
ASL	Additional and Specialist Learning	EFL	English as a Foreign Language
ATI	The Association of Tutors Incorporated	ELAS	Educational Law Association
AQA	Assessment and Qualification Alliance/ Northern Examinations and Assessment Board	EPQ	Extended Project qualification
		ESL	English as a Second Language
		FCoT	Fellow of the College of Teachers (TESOL)
BA	Bachelor of Arts	FEFC	Further Education Funding Council
BAC	British Accreditation Council for Independent Further and Higher Education	FRSA	Fellow of the Royal Society of Arts
		FSMQ	Free-Standing Mathematics Qualification
BAECE	The British Association for Early Childhood Education	GCE	General Certificate of Education
		GCSE	General Certificate of Secondary Education
BD	Bachelor of Divinity	GDST	Girls' Day School Trust
BEA	Boarding Educational Alliance	GNVQ	General National Vocational Qualifications
BEd	Bachelor of Education	GOML	Graded Objectives in Modern Languages
BLitt	Bachelor of Letters	GSA	Girls' Schools Association
BPrimEd	Bachelor of Primary Education	GSVQ	General Scottish Vocational Qualifications
BSA	Boarding Schools' Association	HMC	Headmasters' and Headmistresses' Conference
BSc	Bachelor of Science		
BTEC	Range of work-related, practical programmes leading to qualifications equivalent to GCSEs and A levels awarded by Edexcel	HMCJ	Headmasters' and Headmistresses' Conference Junior Schools
		HNC	Higher National Certificate
Cantab	Cambridge University	HND	Higher National Diploma
CATSC	Catholic Association of Teachers in Schools and Colleges	IAPS	Independent Association of Prep Schools
		IB	International Baccalaureate
CCEA	Council for the Curriculum, Examination and Assessment	ICT	Information and Communication Technology
		IFF	Inspiring Futures Foundation (formerly ISCO)
CDT	Craft, Design and Technology	IGCSE	International General Certificate of Secondary Education
CE	Common Entrance Examination		
CEAS	Children's Education Advisory Service	INSET	In service training
CertEd	Certificate of Education	ISA	Independent Schools Association
CIE	Cambridge International Examinations	ISBA	Independent Schools' Bursars' Association
CIFE	Conference for Independent Education	ISCis	Independent Schools Council information service
CIS	Council of International Schools		
CISC	Catholic Independent Schools' Conference	ISC	Independent Schools Council
CLAIT	Computer Literacy and Information Technology	ISEB	Independent Schools Examination Board
		ISST	International Schools Sports Tournament
CNED	Centre National d'enseignement (National Centre of long distance learning)	ISTA	International Schools Theatre Association

ITEC	International Examination Council
JET	Joint Educational Trust
LA	Local Authority
LISA	London International Schools Association
MA	Master of Arts
MCIL	Member of the Chartered Institute of Linguists
MEd	Master of Education
MIoD	Member of the Institute of Directors
MLitt	Master of Letters
MSc	Master of Science
MusD	Doctor of Music
MYP	Middle Years Programme
NABSS	National Association of British Schools in Spain
NAGC	National Association for Gifted Children
NAHT	National Association of Head Teachers
NAIS	National Association of Independent Schools
NASS	National Association of Independent Schools & Non-maintained Special Schools
NDNA	National Day Nurseries Association
NEASC	New England Association of Schools and Colleges
NFER	National Federation of Educational Research
NPA	National Progression Award
NQ	National Qualification
NQF	National Qualifications Framework
NQT	Newly Qualified Teacher
NVQ	National Vocational Qualifications
OCR	Oxford, Cambridge and RSA Examinations
OLA	Online Language Assessment for Modern Languages
Oxon	Oxford
PGCE	Post Graduate Certificate in Education
PhD	Doctor of Philosophy
PL	Principal Learning
PNEU	Parents' National Education Union
PYP	Primary Years Programme
QCA	Qualifications and Curriculum Authority
QCF	Qualifications and Credit Framework
RSIS	The Round Square Schools
SAT	Scholastic Aptitude Test
SATIPS	Support & Training in Prep Schools/Society of Assistant Teachers in Prep Schools
SBSA	State Boarding Schools Association
SCE	Service Children's Education
SCIS	Scottish Council of Independent Schools
SCQF	Scottish Credit and Qualifications Framework
SEC	The Society of Educational Consultants
SEN	Special Educational Needs
SFCF	Sixth Form Colleges' Forum
SFIA	School Fees Insurance Agency Limited
SFIAET	SFIA Educational Trust

SMA	Schools Music Association
SoH	The Society of Heads
SQA	Scottish Qualifications Authority
STEP	Second Term Entrance Paper (Cambridge)
SVQ	Scottish Vocational Qualifications
SWSF	Steiner Waldorf Schools Fellowship
TABS	The Association of Boarding Schools
TISCA	The Independent Schools Christian Alliance
TOEFL	Test of English as a Foreign Language
UCAS	Universities and Colleges Admissions Service for the UK
UCST	United Church Schools Trust
UKLA	UK Literacy Association
UKCISA	The UK Council for International Education
UWC	United World Colleges
WISC	World International Studies Committee
WJEC	Welsh Joint Education Committee
WSSA	Welsh Secondary Schools Association

Index

Index

I

J

K

L

Index